The Safe and Effective Use of Pesticides
SECOND EDITION

PESTICIDE
APPLICATION
COMPENDIUM

1

The Safe and Effective Use of Pesticides

SECOND EDITION

Patrick J. O'Connor-Marer
Pesticide Training Coordinator
University of California, Davis

University of California
Statewide Integrated Pest Management Project
Agriculture and Natural Resources
Publication 3324

2000

ORDERING
For information about ordering this publication, contact

University of California
Agriculture and Natural Resources
Communication Services—Publications
6701 San Pablo Avenue, 2nd Floor
Oakland, California 94608-1239

Telephone 1-800-994-8849
(510) 642-2431
FAX (510) 643-5470
E-mail: danrcs@ucdavis.edu
Visit the ANR Communication Services website at http://danrcs.ucdavis.edu.

Publication 3324

ISBN 1-879906-43-0
Library of Congress Catalog Card No. 99-070790

 Printed in the United States of America on recycled paper.

Funding for this manual was provided in part by the Extension Service, U.S. Department of
Agriculture, under special project Section 3(d), Pesticide Applicator Training, and through
a National Institute for Occupational Safety and Health cooperative agreement number
U 07/CCU 9066162-02 with the UC Agricultural Health and Safety Center at Davis.

To simplify information, trade names of products have been used. No endorsement of
named or illustrated products is intended, nor is criticism implied of similar products
that are not mentioned or illustrated.

7.5m-rev-11/99

Acknowledgments

This second edition was produced under the auspices of the University of California Statewide Integrated Pest Management Project through a Memorandum of Understanding between the University of California and the California Department of Pesticide Regulation. It was prepared under the direction of Frank G. Zalom, Director, UC Statewide IPM Project, University of California, Davis.

Production

Design and Production Coordination: Naomi Schiff
Photographs: Jack Kelly Clark
Drawings: David Kidd
Editing: Steve Barnett and Diane Clarke

Technical Committee and Principal Reviewers (First Edition)

The following people provided ideas, information, and suggestions and reviewed the many manuscript drafts. Some served on an advisory committee that was formed prior to writing the book; others were key resources and reviewers in specific subject matter areas.

Harry Agamalian, University of California Cooperative Extension
Martin Barnes, University of California, Riverside
James Coburn, Western Farm Service
Susan Cohen, Monterey County Agricultural Commissioner's Office
Clyde Elmore, University of California, Davis
Del Farnham, University of California Cooperative Extension
Mary Louise Flint, University of California, Davis
John Ford, Pesticide Applicators' Professional Association
Tad Gantenbein, John Taylor Fertilizer Company
Beth Grafton-Cardwell, University of California, Davis
James Grieshop, University of California, Davis
Peter Kurtz, California Department of Food and Agriculture
Tom Lanini, University of California, Davis
John Munro, Pest Control Operators of California
Robert Norris, University of California, Davis
A. Paulus, University of California, Riverside
Margaret Rucker, University of California, Davis
Pius Scheuber, Modesto Junior College
Sara Segal, U.S. Environmental Protection Agency

Michael Stimmann, University of California, Davis
Stan Strew, California Agricultural Production Consultants Association
Mac Takeda, California Department of Pesticide Regulation
Michael Tanner, Merced County Agricultural Commissioner

Special Thanks

The following people generously provided information, offered suggestions, reviewed draft manuscripts, or assisted in setting up photographs for the original edition:

Rod Adamchak, University of California, Davis
Harold Alford, Pesticide Impact Assessment Program
Oscar Bacon, University of California, Davis
W. Bagley, Stull Chemical Company
J. Bailey, University of California, Riverside
Rick Barrett, Bugman Pest Control, Inc.
Steve Besemer, University of California Cooperative Extension
J. Borieko, Tingley Rubber Corporation
Les Breschini, John Pryor Company
Steve Brown, California Highway Patrol
Margaret Brush, University of California, Davis
Kate Burroughs, Harmony Farm Supply
Michael Connelly, Yoder Brothers, Inc.
Marilyn Corodemas, San Diego County Agricultural Commissioner's Office
Leonard Craft, Jr., Santa Cruz County Agricultural Commissioner
Arthur Craigmill, University of California, Davis
Vern Crawford, Wilbur Ellis Company
Dave Crutchfield, Pest Control Operators of California
Dan Dahlvang, Racal Airstream, Inc.
John Dibble, University of California, Kearney Agricultural Center
Steve DiGangi, Zabala Vineyards
Robert Donley, Los Angeles County Agricultural Commissioner's Office
Bob Enos, Western Farm Service
Michael Fike, Sacramento-Yolo Mosquito Abatement District
Steve Fleming, Harbor Pest Control
Nancy Frost, U.S. Environmental Protection Agency
T. Fukuto, University of California, Riverside
J. Garcia, Soilserve, Inc.
George Georghiou, University of California, Riverside
Ken Giles, University of California, Davis
Dave Harlow, U.S. Fish and Wildlife Service
J. Hinojos, Bugman Pest Control, Inc.
George Hurley, Western Farm Service
Ken Inouye, Disneyland
Richard Jackson, California Department of Health Services
Tom Jacobs, Tufts Ranch
Marvin Jordan, Wilbur Ellis Company
Bob Kennedy, Hartnell College
Al Keshner, Bugman Pest Control, Inc.

Carl Koehler, University of California, Berkeley

John LaBoyteaux

E. Laird, University of California, Riverside

Michael Lawton, Western Exterminator Company

Chris Lindeman, Lindeman Valley Farm

Ed Littrell, California Department of Fish and Game

Ed Loomis, University of California, Davis

Keith Maddy, California Department of Food and Agriculture

W. McHenry, University of California, Davis

Craig McNamara, Sierra Orchards

Jeff Meyer, University of California, Riverside

Thomas Miller, University of California, Riverside

Leroy Miner, Soilserve, Inc.

J. Mitchell, Tingley Rubber Corporation

Larry Mitich, University of California, Davis

D. Morris, University of California, Davis

Brad Mullens, University of California, Riverside

Robert Nelson, Nelson Manufacturing Company

Richard Neumann, California Department of Health Services

Howard Ohr, University of California, Riverside

Ronald Oshima, California Department of Pesticide Regulation

Michael Parrella, University of California, Riverside

Jo Parker, Cherlor Manufacturing Company

Tom Perring, University of California, Riverside

Mike Ravera, Chevron Chemical Company

Wilbur Reil, University of California Cooperative Extension

Louis Riehl, University of California, Riverside

Terry Salmon, University of California, Davis

Ed Sanders, Bugman Pest Control, Inc.

George Sayre

David Schulteis, Wilbur Ellis Company

David Sites, Soilserve, Inc.

Arthur Slater, University of California, Berkeley

Ted Stamen, University of California Cooperative Extension

Joyce Fox Strand, University of California, Davis

Larry Strand, University of California, Davis

Charles Swanson, Airstream Helmet Company

Robert Van Steenwyk, University of California, Berkeley

Nasario Vasquez, Home Acres Farm

R. Wagner, University of California, Riverside

Gregory Walker, University of California, Riverside

Becky Westerdahl, University of California, Davis

R. Winn, Mine Safety Appliances Company

Wesley Yates, University of California, Davis

Gregg Young, Y and B Ag Services

Melanie Zavala, University of California, Davis

Reviewers and Contributors (Second Edition)

The following people assisted in developing this second edition by reviewing and updating manuscripts and providing additional information:

Chris Betschart, San Diego County Department of Agriculture, San Diego
John Blocker, San Diego County Department of Agriculture, San Diego
Colleen Carr, San Diego County Department of Agriculture, San Diego
Diane Clarke, University of California, Statewide IPM Project, Davis
Steve Dreistadt, University of California, Statewide IPM Project, Davis
Tad Gantenbein, John Taylor Fertilizers, Sacramento
Simone Hardy, San Diego County Department of Agriculture, San Diego
Lyndon Hawkins, California Department of Pesticide Regulation–Environmental Monitoring and Pest Management Branch, Sacramento
Megan Moore, San Diego County Department of Agriculture, San Diego
Dawn Nielsen, San Diego County Department of Agriculture, San Diego
Barbara Ohlendorf, University of California, Statewide IPM Project, Davis
Ted Olsen, San Diego County Department of Agriculture, San Diego
Rick Persky, San Diego County Department of Agriculture, San Diego
Stasi Redding, San Diego County Department of Agriculture, San Diego
Vicente Rodriguez, San Diego County Department of Agriculture, San Diego
Roy Rutz, California Department of Pesticide Regulation–Worker Health and Safety Branch, Sacramento
Karen Stahlman, California Department of Pesticide Regulation–Pesticide Enforcement Branch, Sacramento
Nancy Syzoneko, San Diego County Department of Agriculture, San Diego
Mac Takeda, California Department of Pesticide Regulation–Pesticide Enforcement Branch, Sacramento
Jim Walsh, California Department of Pesticide Regulation–Pesticide Enforcement Branch, Ventura
Rick Walsh, San Diego County Department of Agriculture, San Diego
Melanie Zavala, University of California, Statewide IPM Project, Davis

Contents

Introduction

Pesticide application is a highly skilled occupation requiring specialized training.

HANDLING PESTICIDES requires many special skills and responsibilities. It is an important occupation on its own and a necessary part of many other jobs. If you handle pesticides, you need to recognize their hazards and how to avoid these. Furthermore, you must be familiar with all local, state, and federal laws regulating the sale, use, storage, transportation, application, and disposal of pesticides. If you supervise pesticide handlers, you are responsible for seeing that these employees handle and use pesticides properly and safely.

You may need to become a certified pesticide applicator by taking one or more of the California Department of Pesticide Regulation's (DPR) Qualified Applicator Certificate (QAC), Qualified Applicator License (QAL), or apprentice or journeyman Pest Control Aircraft Pilot's Certificate examinations. If you apply restricted-use pesticides only on property under your control, you will need to take the Certified Private Applicator examination administered by local agricultural commissioner offices. While regulations may not require an applicator to possess one of these credentials, employers frequently require this certification as a condition of continued employment for employees handling pesticides.

This book is Volume 1 in the Pesticide Application Compendium series. The original version was published in 1988. This revised and updated version reflects changes in laws and application technology. Its purpose is to help you learn safe and effective ways of using pesticides. It describes how to prevent accidents and how to avoid injury and environmental problems.

How to Use This Book

Use this book as a study guide if you are preparing for any of the QAC, QAL, or Pest Control Aircraft Pilot's Certificate examinations. The DPR uses these tests to *certify* individuals, pest control businesses, commercial applicators, landscape maintenance personnel, researchers, designated agents, and anyone else applying pesticides as part of their work.

What You Need to Know

The DPR exams assess your competence in handling and/or supervising handling of restricted-use pesticides. Questions on these tests are similar to the review questions at the end of each chapter of this book. These tests cover several areas of skill or *knowledge expectations* that you are required by law to demonstrate in order to handle restricted-use pesticides. The following sections describe what you need to know and where to find that information in this book.

Pests and Pest Management. As a certified pesticide handler, you must recognize common pests and the damage caused by them. You should also understand the concepts of pest management, including principles of *integrated pest management*. See Chapters 1, 2, and 8.

The Pesticide Label. You must demonstrate that you can read and understand pesticide labels and associated labeling information. This includes recognizing restrictions on use of certain pesticides, understanding worker safety and protection requirements, and recognizing and understanding how to protect environmentally sensitive areas. See Chapters 3, 4, and 6.

Mixing and Applying Pesticides. You need to know how to prepare proper concentrations of pesticide for use under particular circumstances. You also must be able to select application equipment and correctly calibrate this equipment. You need to demonstrate your ability to avoid offsite movement of pesticides during application. See Chapters 6, 8, 9, and 10.

Laws and Regulations Affecting Pesticide Use. You must recognize environmentally sensitive areas and protect these from pesticide exposure. You have to show that you know how to protect groundwater and endangered species. You need to be familiar with current regulatory changes and know how to locate regulatory information. See Chapters 4, 5, 6, and 8—also see the *Laws and Regulations Study Guide* from the Department of Pesticide Regulation.

Recognizing and Preventing Pesticide Poisoning. You must recognize common symptoms of pesticide poisoning and demonstrate that you know how to protect yourself and others from exposure by using personal protective equipment. You also need to understand the first aid procedures for pesticide exposure. See Chapters 5, 6, and 7.

Protecting the Environment. You must recognize the negative impact of pesticides on nontarget organisms. You need to understand how environmental contamination occurs and how to prevent it. You must be familiar with endangered species and how to protect them when making pesticide applications. You need to know how to properly handle, store, and dispose of leftover pesticides, pesticide mixtures, and empty containers. See Chapters 5, 6, and 8.

Pesticide Emergencies. You need to know where to get first aid information for pesticide exposure and how to administer first aid to an exposure victim. You must understand the procedures for dealing with pesticide spills and fires. You have to recognize problems associated with misapplication of pesticides and what to do in case it happens. See Chapters 5, 6, and 7.

Using the Review Questions

At the end of each chapter are several review questions to test your grasp of the information presented in that chapter. These questions are the same format as the questions on the DPR examinations. If you have had experience with handling pesticides, you will probably be able to answer many of the questions without studying the information in the chapter.

Begin your study of each chapter by reading through the review questions. Make notes of the subject material you do not fully understand. Then, review the chapter to locate the sections that deal with that information. Read those sections carefully before you review the rest of the chapter.

When you finish studying the chapter, answer each of the review questions. Check your answers with the correct answers on page 314. If you missed any of the questions, go back and reread the appropriate sections of the chapter that cover that information.

Useful Pesticide Resources

This and the other volumes in the Pesticide Application Compendium series are useful references for growers, structural pest control operators, pest control advisers, pest management students, homeowners, or anyone involved in pesticide use decisions. Books in this series are also helpful instructional guides for training people to use pesticides properly and safely.

Other volumes of the Pesticide Application Compendium cover the many different occupational areas in which people use pesticides (Table 1). Applicants for a Qualified Applicator Certificate or Qualified Applicator License must take an examination in one or more of these specialized areas.

Besides this text, there are two important sources you should rely on for information regarding pesticides and pest management:

- **County agricultural commissioners** (CACs) are regulatory officials of the DPR. Their offices throughout the state have the responsibility, among other functions, for issuing permits for restricted-use pesticides; monitoring pesticide use, storage, and disposal; and enforcing pesticide laws and regulations. Agricultural commissioners' offices provide local information on pesticide use, storage, transportation, disposal, and hazards. Contact your local CAC office if there is any pesticide emergency.

- **The University of California,** through its Cooperative Extension program, maintains offices in most counties of the state. Specialists who staff these offices are able to provide pest identification, pest management, and pesticide use information for home, structural, agricultural, livestock and poultry, rangeland, wildlife, turf and landscape, forest, and aquatic areas. Farm advisors work closely with other University of California researchers and specialists.

TABLE 1.

Specialized Areas of Pesticide Application.

SPECIALIZED AREA	DESCRIPTION OF PESTICIDE APPLICATOR'S WORK	TYPE OF PESTS
Residential, Industrial, and Institutional Pest Control	Performs pest control in apartments, restaurants, hospitals, offices, warehouses, grocery stores, and other similar buildings as part of employment by owner or operator of the building. Selects pest control methods and pesticides to use. Performs postharvest fumigation and insecticide and fungicide applications to agricultural products. Applies pesticides to stored agricultural products. Controls weeds around commercial and industrial structures. Work is often closely associated with people and their pets. Special subsections of this category, which require separate examinations, relate to the application of: (1) pesticides for preservation of wood products such as lumber, posts, and other structural wood; (2) antifouling paints to boat hulls; and (3) pesticides to control roots in sewer lines.	*Invertebrates:* cockroaches, bugs, stored product pests, flies, fleas, mosquitoes, termites, ants, and other insects; spiders and mites; marine organisms. *Vertebrates:* rats, mice, bats, and birds. *Weeds:* weeds and unwanted vegetation; tree roots in sewer lines. *Microorganisms:* wood-decaying fungi.
Landscape Maintenance Pest Control	Controls pests on or around ornamental and fruit trees, shrubs, small fruits and berries, turf, and flowers; works around homes, businesses, cemeteries, theme parks, public parks, indoor malls, and house plants. Pesticide application is often part of a landscape maintenance business. Applicator makes decisions regarding pest control methods, irrigation, and plant nutrition. Work is closely associated with human activities.	*Invertebrates:* aphids, scales, flies, bees, wasps, earwigs, moths, beetles, and bugs; spiders, mites, and centipedes; snails and slugs. *Vertebrates:* rats, mice, gophers, moles, squirrels, rabbits, birds, snakes, and lizards. *Microorganisms:* fungi, bacteria, and viruses. *Weeds:* various types of terrestrial weeds.
Right-of-Way Pest Control	Performs pesticide applications along roads, rail lines, utility accesses, and drainage ditches to keep these areas free of undesirable weeds and to prevent fire hazards and obstruction of access or view. Applies pesticides for control of vertebrates and insects that interfere with desirable foliage or water drainage. A special subsection of this category, which requires a separate examination, relates to the application of pesticides for the preservation of wood products and utility poles.	*Invertebrates:* pests of foliage and wood products. *Vertebrates:* squirrels, mice, gophers, moles, rabbits, and birds. *Weeds:* various types of terrestrial weeds.

SPECIALIZED AREA	DESCRIPTION OF PESTICIDE APPLICATOR'S WORK	TYPE OF PESTS
Forest Pest Control	Applies pesticides in forest locations and commercial Christmas tree plantations. Is responsible for protecting wildlife, watersheds, and lakes and streams.	*Invertebrates:* boring and defoliating insects of forest trees; mites. *Vertebrates:* squirrels, voles, gophers, rabbits, deer, and others. *Weeds:* mostly undesirable plant species competing with forest trees; parasitic plants. *Microorganisms:* plant disease agents affecting forest trees.
Aquatic Pest Control	Applies pesticides for control of aquatic weeds, pest fish, arthropods, and mollusks. Requires special skills to protect aquatic environments and nontarget organisms. Familiarity with aquatic ecosystems and the ultimate use of water is very important to protect people, crops, and the environment.	*Invertebrates:* snails, clams, mussels, and crabs. *Vertebrates:* pest fish, rodents, beavers, and others. *Weeds:* aquatic weeds; algae.
Plant Agriculture Pest Control	Applies pesticides in and around agricultural crops. Often employed by a commercial applicator. Usually supervises pest control applicator. Responsible for protecting fieldworkers, groundwater, and environment. May work with highly toxic materials.	*Invertebrates:* many different agricultural pest insects, mites, snails, and nematodes. *Vertebrates:* squirrels, gophers, rabbits, and birds. *Weeds:* many types of agricultural weeds and poisonous plants. *Microorganisms:* fungi, bacteria, viruses, and other microorganisms that cause crop diseases.
Animal Agriculture Pest Control	Applies pesticides for control of livestock and poultry pests. Requires familiarity with livestock and poultry and unique pest control techniques. Pesticide use is closely associated with animals.	*Invertebrates:* mosquitoes, lice, flies, and bugs; ticks and mites. *Vertebrates:* livestock and poultry predators. *Weeds:* poisonous plants and undesirable range weeds.
Seed Treatment	Performs or supervises the application of insecticides and fungicides to seeds used to produce agricultural crops. Requires familiarity with different methods of protecting seeds. Usually employed by a seed treatment company.	*Invertebrates:* seed-feeding or damaging insects. *Microorganisms:* fungi and bacteria.
Regulatory Pest Control	Involved in detecting and eradicating imported pests that pose threats of economic harm to agriculture, livestock and poultry, or other segments of society. Must be familiar with suppression and eradication methods. Requires understanding of how pests enter and disperse through an area. Usually works for a public agency.	*Invertebrates:* exotic insects and mites that threaten to cause economic or health damage. Nematodes, snails, clams, mussels, and crabs—damaging species that might be introduced from other areas. *Weeds:* aquatic, terrestrial, and exotic weeds. *Vertebrates:* reptiles, birds, and rodents and other mammals. *Microorganisms:* exotic plant disease organisms.
Demonstration and Research Pest Control	Evaluates pesticides for efficacy. Studies interactions between pests, nonpests, and environmental factors when pesticides are applied. Demonstrates proper and effective methods of using pesticides. May be pesticide chemical company field representative, farm advisor, university researcher, independent consultant, or contract researcher.	All types of agricultural and nonagricultural pests may be involved.
Public Health Pest Control	Involved in applying pesticides to control pests that transmit disease organisms to people. Usually employed by public agencies. Pesticide use is often closely associated with homes and workplaces or public areas.	*Invertebrates:* flies, fleas, cockroaches, mosquitoes, lice, and bugs; ticks, mites, and spiders. *Vertebrates:* rats, mice, bats, and birds.

1

Pest Identification

Close examination may be necessary to identify pests that are causing damage.

PESTS ARE ORGANISMS that cause problems in various ways. Some compete with people for food or fiber. Others interfere with raising crops, livestock, or poultry. Certain types of pests damage property and personal belongings or disfigure ornamental plantings. A few transmit or cause plant, animal, or human diseases.

Before trying to control a pest, you need to identify it. Be certain any injury or observed damage is actually due to the identified pest and not some other cause. Once you have identified the pest and confirmed that it is causing damage, become familiar with its life cycle, growth, and reproductive habits. Then, use this information to form your pest control plans. Misidentification and lack of information about a pest could cause you to choose the wrong control method or apply the control at the wrong time. These are the most frequent causes of pest control failure.

This chapter reviews some of the ways to identify pests. Four main groups of pests include

- weeds (undesired plants)
- invertebrates (insects and their relatives, nematodes, snails, and slugs)
- vertebrates (birds, reptiles, amphibians, fish, and rodents and other mammals)
- disease agents (bacteria, viruses, fungi, mycoplasmas, other microorganisms, and nonliving factors)

HOW PLANTS AND ANIMALS ARE NAMED

Names of plants and animals are your doorways to information about them. Once you know the name of a pest, you can more easily select control methods. Control methods include specific pesticides that prevent this pest from causing injury.

Scientific Names

Classification systems are sets of rules used for organizing and naming living things. An elegant, standardized classification system used throughout the world is the basis for the scientific names given to plants and animals. This system reveals relationships among different species of plants or animals. Scientific names are very useful when trying to locate information about organisms.

Living organisms belong to one of two major groups—the *plant kingdom* or the *animal kingdom*. Usually it is easy to distinguish between living organisms and nonliving objects and between plants and animals. However, microorganisms and algae are more difficult to classify because of characteristics that make them intermediate between plants and animals.

There are six subcategories within a kingdom in the standardized classification system—*phylum*, *class*, *order*, *family*, *genus*, and *species*. Unique physical characteristics set some organisms apart from others. For example, in the phylum Arthropoda all organisms have jointed appendages and external skeletons. Animals in the phylum Chordata

 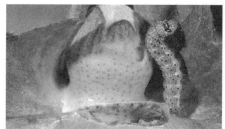 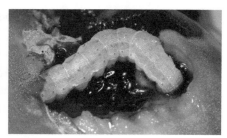

FIGURE 1-1

Common names are often not a dependable way to identify pests because some pests may have more than one common name. The Helicoverpa zea *shown here, for example, becomes the corn earworm, bollworm, or tomato fruitworm, depending on which crop it is infesting.*

have backbones, spinal nerve cords, and internal skeletons. Within a phylum there are several orders, each containing one or more families. A family is a group of related genera (the plural of *genus*), and a genus is a collection of species. A species is unique from all other organisms. The genus and species names make up an organism's scientific name. There may be variations among individuals of the same species. These include color and size differences and ability to attack a specific type of crop or plant. There may even be differences in the ability to resist certain pesticides.

Common Names

Besides a scientific name, most plants and animals have one or more common names. Pesticide labels refer to most pests by their common names. These names are usually descriptive, such as housefly, American cockroach, roof rat, field bindweed, yellow foxtail, apple scab, and fire blight. The disadvantage of using common names is that they do not provide any information about the relationship of one organism to another. For example, johnsongrass (*Sorghum halepense*) is a weed, while Sudan grass, grain sorghum, and milo (all *Sorghum bicolor*) are grains. All three belong to the genus *Sorghum*, but their common names do not indicate any relationship. However, their scientific names show they all belong to the genus *Sorghum*, indicating a close relationship.

Because common names vary with locality or host, an organism will often have more than one common name. The insect *Helicoverpa zea*, for example, is the corn earworm, bollworm, and tomato fruitworm, depending on which crop it is attacking (Figure 1-1). Organizations such as the Weed Science Society of America and the Entomological Society of America have developed lists of accepted common names.

WAYS TO IDENTIFY PESTS

Identify pests by using the guidelines included in this chapter and then consulting identification books. Or, have the pest examined and identified by specialists. When having pests identified, always collect several specimens.

The difficulty in identifying certain insects and most mites, nematodes, and plant pathogens in the field is their small size. Accurate identification requires the use of a hand lens or microscope, special tests, or careful analysis of damage. Often the pest's host association and location are important to making positive identifications. Information on the environmental conditions where you collect pests and the time of year of collection provides clues to the pest's identity.

Pest species may have different physical forms depending on their life cycles or the time of year. Weed seeds, for example, do not resemble seedlings or mature weeds. Many insect species undergo extreme changes in appearance as they develop from eggs through larval, pupal, and adult stages.

Identification Experts

Only trained experts, using special techniques and equipment, can positively identify some pests such as nematodes and most pathogens. Private laboratories exist that can identify nematodes, mites, insects, plant pathogens, and other pests. Farm advisors in each county have expertise in pest identification. Also, they are in close contact with other University of California experts. County agricultural commissioners and their staff are helpful resources. In addition, the California Department of Food and Agriculture maintains a pest identification laboratory. Many pest control companies have licensed pest control advisers on their staffs. These experts can identify some types of pests.

When sending samples for identification, be sure to keep the material fresh and undamaged. Provide complete information on where you found the pest and, if appropriate, include examples of pest damage. Weeds, pathogens, and arthropods all require different types of sampling and handling. Sidebars in the following sections provide suggestions on how to collect and prepare specimens for shipment to an expert or identification laboratory.

Identification Keys

Identification keys are useful tools. They provide descriptive clues to the identity of living organisms. Unless you are familiar with the terms used to describe the pest's physical structures, many keys are difficult to use. This is because experts develop these keys for use by other experts. However, simple keys are usually available for common pests. A *dichotomous key* consists of a series of sequentially paired statements. To use a key, begin by selecting the descriptive statement from the first pair that best fits the pest you are trying to identify. The statement you select will lead you to another pair of statements. Continue working through the paired statements in this manner until the key leads you to the pest's identity. Dichotomous keys mainly use structural features, but they sometimes rely on the organism's color or size, especially with weeds. Many keys include photographs or drawings to help illustrate features referred to in the key. Table 1-1 is an example of a dichotomous key.

Photographs and Drawings

Whenever possible, use photographs and drawings for identification because they provide good visual descriptions of the pest (Figure 1-2) and its damage. They help you locate the pest's unique or distinguishing features. Use publications such as the California Department of Food and Agriculture *Vertebrate Pest Control Handbook* and the University of

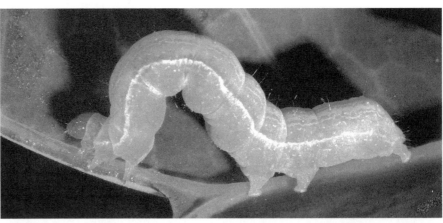

FIGURE 1-2

Photographs such as these of a cabbage looper egg and larva show the unique physical characteristics or coloration patterns that are useful identification aids.

TABLE 1-1.

Example of a Dichotomous Key.

KEY TO COMMON ADULT COCKROACHES*	
CHARACTERISTICS	SPECIES
1a. Small, about ⅜ in or shorter	go to line 2
1b. Medium to large, longer than ⅜ in	go to line 4
2a. Pronotum without longitudinal black bars	go to line 3
2b. Pronotum with 2 longitudinal black bars	German cockroach (*Blattella germanica*)
3a. Wings covering about half of abdomen Pronotum narrower	wood roach (*Parcoblatta* spp.)
3b. Wings covering nearly all of abdomen or extending beyond; pronotum narrower	brownbanded cockroach (*Supella suplongipalpa*)
4a. Wings covering abdomen, often extending beyond	go to line 5
4b. Wings absent or shorter than abdomen	Oriental cockroach (*Blatta orientalis*)
5a. Pronotum more than ¼ in wide	go to line 6
5b. Pronotum about ¼ in wide with pale border	wood roach (*Parcoblatta* spp.)
6a. Front wing without pale streak; pronotum solid color, or with pale design only moderately conspicuous	go to line 7
6b. Front wing with outer pale streak at base; pronotum strikingly marked	Australian cockroach (*Periplaneta australasiae*)
7a. Pronotum usually with some pale area; general color seldom darker than reddish chestnut	go to line 8
7b. Pronotum solid dark color; general color very dark brown to black	smokybrown cockroach (*Periplaneta fuliginosa*)
8a. Last segment of cercus not twice as long as wide	brown cockroach (*Periplaneta brunnea*)
8b. Last segment of cercus twice as long as wide	American cockroach (*Periplaneta americana*)

*Adapted from "Pictorial Key to Some Common Adult Cockroaches" by H. D. Platt, Department of Health, Education, and Welfare, Public Health Service Communicable Disease Center, Atlanta, GA, October 1953.

California *Grower's Weed Identification Handbook, Pests of Landscape Trees and Shrubs, Pests of the Garden and Small Farm, Wildlife Pest Control Around Gardens and Homes,* and the various Integrated Pest Management Manuals. Other pest management publications, textbooks, and field guides also contain useful photographs and drawings.

Preserved Specimens

Experts preserve identified plants, insects and other arthropods, reptiles, and mammals for study and comparison (Figure 1-3). Museums and herbaria at universities or other institutions are the most common locations for large collections of preserved speci-mens. You can also buy individual specimens and small collections of more common household and structural pests. Collections of weed seeds are available as helpful identification aids. Most preserved material is fragile, so handle it carefully. Store specimens in a cool and dry place to prevent damage and deterioration.

Characteristic Signs

Pests may leave signs of their presence that help you determine what they are. Birds and rodents build nests that are often characteristic to each species. The type of feeding damage helps you identify many insects. Rodents and some other mammals dig unique burrows in

FIGURE 1-3

Preserved specimens, such as these mounted insects, aid in pest identification. These are the adults of (a) the variegated cutworm, (b) the beet armyworm, (c) the cabbage looper, (d) the tomato fruitworm, (e) the tobacco budworm, and (f) the western yellowstriped armyworm.

the ground and often leave identifying gnaw marks on tree trunks or other objects. Sometimes trails in grass or tracks in dirt are helpful clues to rodent identification. Rodent fecal pellets and insect frass also are distinctive and important identification aids. Weeds may have unique flowers, seeds, fruits, or unusual growth habits. Also look for remains of weed plants from the previous season. Fungi and other pathogens sometimes cause specific types of damage, deformation, or color changes to host tissues.

Weeds

Weeds are plants that interfere with the growing of crops or ornamental plants or cause other types of problems. Some weeds are noxious and endanger livestock. Others affect the health of people or interfere with the safety or use of roads, utilities, and waterways. Many weeds are visual or physical nuisances due to their growth habits and size. Grasses, broadleaved herbaceous plants, shrubs, and even trees are "weeds" if they interfere with the activities of people (Figure 1-4).

Important weeds, however, possess special characteristics that distinguish them from the occasional out-of-place plant. *True* weeds adapt well to local climates, soils, and other external conditions. They compete successfully with cultivated plants for available resources. Most weeds produce large quantities of seeds, even under adverse conditions. Seeds of some weeds remain dormant in the soil for extended periods, sometimes 20 years or more, before germinating. Some weed seeds or fruits have special adaptations to promote dispersal (Figure 1-5). Because many weeds are capable of reproducing through vegetative structures, such as stolons, rhizomes, and tubers (see page 18), cultural activities that break up these structures, such as hoeing, mowing, or discing, produce new plants (Figure 1-6). Consequently, many weeds are persistent and difficult to eliminate.

FIGURE 1-4

Weeds are plants that interfere with the growing of agricultural or landscape plants or endanger the health or safety of people or animals. This photo shows an infestation of field bindweed in a tomato field.

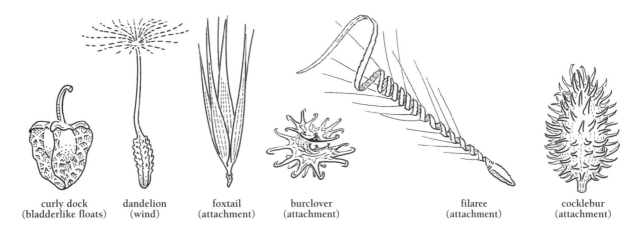

curly dock
(bladderlike floats)

dandelion
(wind)

foxtail
(attachment)

burclover
(attachment)

filaree
(attachment)

cocklebur
(attachment)

FIGURE 1-5

Weed seeds such as those shown here have many adaptations enabling them to disperse. These special characteristics are among some of the ways weeds compete with other plants.

FIGURE 1-6

Cultural activities such as discing can disperse some weeds. Cultivation breaks plants up into smaller segments that can reroot and form new plants.

Some weeds are native plants, while most are *exotic* species imported inadvertently or intentionally from other parts of the world. In their new location, many imported weeds become serious pests. This is because natural enemies or diseases are not present to suppress them. The weeds thrive if local environments are ideal for their growth.

Weed experts consider only about 3% of the identified plant species found in the world to be weeds. Usually, there are no more than 25 to 35 weed species at any one crop or landscape site. It is common for specific settings to have certain groups of weed species associated with them. Weeds found in crops or other cultivated areas are usually the most difficult ones to control with herbicides. This is because they are often similar to the cultivated plants. At the end of this section are discussions and illustrations of some of the major weed families.

How Weeds Are Pests

Weeds compete with agricultural crops for water, nutrients, light, and space, and they may also interfere with farming operations. Some weed species are toxic to livestock. Others release toxins into the soil, and these toxins inhibit the growth of other plants. Weeds clog irrigation canals and drainage ditches. Uncontrolled weeds contaminate products at harvest and harbor insects and pathogens.

Around homes, businesses, and industry, heavy populations of weeds often infest lawns, groundcovers, and ornamental plantings. Weeds sometimes harbor insect or vertebrate pests and detract from the appearance of landscaping. Dry weeds are fire hazards. Various weed pollens cause allergies in some people, and certain weeds produce skin irritation. Some weeds are poisonous to people and animals.

Along roadsides and rights-of-way, large weeds interfere with travel and maintenance operations. Tall roadside weeds obscure signs, while creeping species clog road drains or erode pavement edges. In commercially operated forests, weeds compete with tree seedlings and become fire hazards. They interfere with normal cultural activities. Some weeds, such as mistletoe, parasitize trees. Overgrown aquatic weeds clog irrigation canals, ditches, streams, rivers, and lakes. These cause harm to native aquatic life and make the use of waterways difficult for people and animals. Large infestations of aquatic weeds also hinder fish growth and reproduction. Aquatic weeds promote mosquito problems by decreasing normal water flow and wave action.

Identifying Weeds

A simple way to identify common weeds is to compare specimens with color photographs and drawings. If you are unable to determine the species from these sources, refer to identification keys or compare the weeds to preserved specimens. You may need to send some weed plants to an expert for identification (see Sidebar 1).

Specialists identify plants, including weeds, by recognizing differences and similarities among flowers, leaves, stems, and roots. Fruits, seeds, and special structures such as tubers or rhizomes are also useful identification characteristics, as are the plant's growth habits.

Weed Classification. Most weeds fall within two major land-plant groups, the *dicots* and the *monocots*. Dicots, also called *broadleaves*, are plants that produce two seedling-leaves (cotyledons). Leaves of dicots usually have netlike veins. Dicots generally grow as *herbaceous* plants (leafy and herblike) or as *woody* plants (shrub- or treelike).

Monocots produce only a single grasslike leaf in the seedling. Leaves of these plants typically have veins that run parallel to their length. Grasses, sedges, and rushes are monocots.

Mosses (and liverworts) belong to a unique group of plants known as *bryophytes*. Mosses are different from land plants because they lack a vascular system. They are occasional pests in aquatic settings and sometimes cause problems in greenhouses or on buildings or ornamental plants.

Algae are nonflowering primitive aquatic plants that often clog streams, lakes, drainage ditches, and rice fields. Pest managers usually include algae among weed pests. Like more highly developed plants, algae carry out photosynthesis to convert light into energy. However, algae lack true stems, leaves, and flowers that are characteristic of higher plants. They reproduce through cell division, or they produce spores.

It is usually easy to determine if the weed is a land plant, moss, or alga. However, when identifying land weeds, you must distinguish between a woody or herbaceous dicot (broadleaf) or a monocot (grass, rush, or sedge).

Weed Development. Most weeds pass through several stages of development, beginning with the seed. Sprouted seeds, known as seedlings, are usually tender and vulnerable to environmental extremes and are often quite susceptible to herbicides. Seedlings differ in appearance from mature plants and so may be difficult to identify. Because they are the stage most readily controlled, learn to identify the seedlings.

From seedlings, weeds continue their vegetative growth stage marked by rapid foliage development as they attain their maximum size. Plants then enter a reproductive period in which they divert most of their energy to flowering and seed production. Once they form seeds, weeds reach maturity, a postreproductive period. Perennial plants continue to repeat vegetative growth and reproductive cycles each year.

For identification, learn to recognize the different growth stages of weeds.

Understanding the growth stages is also important when selecting herbicides or other methods of weed control.

Weed Life Cycles. Weed life cycles are either *annual*, *biennial*, or *perennial*. Occasionally, some weed species with one type of life cycle may behave as if they have a different life cycle. This may be due to favorable weather or abnormal or unusual changes in environmental influences. Milder temperatures, for example, promote longer life cycles. Once you are familiar with the life cycle of a weed, you can properly time herbicide applications. For instance, most perennial weeds are not susceptible to herbicides during early bloom stages.

Annual weeds live one year or less. They sprout from seeds, mature, and produce seeds for the next generation during this period. Annual weeds are either *summer annuals* or *winter annuals* (Figure 1-7). Seeds of summer annuals sprout in the spring, and the plants produce seeds and die during the summer or fall. Some common summer annual weeds include pigweed, puncturevine, barnyardgrass, Russian thistle, common purslane, and yellow foxtail. Seeds of winter annuals sprout in the fall, then grow over the winter. These plants produce seeds in the spring and usually die before summer. Mustard, wild oat, annual bluegrass, burclover, and filaree are examples of winter annual weeds.

Biennial plants live for two growing seasons. They sprout and undergo vegetative growth during the first season, then flower, produce seed, and die the following season. Bristly oxtongue, poison hemlock, wild carrot, mullein, and Scotch thistle are biennials.

Perennial weeds live 3 or more years; some species live indefinitely. Many perennials lose their leaves or die back entirely during the winter (herbaceous perennials). These plants regrow each spring from roots or underground storage organs such as tubers, bulbs, or

SIDEBAR 1

Sampling and Sending Weeds for Identification

■ SAMPLING

1. Choose several plants that represent the species.

2. Include stems, leaves, flowers (if present), and roots.

3. Dig up weeds to prevent damage to roots.

4. Shake plants lightly after digging to remove excess soil.

■ PREPARATION

1. Keep plants in an ice chest while you are in the field. If they cannot be shipped immediately, store them in a refrigerator.

2. Place plants in plastic bags without moisture, or press them between sheets of absorbent paper and encase in heavy cardboard for protection.

■ LABELING

Attach a label to the outside of each sample. Include the following information on labels:

1. Location where samples were taken, including names of nearby crossroads.

2. Description of specific characteristics of the site where the weeds were growing.

3. Whether plants are annuals or perennials.

4. Your name, address, and telephone number.

5. Date samples were taken.

6. Any other information that would help in the identification of the weeds.

■ SHIPPING

1. Contact the person or laboratory who will receive samples to determine the best method of shipping and to inform them that samples will be arriving.

2. Pack samples in a sturdy, well-insulated container to prevent crushing or heat damage.

3. Mark package clearly and request shipper to keep it in a cool location.

4. Ship packages early in the week so they will arrive before a weekend.

FIGURE 1-7

This illustration shows the difference in the growth periods of winter and summer annual weeds.

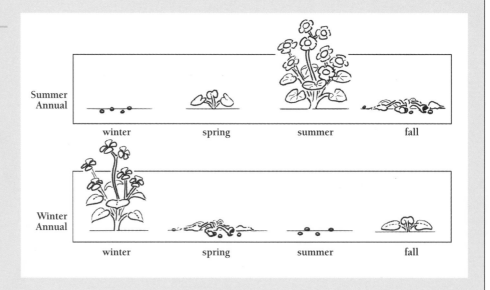

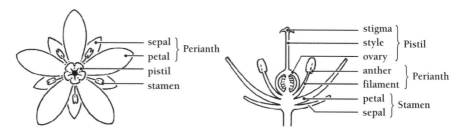

FIGURE 1-8

Weed flowers have important parts that are useful in identifying them.

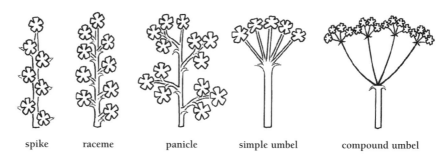

spike   raceme   panicle   simple umbel   compound umbel

FIGURE 1-9

As shown here, there are several types of inflorescences. Use these characteristics in weed identification.

rhizomes. These storage organs provide the chief means of dispersal for a number of major perennial weeds as well. Examples of perennial weeds include curly dock, silverleaf nightshade, field bindweed, alkali sida, dandelion, yellow nutsedge, Pacific poison oak, johnsongrass, and bermudagrass. Woody plants such as trees and shrubs are perennials and can be weeds under certain circumstances. Perennial weeds are the most difficult type of weed to control with herbicides, cultural controls, or mechanical methods.

Physical Features of Weeds. Weeds (and most other plants) have unique physical features that experts use for identification. These include flowers, leaves, stems and special rooting structures, roots, and fruits and seeds.

Flowers. Flowers contain sexual reproductive organs and differ widely among species. These differences help in weed identification. To use flowers as an identification aid, become familiar with the different flower parts (Figure 1-8). Flowers occur singly or as compound *inflorescences*, groups of flowers arising from a common main stem. Various names, such as *panicle, raceme, spike, head, umbel,* and *catkin,* describe the arrangement of flowers in an inflorescence (Figure 1-9).

Leaves. The arrangement and shape of leaves, vein patterns, and presence of spines or hairs are helpful identifying characteristics. When identifying seedlings, leaves are the only easily visible structures. Cotyledons and occasionally the first true leaves of broadleaved plants differ from the plant's mature foliage. For grasses, experts rely on the collar region of the plant, where leaves separate from the main stem.

Stems. Stems form the weed's basic framework or skeleton. They connect roots to other structures, providing support for leaves and flowers as well as channels for transport of nutrients and

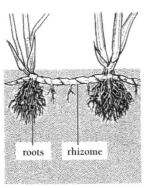

JOHNSONGRASS RHIZOME

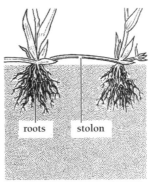

BERMUDAGRASS STOLON

CANADA THISTLE
CREEPING ROOT

water. Specialized stem modifications enable some weeds to reproduce vegetatively (Figure 1-10). *Rhizomes* are elongated underground stems that grow horizontally from the plant. *Tubers* also grow underground and are enlarged fleshy growths arising from stems or roots. A *stolon* is a stem that grows horizontally above the ground surface and roots at nodes.

Roots. Roots *absorb* water and nutrients from the soil and store food. The creeping roots of some plants give rise to stems. Some weeds have thick, elongated taproots from which short lateral rootlets grow (dandelions, for example). Other weeds have networks of fine branching *fibrous* roots, as seen in grasses. Roots provide helpful clues in weed identification.

Fruits and Seeds. A fruit is the ripened ovary of a plant's flower. Seeds are the primary way weeds reproduce. Fruits and seeds are useful structures for identifying weeds, because they are unique in their shape, size, markings, and color.

Algae

Important Characteristics. Algae are primitive plants closely related to some fungi and protozoans. They reproduce by means of spores, cell division, or fragmentation. There are more than 17,000 identified species of algae. Pest algae fall within three general groups: planktonic or microscopic, filamentous, and attached-erect (Figure 1-11). Microscopic algae impart greenish or reddish colors to water. They often float on the water surface as scums. Filamentous algae form dense free-floating mats or mats attached to aquatic plants or rocks. Attached-erect algae, known as *Chara* and *Nitella*, resemble flowering plants with leaflike and stemlike structures.

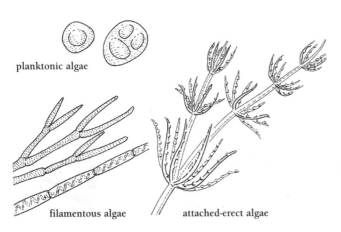

planktonic algae

filamentous algae   attached-erect algae

FIGURE 1-11

There are three types of algae: planktonic, filamentous, and attached-erect. (Drawings are greatly enlarged.) Algae often clog waterways, as seen in the photograph.

Algae clog irrigation channels, irrigation equipment, waterways, and ponds, and render swimming pools unsightly. Large algal buildup may deplete oxygen within a body of water and kill fish. Some forms release toxins into water as they decompose, which may poison people or livestock.

Where Found. Algae occur in swimming pools, ponds, lakes, streams, rivers, and other bodies of water. They also become pests in irrigation canals. Some forms of algae are problems in flooded rice fields.

Sedge Family

Important Characteristics. Many sedges (Figure 1-12) are perennial plants. They are grasslike and have fibrous root systems, and their perennial species produce rhizomes or tubers. Elongated leaves are V shaped and arise from 3-sided stems. This unique stem shape distinguishes them from grasses.

Where Found. Sedges are pests in orchards, vineyards, irrigated crops, and home gardens. They cause severe problems in rice fields. Sedges usually occur in marshy or poorly drained areas and along edges of ditches and ponds.

Examples. Yellow nutsedge or "nutgrass" (*Cyperus esculentus*), purple nutsedge (*C. rotundus*), blunt spikerush (*Eleocharis obtusa*), hardstem bulrush (*Scirpus acutus*), and river bulrush (*S. fluviatilis*) are examples of sedges.

Grass Family

Important Characteristics. Grasses (Figure 1-13) are a large family of annual or perennial plants. They include many notable weeds as well as important cultivated crops such as grains. Some species provide substantial food sources for grazing livestock. Roots of grasses are dense and fibrous; several species reproduce by rhizomes. A major feature used in grass identification is the collar region (Figure 1-14). A unique structure known as the *ligule* occurs at the collar region in many species of grasses.

Several important grassy weeds are winter annuals. Wild oat, for example, is one of the most widely distributed, troublesome winter annual weeds in California.

Where Found. Most cultivated and natural areas contain grassy weeds. They are often pests in fields, pastures, rangelands, orchards, vineyards, landscaped areas, turf, along roadsides and ditchbanks, and in other locations.

FIGURE 1-12

Sedges are grasslike plants with fibrous root systems. They are usually found in marshy or poorly drained areas.

FIGURE 1-13

Grasses, like the wild oat shown here, are one of the largest families of important weeds.

Examples. Grass weeds include wild oat (*Avena fatua*), foxtail brome (*Bromus rubens*), bermudagrass (*Cynodon dactylon*), smooth crabgrass (*Digitaria ischaemum*), barnyardgrass (*Echinochloa crus-galli*), deergrass (*Muhlenbergia rigens*), dallisgrass (*Paspalum dilatatum*), annual bluegrass (*Poa annua*), yel-low foxtail (*Setaria glauca*), and john-songrass (*Sorghum halepense*).

Mallow Family

Important Characteristics. Mallows are annual or perennial broadleaved weeds, depending on the species (Figure 1-15). Most are resistant to many of the widely used herbicides, making them persistent pests. Most species are herbaceous plants that grow from ½ to 7 feet tall. They produce capsule or disclike fruits that enclose several seeds. Their leaves are usually round with serrated edges and have a characteristic palmate vein structure (the veins radiate from a common center). The cotyledons are roundish to heart shaped or pear shaped.

Where Found. Weeds in the mallow family are pests in annual crops, orchards, vineyards, and along roadsides, ditch banks, and in waste areas.

Examples. Venice mallow (*Hibiscus trionum*), velvetleaf (*Abutilon theophrasti*), little mallow (*Malva parviflora*), and alkali sida (*Malva leprosa*) are representative weeds of this family.

Mustard Family

Important Characteristics. Mustards are usually upright broadleaved weeds that grow from 1 to 5 feet tall, depending on the species (Figure 1-16). Many have yellow flowers. Seedlings usually

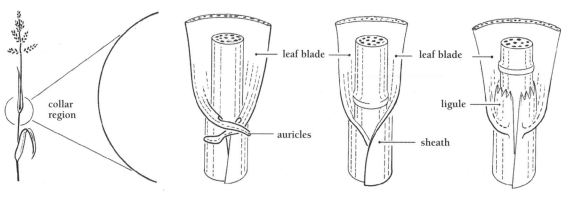

FIGURE 1-14

The collar region of a grass leaf contains unique structures that are very important in identifying grass species.

have broad cotyledons, which in some species are kidney shaped or indented at the tip. They have annual or biennial life cycles.

Where Found. Mustards occur in fields, orchards, vineyards, pastures, along roadsides and ditchbanks, and in vacant lots and waste areas.

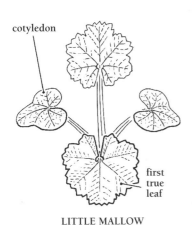

LITTLE MALLOW

FIGURE 1-15

Malva parviflora—*mallow family.*

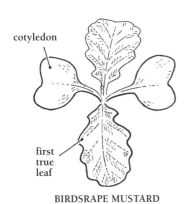

BIRDSRAPE MUSTARD

FIGURE 1-16

Brassica rapa—*mustard family.*

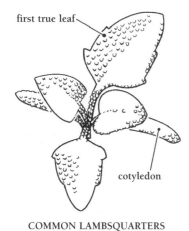

first true leaf

cotyledon

COMMON LAMBSQUARTERS

FIGURE 1-17

Chenopodium album—*goosefoot family.*

Examples. Common weedy mustards include black mustard (*Brassica nigra*), birdsrape mustard (*Brassica rapa*), shepherdspurse (*Capsella bursa-pastoris*), hoary cress (*Cardaria draba*), wild radish (*Raphanus raphanistrum*), and London rocket (*Sisymbrium irio*).

Goosefoot Family

Important Characteristics. Weeds of the goosefoot family include annuals, biennials, and perennials (Figure 1-17). Plants are variable in size depending on the species and where they are growing. Some reach heights of 6 feet; other species range in height from 8 to 24 inches. Mature leaves often have notches and usually are tinged with purple. Many species have elongated cotyledon leaves that are 4 to 6 times longer than their width.

Where Found. Weeds in the goosefoot family are widespread and are found in agronomic, horticultural, and vegetable crops. They grow abundantly in waste places, along roadsides, and along irrigation and drainage ditches.

Examples. Weeds in the goosefoot family include Australian saltbush (*Atriplex semibaccata*), common

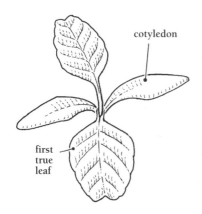

cotyledon

first
true
leaf

REDROOT PIGWEED

FIGURE 1-18

Amaranthus retroflexus—*amaranth family.*

lambsquarters (*Chenopodium album*), nettleleaf goosefoot (*C. murale*), and Russian thistle (*Salsola iberica*).

Amaranth Family

Important Characteristics. Amaranths are mostly upright herbaceous plants. Some species reach 8 feet in height (Figure 1-18), but there is also a low-growing prostrate species. Amaranths have small, inconspicuous greenish flowers. The cotyledons are narrow and elongate, and 4 to 5 times as long as they are wide. Seedling leaves are dull green to reddish on upper surfaces and magenta to bright red underneath. Some amaranths can cause nitrate poisoning in livestock under certain environmental conditions.

Where Found. Amaranths are pests in most cultivated crops, orchards, and vineyards. They often grow along ditch banks and roadsides and in waste areas.

Examples. Amaranths include tumble pigweed (*Amaranthus albus*), prostrate pigweed (*A. blitoides*), and redroot pigweed (*A. retroflexus*).

Morningglory Family

Important Characteristics. Weeds in the morningglory family include annuals and perennials. These are low-growing vines (Figure 1-19). One species, field bindweed, is one of the most difficult perennial broadleaf weeds to control in California. Cotyledons of plants in this family are large and roundish

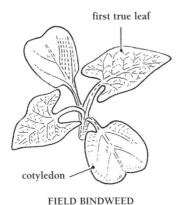

first true leaf

cotyledon

FIELD BINDWEED

FIGURE 1-19

Convolvulus arvensis—*morningglory family.*

and notched on the end. The first true leaves are triangular.

Where Found. Weeds of the morningglory family occur in all agronomic and vegetable crops as well as along roadsides and ditchbanks.

Examples. Field bindweed (*Convolvulus arvensis*), ivyleaf morningglory (*Ipomoea hederacea*), and tall morningglory (*I. purpurea*) are examples of important weeds in the morningglory family.

Potato Family

Important Characteristics. The potato family contains a large number of pest weeds. Most are low-growing, bushy plants reaching heights of about 3 feet (Figure 1-20). Tree tobacco grows to 12 feet. Cotyledons are longer than they are wide, sometimes by as much as 8 to 10 times. This leaf gently tapers to a point at the end. Some species produce thorny seedpods, while others produce rounded berries with many seeds. Several species are poisonous to people and livestock because seeds and young leaves contain high levels of alkaloids.

Where Found. Weeds in the potato family occur in agronomic crops and along roadsides, ditch banks, and fencerows. They are also pests in vineyards and orchards.

Examples. This large family includes Chinese thornapple (*Datura ferox*), jimsonweed (*D. stramonium*), Indian tobacco (*Nicotiana quadrivalvis*), tree tobacco (*N. glauca*), Wright groundcherry, lanceleaf groundcherry, and tomatillo groundcherry (*Physalis* spp.). It also includes silverleaf nightshade, black nightshade, and hairy nightshade (*Solanum* spp.).

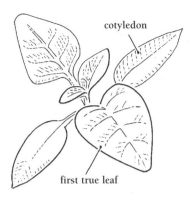

cotyledon

first true leaf

BLACK NIGHTSHADE

FIGURE 1-20

Solanum nigrum—*potato family.*

Aster Family

Important Characteristics. The very large aster family contains many important annual and perennial weeds. Many weeds in this family are "thistles" (Figure 1-21), characterized by spines on their leaves, stems, or flowers. These weeds are usually erect plants; many grow to heights of 1 to 3 feet while others are much taller. Most have showy flowers.

Where Found. Weed species in this family grow in almost all open or cultivated areas. These include rangelands, along roadsides and ditch banks, along fencerows, and in vacant lots, cultivated crops, orchards, vineyards, and lawns.

Examples. Weeds in the aster family include common yarrow (*Achillea millefolium*), California mugwort (*Artemisia douglasiana*), Russian knapweed (*Acroptilon repens*), yellow starthistle (*Centaurea solstitialis*), Canada thistle (*Cirsium arvense*), bull thistle (*C. vulgare*), common sunflower (*Helianthus annuus*), Jerusalem artichoke (*H. tuberosus*), telegraphplant (*Heterotheca grandiflora*), prickly lettuce (*Lactuca serriola*), pineapple weed (*Matricaria matricarioides*), Scotch thistle (*Onopordum acanthium*), bristly oxtongue (*Picris echioides*), common groundsel (*Senecio vulgaris*), California goldenrod (*Solidago californica*), annual sowthistle (*Sonchus oleraceus*), dandelion (*Taraxacum officinale*), and common cocklebur (*Xanthium strumarium*).

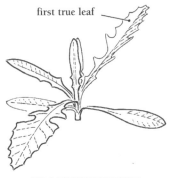

first true leaf

YELLOW STARTHISTLE

FIGURE 1-21

Centaurea solstitialis—*aster family.*

Invertebrates

Invertebrates are animals without backbones (vertebrae). These include nematodes and all other worms, snails and slugs, and also the arthropods (insects, spiders, mites, and their relatives). Pest invertebrates affect people in many different ways. Some are parasites of livestock, poultry, or human beings; they feed on skin, hair, and blood or invade internal tissues. Many invertebrates transmit disease organisms to people, pets, livestock, poultry, or plants. A large number of invertebrate pests feed on growing plants. Invertebrates also consume or contaminate stored food products. Some even damage buildings and other structures, as well as books, fabrics, furniture, equipment, and other items.

Arthropods

Arthropods are one of the largest groups in the animal kingdom. The word *arthropod* means "jointed foot" and refers to organisms with an external skeleton and jointed body parts. Insects, spiders, ticks, and mites are part of this group, as are crabs, crayfish, shrimp, and lobsters. Centipedes, millipedes, scorpions, and sowbugs are also arthropods. Only about 3% of the arthropod species that occur in the United States are pests, however. Table 1-2 lists some of the ways that arthropods interfere with human activities. Many arthropod

TABLE 1-2.

Ways in Which Arthropods Are Pests.

TYPE OF PEST	TYPE OF DAMAGE	EXAMPLE OF ARTHROPOD PEST
PLANT PESTS	chewing on leaves	caterpillars, beetles, grasshoppers
	boring or tunneling into leaves, stems, or fruit	twig borers, leafminers, beetles
	sucking plant juices	aphids, mites, scales, thrips, plant bugs
	feeding on roots	beetles, aphids, flies
	feeding on fruits, nuts, berries	moth larvae, beetles, earwigs
	causing malformations such as galls	flies, wasps, mites
	transmitting diseases	aphids, mites, leafhoppers
PESTS OF ANIMALS AND PEOPLE	have venomous bite or sting	bees, wasps, ants, spiders, scorpions
	feed on flesh or blood	flies, mosquitos, bugs, ticks, fleas, lice, mites
	transmit diseases	mosquitos, bugs, flies, fleas, ticks, cockroaches
	cause allergic reactions	bugs, bees, wasps, mites
	have offensive odors	beetles, lacewings, bugs
	cause fear or are nuisances	insects, spiders, scorpions, centipedes
	cause loss in livestock weight gain or reduction of milk or egg production	fleas, ticks, mites
	damage and devalue hides and pelts; cause loss of carcasses used for meat	sheep ked, lice, ticks, mites, cattle grubs
	cause reduction in livestock's worth and reproduction efficiency	flies, mites
STORED PRODUCT PESTS	eat or damage grains and other stored products	beetles, cockroaches, moths, crickets
STRUCTURAL PESTS	damage buildings and other wood structures	termites, beetles, ants, bees
PESTS OF HUMAN BELONGINGS	feed on clothing, carpeting, and paper products	moths, beetles, cockroaches, crickets
	feed on furniture and other wood products	termites, beetles

TABLE 1-3.

Beneficial Arthropods.

TYPE OF BENEFIT	ARTHROPOD
USEFUL PRODUCTS	
silk	silkworm moths
beeswax, honey	honey bees
shellac	scale insects
pigments and dyes	scale and gall insects
POLLINATION	
figs	wasps
many fruits and vegetables	honey bees, wild bees, bumble bees, flies, other insects
FOOD	
for fish	mosquitoes, flies, many others
for birds	butterflies, moths, beetles, many more
PARASITES AND PREDATORS OF HARMFUL INSECTS AND MITES	
parasites	wasps, flies
predators	beetles, lacewings, flies, bugs, spiders, wasps, mites
NATURAL CONTROL OF WEEDS	
feeding damage	moths, beetles, others
introducing disease agents	beetles
IMPROVED SOIL CONDITIONS	beetles, other soil-inhabiting insects
SCAVENGERS OF DEAD PLANT AND ANIMAL MATTER	beetles, flies, many others
USE IN SCIENTIFIC STUDIES	fruit flies, cockroaches, others
MEDICINAL USES	bees, wasps, flies

species are beneficial to people, plants, or livestock (Table 1-3).

Sometimes an arthropod may be a pest in one situation but beneficial in another. For example, poisonous spiders are pests when they disturb or endanger people or animals. However, in gardens and agricultural situations they help control harmful insects and other arthropod pests.

How to Identify Arthropods. Arthropods may range from several inches in length to microscopic in size. Identify most important arthropod pests by comparing them to photographs or drawings. Use a microscope or hand lens to examine small specimens. Identification keys help you identify some arthropods. Since these usually require a knowledge of body parts and structures, identification keys are more difficult to use. Because it is not always easy to identify arthropods, you may need the help of a trained specialist. Sidebar 2 explains how to prepare arthropods for shipment to identification specialists.

Identify pest arthropods by distinguishing between the various types of body structures that are unique to different groups. Some insects undergo changes in their body form during their life (for example, caterpillars turn into moths or butterflies). Also learn to recognize developmental stages, because the immature forms are often the ones that damage plants or products. Adults of many pest insects possess wings that can be used for identification. Insect mouthpart types are also helpful characteristics for identification: insects usually have specialized mouthparts for sucking, biting, and chewing, or a combination of these.

Arthropod Body Structure

Insects. The body of an adult insect has three distinct parts—the head, thorax, and abdomen (Figure 1-22). Eyes and one pair of antennae arise from the head. Also on the head are usually several pairs of appendages that make up the mouthparts. The thorax has three pairs of legs and often one or two pairs of wings. Insects have segmented abdomens. Sometimes the folded wings partially or entirely cover the abdomen. Some insects have appendages extending from the tip of the abdomen, such as pinchers, a sting, or other structures.

Spiders. Spiders have two major body parts (Figure 1-23). The head and thorax combine into one section called a *cephalothorax*. The cephalothorax gives rise to four pairs of legs, eyes, and mouthparts including a pair of fangs (chelicerae). The remaining body part is a nonsegmented abdomen that terminates with several pairs of spinnerets, the spider's web-spinning organs.

Ticks and Mites. Ticks and mites have only two body segments, but these are different from spiders (Figure 1-24). A small head (called a *gnathosoma*) with a few mouth appendages is attached to a large, combined thorax and abdomen called an *idiosoma*. Adult mites and ticks have four pairs of legs arising from the idiosoma. Immature forms usually have only three pairs.

Other Arthropods. Other arthropod groups have varying arrangements of body parts and legs. For example, centipedes and millipedes have many body segments with large numbers of legs (Figure 1-25). Scorpions have a long, segmented tail.

Arthropod Developmental Stages

Arthropods hatch from eggs and increase in size by shedding their outer body covering and growing a new, larger one. This is the process of *molting*. The period between one molt and the next is an *instar*. Immature arthropods pass through several instars before becoming adults.

The developmental changes from egg to adult that take place in most insects are unique among the arthropods. In many insect orders, the young have a different form than the adults. Immature insects in these orders undergo a change in form known as *metamorphosis*. These insects pass through a larval (usually wormlike) stage, a pupal stage, and an adult stage. However, in a few orders the young resemble adults but are wingless. As they grow, they pass through a gradual metamorphosis. If the insects are winged as adults, the young insects develop wing buds externally and these gradually grow until they reach the adult stage.

SPIDERS: Class Arachnida— Order Araneae

Important Characteristics. Spiders have four pairs of legs and an unsegmented abdomen. The abdomen attaches to the other main body part (the cephalothorax) by a narrow waist. At the tip of the abdomen are spinnerets, special organs used for producing different types of webbing.

Life Cycle. Immature spiders hatch from eggs and pass through several instars before becoming adults. Each instar begins by molting. This is a process in which the spider sheds its outer body covering, allowing it to grow larger. Most spiders live for 2 or 3 years, although some species may live as long as 20 to 30 years. Females generally live longer than males. Spiders feed on insects and other small arthropods.

Where Found. In buildings, spiders congregate in corners of ceilings, behind and underneath furniture, and in basements, attics, and crawl spaces. Outdoors, spiders appear in most types of environments. They frequently live among agricultural crops and landscape plants.

Sampling and Sending Arthropods for Identification

■ SAMPLING

1. Collect plant-feeding insects and mites by snipping off portions of foliage or stems containing the pest and placing these into a plastic bag.

2. Use an insect net to collect flying insects.

3. For other insects, shake plant foliage onto a light-colored cloth sheet and funnel arthropods into a plastic bag or glass or plastic jar.

4. Keep all collected specimens cool by placing them into an ice chest or refrigerator.

■ PREPARATION

1. Place insects, mites, and other arthropods into a glass vial with 70% isopropyl alcohol ("rubbing" alcohol also may be used). Vials must be sealed so that alcohol cannot leak out.

2. Include more than one individual of each species whenever possible. If other life stages are present (eggs, larvae, pupae, adults), include representative samples of these.

3. If the pest is associated with plants, send samples that show pest damage. Do not put plant material in the alcohol. Keep plants as fresh as possible by keeping them cool.

■ LABELING

Attach a label to the outside of each vial and plant sample bag. Include the following information on labels:

1. Your name, address, and telephone number.

2. Name and variety of host plant, if applicable.

3. Date specimens were collected.

4. Whether pest is in commercial, agricultural, residential, nursery, or other setting. If the pest is not associated with plants, describe the site where it was collected.

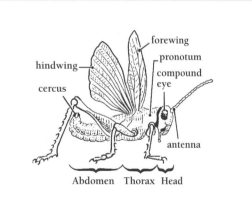

FIGURE 1-22

The body parts of this grasshopper represent the general structures that you usually see on most adult insects. Some adult insects are wingless, however.

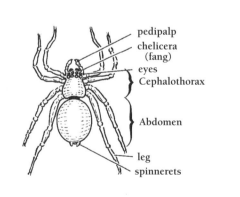

FIGURE 1-23

Spiders have two main body regions rather than the three found in insects. They have four pairs of legs, a pair of pedipalps, and a pair of chelicerae. The chelicerae terminate in fangs that spiders use to inject venom. At the end of the abdomen is a cluster of spinnerets, part of the spider's web-producing mechanism.

5. Location of area where specimens were collected, including names of nearest cross-roads.

▮ SHIPPING

1. Contact the person or laboratory who will receive samples to determine the best method of shipping and to inform them that samples will be arriving.

2. Pack samples in a sturdy, well-insulated container to prevent crushing or heat damage.

3. Mark package clearly and request shipper to keep it in a cool location.

4. If plant material is included, ship packages early in the week so they will arrive before a weekend.

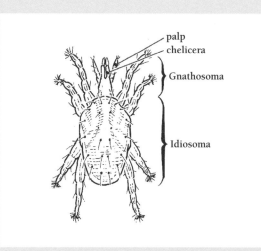

FIGURE 1-24

The body arrangement of mites and ticks is different from insects or spiders. Adults generally have four pairs of legs; immature forms usually have three pairs.

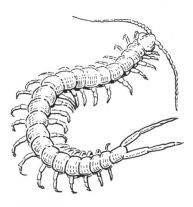

FIGURE 1-25

Centipedes have many body segments, most of which give rise to pairs of legs. Centipedes have a pair of poisonous fangs that arise from the head segment.

Damage. In California, black widow, brown recluse, hobo spiders, and a few other species can inflict painful bites. These bites may require prompt medical attention. Other large spiders may bite occasionally. Spiders leave unattractive webbing on inside and outside surfaces of buildings. Their presence in shipped produce has caused concern.

Beneficial Aspects. Spiders are general predators of arthropods, including insects, and contribute to the natural control of many pest species.

TICKS AND MITES: Class Arachnida—Order Acari

Important Characteristics. Mites and ticks have their abdomen broadly joined to the head and thorax (Figure 1-26). Adults usually have four pairs of legs, while immature mites and ticks most often have three or fewer pairs. Some species of mites produce fine webbing from silk glands located near their mouth. Most mites are very small and difficult to see without the aid of a hand lens or microscope.

Life Cycle. Ticks and mites hatch from eggs and pass through several immature stages before becoming adults. Immature ticks and mites resemble adults. Mites usually develop quickly from eggs to adults; some overwinter as adults, while other species overwinter as eggs. Ticks generally live much longer. Some require 1 to 2 years to reach maturity and may live an additional 2 or 3 years as adults.

Where Found. Depending on the species, mites are parasites on plants or animals. Certain species are predatory on other mites. Ticks are blood-feeding parasites of vertebrates and require blood meals to develop and reproduce. They commonly occur on animal hosts or in or near their nests. Plant-feeding mites live on upper or lower leaf surfaces.

SIZE RELATIONSHIPS

The actual body lengths (not including legs, antennae, or wings) of arthropods in drawings such as the tick at the right are indicated by a size bar. ⊢——————⊣
This magnifying glass symbol indicates arthropods whose body length is 0.1 inch or smaller, such as the mite shown at the right.

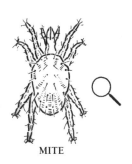
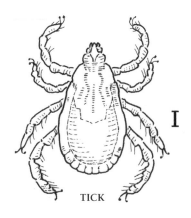

MITE

TICK

FIGURE 1-26

Ticks and mites are closely related, although ticks are much larger. Ticks are parasites of vertebrates and feed on blood. Some mites are parasites of vertebrates, although many are serious plant pests.

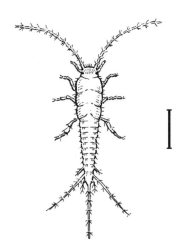

COMMON SILVERFISH

FIGURE 1-27

Silverfish—Order Thysanura.

DIFFERENTIAL GRASSHOPPER

FIGURE 1-28

Grasshopper—Order Orthoptera.

Damage. Plant-feeding mites often produce serious economic or visual damage, including leaf discoloration and defoliation. Some plant-feeding mites transmit disease-causing microorganisms. Feeding injuries produced by mites that infest animals and people may itch severely. Toxins injected by ticks during feeding sometimes cause paralysis of hosts; some tick species transmit disease-causing microorganisms.

Beneficial Aspects. Several species of mites are predatory on pest mites. These serve as an important component of natural and biological control programs.

BRISTLETAILS: Class Insecta— Order Thysanura (Silverfish and Firebrats)

Important Characteristics. Silverfish and firebrats have no wings. They usually have two or three long taillike structures (Figure 1-27). Mouthparts are of the chewing type. Most are brownish or silver in color. They are often nocturnal.

Life Cycle. Thysanurans undergo simple metamorphosis, so the young resemble adults, but are smaller. Individuals of some species live for 2 to 3 years.

Where Found. Silverfish and firebrats occur in homes, businesses, and libraries. They hide in cracks and crevices and other dark places. Silverfish prefer areas of high humidity and often may become trapped in sinks and tubs. Firebrats prefer drier habitats.

Damage. These insects infest paper, cereals, and fabrics (including synthetics). They also feed on resins and glue used in books and picture mountings.

ORTHOPTERANS: Class Insecta— Order Orthoptera (Crickets, Grasshoppers, Locusts, and Katydids)

Important Characteristics. Immature orthopterans resemble adults. They have chewing mouthparts and many species have wings, although most are not good fliers (Figure 1-28). Wingless species also exist. They have powerful hind legs that they use for jumping. Crickets, locusts, and katydids make distinguishing chirping or buzzing sounds. Many grasshopper species make clicking or buzzing sounds when they fly.

Life Cycle. Orthopterans hatch from eggs that adult females glue to plant surfaces, insert into plant tissues, lay in soil, or lay freely on the ground. Immature forms do not have wings; they pass through a series of instars before reaching the adult stage. Most orthopterans live 1 or more years.

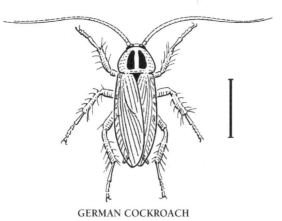

GERMAN COCKROACH

FIGURE 1-29

Cockroach—Order Blattodea.

Where Found. Orthopterans occur in most agricultural crops, landscaped areas, and gardens. Many live in the soil, while others live in trees or shrubs.

Damage. Grasshoppers, locusts, and katydids feed on plants and cause serious injury or defoliation. Crickets sometimes infest residences and stain or damage fabrics and paper products.

COCKROACHES: Class Insecta— Order Blattodea

Important Characteristics. Most cockroaches are poor fliers. Immature cockroaches resemble adults. They have chewing mouthparts. A great range of size differences exists among species. Although there are more than 50 described species of cockroaches in the United States and more that 3,500 worldwide, only 5 species are major pests in California (Figure 1-29). Cockroaches are nocturnal. They hide in dark, warm areas, especially narrow spaces where surfaces touch them on both sides. Cockroaches tend to congregate in corners and generally travel along the edges of walls or other surfaces.

Life Cycle. Cockroaches hatch from eggs that are usually laid in capsules made by the adult female. Females of some species carry their egg capsules about with them. Young pass through a series of instars before reaching the adult stage. Adults usually live from one to two years.

Damage. Several species of cockroaches inhabit buildings and may become persistent and troublesome pests. They are capable of transmitting bacteria responsible for food poisoning, such as *Salmonella* and *Shigella*, and viral hepatitis organisms. German cockroaches are also believed capable of transmitting staphylococcus, streptococcus, and coliform bacteria and are known to be responsible for allergy and asthma problems. In addition, German cockroaches have been implicated in the spread of typhoid, dysentery, and leprosy organisms.

EARWIGS: Class Insecta— Order Dermaptera

Important Characteristics. Earwigs are elongated, sometimes wingless insects having characteristic forceplike pinchers (cerci) extending from the end of the abdomen (Figure 1-30). They use these pinchers for defense and for catching prey. The pinchers of females of the European earwig are straight, while those of males are curved. Earwigs have chewing mouthparts.

Life Cycle. Earwigs hatch from eggs deposited in a nest in the soil. Adult females protect their eggs and newly hatched young. Earwigs pass through gradual metamorphosis. They develop from egg to adult in 2 to 3 months. They hibernate as adults.

Where Found. Earwigs usually nest in the ground and hide under boards, stones, and ground litter. Earwigs are very common insects in some parts of California.

Damage. Earwigs feed on vegetables, ripe fruit, garden flowers, and garbage; some are predaceous. They are occasional nuisances in buildings when they wander in from outdoors.

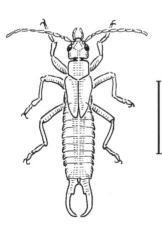

EUROPEAN EARWIG

FIGURE 1-30

Earwig—Order Dermaptera.

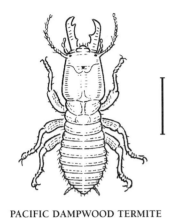

PACIFIC DAMPWOOD TERMITE
(SOLDIER)

FIGURE 1-31

Termite—Order Isoptera.

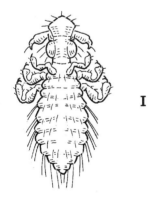

CHICKEN HEAD LOUSE

FIGURE 1-32

Chewing lice—Order Mallophaga.

TERMITES: Class Insecta—Order Isoptera

Important Characteristics. Termites superficially resemble ants but have an abdomen broadly joined to the thorax. When compared to ants, there also are differences in body coloration and the shape and size of wings and antennae (Figure 1-31). Some termites have wings but lose them after dispersing from the colonies where they hatched. Termites' wings are much longer than the body and both pairs of wings are of equal length. The wings of ants are shorter—no longer than the body, with the front pair of wings being longest. Termites live in colonies having different subgroups of individuals, called *castes.* Each caste performs specific functions in the colony. Many soldiers have enlarged heads with powerful pincerlike jaws. Queens have greatly enlarged abdomens. Termites have chewing-type mouthparts.

Life Cycle. Adult termites feed and tend to newly hatched termites. The nymphal stage lasts 3 to 4 months or longer. Adult workers may live 3 to 5 years, while queens live much longer. Termite colonies survive for many years as younger individuals replace older ones.

Where Found. Some species of termites live in the soil, but others construct nests in trees and wooden structures. Soil-nesting species usually construct tunnels or tubes to the wood sources they use as food.

Damage. Termites cause serious damage to wood structures by feeding and constructing tunnels or galleries.

CHEWING LICE: Class Insecta—Order Mallophaga

Important Characteristics. Chewing lice (Figure 1-32) are very small oval or elongated wingless insects with chewing mouthparts. They have flattened bodies, sometimes with dark brown or black spots or bands. Chewing lice have a head that is wider than their thorax. You need a hand lens or microscope to examine these tiny insects.

Life Cycle. Chewing lice lay their eggs on hosts, usually attached to hair or feathers. They may pass through three or more nymphal stages before developing into adults. Most chewing lice develop into adults within 2 or 3 weeks after hatching.

Where Found. Chewing lice are parasites of birds, fowl, and a few mammals. Species are host-specific—each species occurs only on one type of animal.

Damage. These parasites feed on feathers and the outer skin and skin debris of birds, and on hair, blood, and skin of mammals. Poultry infested with chewing lice usually become restless and uncomfortable, have decreased weight gain, and have lowered egg production.

SUCKING LICE: Class Insecta—Order Anoplura

Important Characteristics. Sucking lice (Figure 1-33) are flat-bodied, wingless insects with piercing-sucking mouthparts. The head is narrower than the thorax. A hand lens or microscope is necessary to examine these insects.

Life Cycle. Females cement their eggs to hairs of the host. After hatching, sucking lice pass through several instars and become adults within 1 to 2 weeks. Sucking lice pierce the skin of their hosts to feed on blood.

Where Found. Sucking lice are all host-specific parasites of mammals, including people. The human body louse remains on clothing when removed and can survive off its host for short periods of time. Other species must always remain on their hosts.

Damage. Feeding by sucking lice causes irritation and itching. Some lice

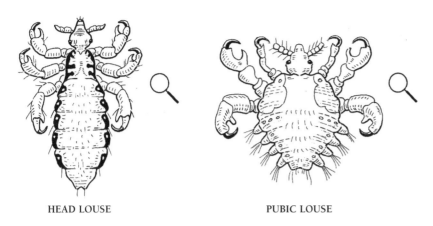

HEAD LOUSE   **PUBIC LOUSE**

FIGURE 1-33

Sucking lice—Order Anoplura.

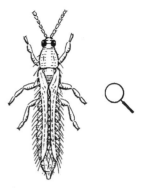

WESTERN FLOWER THRIPS

FIGURE 1-34

Thrips—Order Thysanoptera.

are capable of transmitting disease-causing organisms.

THRIPS: Class Insecta—Order Thysanoptera

Important Characteristics. Thrips are tiny, elongated insects with two pairs of wings (Figure 1-34). Their wings have a fringelike appearance. Thrips have modified sucking-rasping mouthparts.

Life Cycle. Thrips hatch from eggs, and most species pass through four instars. Thrips actively feed during their first two instars. The final instars are more of a resting stage, which often takes place in the soil. Wings are present after the thrips' final molt.

Where Found. Thrips commonly infest plants, often in flowers and on tender, developing parts of leaves and fruits.

Damage. Thrips puncture plant cells and then suck up the fluid that escapes. This type of feeding damages cells, resulting in deformed fruit and other plant structures. Some thrips are serious pests in greenhouses, gardens, and agricultural areas.

Beneficial Aspects. A few species of thrips are predatory. Predatory thrips play an important role in the natural control of several plant pests, including aphids and mites.

TRUE BUGS: Class Insecta—Order Heteroptera (Bed Bugs, Plant Bugs, Damsel Bugs, Assassin Bugs)

Important Characteristics. You can recognize most true bugs (Figure 1-35) by the triangular-shaped plate or scale on the thorax (*scutellum*) seen from above. They also have a long, needle-like beak (piercing-sucking mouthparts) that folds under their bodies. True bugs are various sizes depending on the species; some are nearly 2 inches long. They have two pairs of wings and most fly well. The second pair of wings are not visible while the insect is at rest. They sometimes have brightly colored wings.

Life Cycle. True bugs undergo gradual metamorphosis after hatching from eggs. Young resemble adults but without wings. Life cycles vary among the many species of true bugs.

Where Found. True bugs feed on plants and animals, depending on the species. Most are free-living, searching out appropriate hosts for food. There are several aquatic species.

Damage. Some species feed on blood of livestock, birds, rodents, and people. Feeding sites may become inflamed or infected and usually are very tender. A few species of true bugs transmit disease-causing organisms. Plant-feeding bugs damage plant cells. This causes

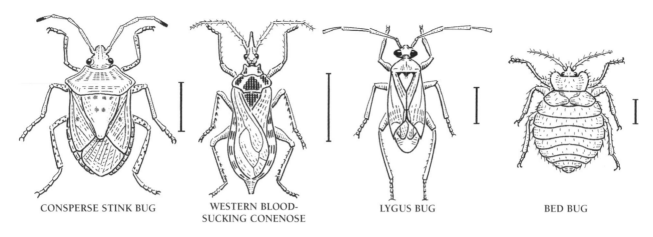

CONSPERSE STINK BUG

WESTERN BLOOD-SUCKING CONENOSE

LYGUS BUG

BED BUG

FIGURE 1-35

True bug—Order Heteroptera.

FIGURE 1-36

Leafhopper, whitefly, scale, and aphid—Order Homoptera. The photograph shows frosted scale insects on an English walnut tree. The round holes on some of the scales' outer body coverings are exit holes made by parasitic wasps.

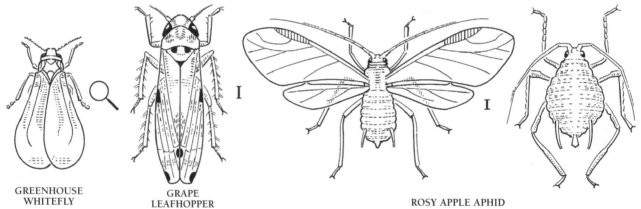

GREENHOUSE WHITEFLY

GRAPE LEAFHOPPER

ROSY APPLE APHID

deformities of fruits and other plant parts. Some bugs also inject chemicals into the plant that prevent or alter the plant's normal growth. Bugs are often serious plant pests in agricultural, home garden, and landscaped settings.

Beneficial Aspects. Some species of heteropterans are predators of other insects, including many insect pests. Examples of these are assassin bugs, bigeyed bugs, and minute pirate bugs.

HOMOPTERANS: Class Insecta— Order Homoptera (Aphids, Leafhoppers, Cicadas, Psyllids, Whiteflies, Mealybugs, Scales, Phylloxerans, Spittlebugs, and Treehoppers)

Important Characteristics. Homopterans are a diverse group of somewhat soft-bodied insects. Most are winged or have some winged forms. They all have piercing-sucking mouthparts. Figure 1-36 shows some of the different homopterans.

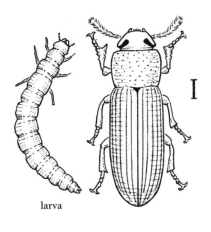

larva

CONFUSED FLOUR BEETLE

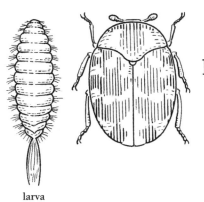

larva

CARPET BEETLE

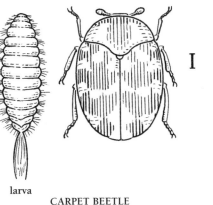

GRANARY WEEVIL

FIGURE 1-37

Beetles (left, middle), and weevil (right)—Order Coleoptera.

Life Cycle. Because this group is so diverse, it is not possible to describe a typical life cycle. Some, such as the periodical cicada, have life cycles as long as 17 years. However, many homopterans live less than 1 year.

Where Found. Homopterans are plant feeders, so they are usually found on or near plants. Some occur in greenhouses and indoors on houseplants. Phylloxerans often occur beneath the soil surface, where they feed on plant roots.

Damage. Homopterans pierce plant tissues and suck out liquids. Feeding usually causes deformed leaves and fruit, loss of plant vigor, stunted growth, and dieback of plant parts. Most homopterans excrete a sticky substance called honeydew that supports the growth of black sooty mold fungi. Many species transmit disease-causing pathogens to host plants.

COLEOPTERANS: Class Insecta— Order Coleoptera (Beetles and Weevils)

Important Characteristics. Adult beetles and weevils range from "pinhead" size to several inches in length, depending on the species (Figure 1-37). Most adults have a pair of hardened and often black wings (*elytra*). These completely cover the abdomen and hide the insect's second pair of wings when it is not flying. Larvae are very diverse in appearance. Both larvae and adults have chewing mouthparts.

Life Cycle. Coleopterans undergo complete metamorphosis. Larvae pass through several instars before pupating; pupation usually takes place in the soil. Some adults survive adverse weather by going into a resting or dormant phase—*hibernation* during cold winter periods or *aestivation* during hot or dry periods.

Where Found. Beetle and weevil pests infest plants, stored food products, wood, furniture, fabrics, and animal products; some even bore into metal. Many species actively bore into items they use for food.

Damage. Beetles and weevils damage or destroy agricultural products, forest trees, stored foods, fabrics, furs, carpets, wood items, and landscape plants.

Beneficial Aspects. Several species of beetles are predatory on other insects. These contribute to the control of plant-feeding pests such as aphids and mites.

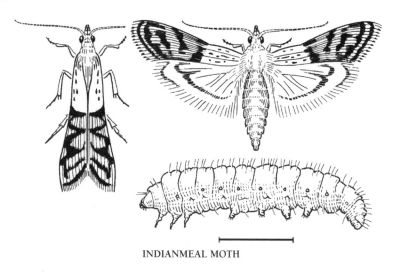

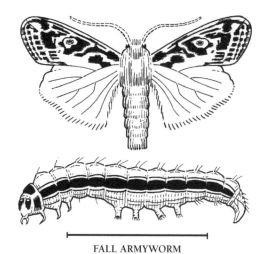

INDIANMEAL MOTH

FALL ARMYWORM

FIGURE 1-38

Moths—Order Lepidoptera.

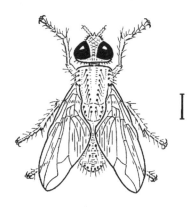

HOUSE FLY

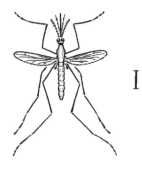

WESTERN MALARIAL MOSQUITO

FIGURE 1-39

Fly (top) and mosquito (bottom)—Order Diptera.

LEPIDOPTERANS: Class Insecta—Order Lepidoptera (Butterflies, Moths, and Skippers)

Important Characteristics. Adult butterflies, moths, and skippers (Figure 1-38) are distinguishable from other insects by their large, scale-covered and often brightly colored wings. Larvae are wormlike with chewing mouthparts. Adults have modified mouthparts in the form of a coiled tube that they extend to suck up liquids. Butterflies and skippers differ from moths by their antennae. Moths have tapering hairlike or feathery antennae while those of butterflies and skippers are clubbed. (Some exceptions exist where moth antennae resemble butterflies'—these are rare, however.) Skippers have shorter, thicker bodies and smaller wings, setting them apart from butterflies. Moths are primarily nocturnal, while butterflies and skippers fly mostly during the day.

Life Cycle. Lepidopterans undergo complete metamorphosis. After hatching from eggs, larvae pass through several instars then enter the pupal stage and change into winged adults. Pupation sometimes takes place in the soil. Many pest lepidopterans overwinter as pupae. Life cycles from egg through adult vary according to the species. Many of the pest species produce three or four generations per year.

Where Found. Lepidopteran pests occur on or in plant parts (including fruits), in stored food products, and in fabrics. Adult moths are commonly attracted to lights.

Damage. Moth larvae are one of the most serious agricultural pests. They cause considerable damage to fruits and vegetables, nuts, grains, cotton, and forage crops. Moths are also prominent pests in stored foods and cause extensive damage to fabrics.

DIPTERANS: Class Insecta—Order Diptera (Flies, Mosquitoes, Gnats, and Midges)

Important Characteristics. Adult dipterans (Figure 1-39) have only one pair of wings. In place of the second pair of wings are small clublike organs (*halteres*) believed to assist in balance. Larvae, known as maggots, are usually wormlike. Most adults have modified mouth structures for sucking, lapping, or piercing. Some adults have biting mouthparts.

Life Cycle. Dipterans undergo complete metamorphosis. Most species deposit eggs onto surfaces or into tissues of hosts. In a few species the eggs hatch inside the female's body, and these females deposit larvae rather than eggs. Many species undergo rapid development from eggs through the adult stages. This development may take as little as 3 or 4 days. Others have extended life cycles taking 2 or more years to complete. Many species survive periods of adverse environmental conditions as resting pupae in the soil.

Where Found. Flies, mosquitoes, gnats, and midges occur in most outdoor areas and inside buildings. Some larvae are internal parasites of animals; others invade plant tissues. Larvae of mosquitoes live in aquatic habitats. Housefly larvae congregate in garbage and on animal feces.

Damage. Many dipteran species are serious pests. Larvae of some invade living animal tissues. Adult mosquitoes and the adults of some species of flies, midges, and gnats are blood-feeding. Many of these insects transmit several serious disease-causing pathogens. Some species of flies are pests in agricultural crops and landscape settings. Others are nuisances in and around buildings and livestock or poultry areas.

Beneficial Aspects. A few fly species are parasitic on pest insects, and others are predators. These are often important natural and biological control agents.

FLEAS: Class Insecta—Order Siphonaptera

Important Characteristics. Adult fleas are tiny dark-brown or black wingless insects with laterally compressed bodies (Figure 1-40). Fleas are capable of hopping great distances for their small size. Cat fleas have been observed to jump 8 inches vertically and 15 inches horizontally. Larvae are wormlike. Fleas have piercing-sucking mouthparts.

Life Cycle. Fleas undergo complete metamorphosis. They usually pass through one complete cycle, from eggs to adults, in 30 to 40 days.

Where Found. Females lay their eggs on the host, although the eggs usually drop off before hatching. Larvae are free-living, usually on the ground. They feed on skin debris and hair of their host. Adults must feed on the blood of warm-blooded animals. Therefore, they live on their hosts or in their host's nest. They are usually host-specific.

Damage. Flea bites are uncomfortable and may cause an allergic reaction in some people and animals. Some species of fleas can transmit pathogens of diseases such as bubonic plague and murine typhus. Certain fleas serve as the intermediate hosts of tapeworms.

HYMENOPTERANS: Class Insecta—Order Hymenoptera (Bees, Wasps, Ants, Sawflies, and Horntails)

Important Characteristics. Adult hymenopterans differ from other orders of insects by usually having their abdomen joined to the thorax by a very narrow "waist" (Figure 1-41). Winged forms have two pairs of transparent, sometimes colored wings. Larvae are grublike. Certain species of bees, wasps, and ants are venomous; they have a sting at the tip of their abdomen. Several species are social rather than solitary. Large numbers of individuals live together in a colony and members of the colony perform different tasks, depending on their caste. Larvae and some adult hymenopterans have chewing mouthparts.

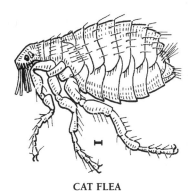

CAT FLEA

FIGURE 1-40

Flea—Order Siphonaptera.

FIGURE 1-41

Bee (left), wasp (center), and ant (right)—Order Hymenoptera.

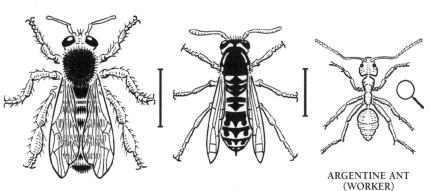

HONEY BEE   YELLOWJACKET   ARGENTINE ANT (WORKER)

Life Cycle. Hymenopterans undergo complete metamorphosis. Their larvae may be internal or external parasites of insects, spiders, and other arthropods; some species are plant parasites. Species that live in colonies forage for food for their larvae. Colonies of social hymenopterans live for many years, although individuals survive for only a few months to 1 or 2 years. Some species produce several generations per year.

Where Found. Adult hymenopterans forage for food on flowers and other plant parts. Many congregate on sweets and meat. Social species live in nests in the ground or in buildings, trees, and other structures.

Damage. Many species of hymenoptera are venomous and inflict painful stings that, in some people, may be fatal. Certain species of sawflies are serious agricultural and forest pests. Many bees and wasps are nuisances around homes and outdoor areas. Ants are persistent pests in food preparation areas and in agricultural crops. Some bees and ants damage wood structures.

Beneficial Aspects. Bees and other species of hymenoptera are important pollinators of agricultural and horticultural plants. Parasitic wasps play an extremely important role in the control of pest insects. Some are egg parasites and others attack the larval or adult stages of their hosts.

Nematodes

Nematodes (Figure 1-42) are a large group of unsegmented worms. Most stages are eellike in shape, pointed at both ends, and quite distinct from segmented worms such as earthworms. Mature females of some species have various rounded shapes. Most species are microscopic. Some are plant parasites and others are animal parasites, but most species are nonparasitic. Beneficial nematodes attack insects, plants, and other nematodes.

Most plant-parasitic nematodes are internal or external parasites of plant roots. Some species inject tissues with salivary secretions. These secretions cause root cells to enlarge and form knots or galls in which the nematodes live and feed. Others feed on root tips or in inconspicuous lesions on the root surface. Root damage caused by nematode feeding or migration prevents the plant from getting water and nutrients required for normal growth. Symptoms include stunting, loss of vigor, yellowing, and general decline. Although nematodes seldom cause the death of plants, nematode-infested plants are highly susceptible to injury from other pests or environmental stresses. Some nematodes transmit viruses to plants. Grapevine fanleaf virus, tobacco rattle virus, arabis mosaic virus, and tomato black ring virus are examples. A few nematode species attack aboveground parts of plants. This causes stunting or production of galls in the place of seeds.

Nematodes are common parasites of many animals, such as insects, snails, toads, frogs, birds, and most vertebrates (including human beings, poultry, and livestock). Hookworms and intestinal pinworms, for example, are nematodes. The canine heartworm, transmitted to dogs by a mosquito, is a nematode.

You can control plant-damaging nematodes through soil-applied pesticides, although control is difficult. Physicians or veterinarians, rather than certified pesticide applicators, control human and animal internal parasites.

Nematodes are difficult to identify because of the large number of species, their morphological complexity, and their generally microscopic size. Table 1-4 lists important genera and species. Many species of nematodes feed on fungi, insects, bacteria, and other nematodes. Some of these nematodes are biological control agents for insect pests.

TABLE 1-4.

Important Genera and Species of Nematodes.

COMMON NAME	SCIENTIFIC NAME
PLANT PESTS	
citrus nematode	*Tylenchulus semipenetrans*
cyst nematode	*Heterodera* spp.
dagger nematode	*Xiphinema* spp.
foliar nematode	*Aphelenchoides* spp.
lesion nematode	*Pratylenchus* spp.
needle nematode	*Logidorus africanus*
pin nematode	*Pratylenchus* spp.
potato rot nematode	*Ditylenchus distructor*
rice root nematode	*Hirschmanniella* spp.
ring nematode	*Criconemoides* spp.
root-knot nematode	*Meloidogyne* spp.
seed-gall nematode	*Anguiana* spp.
stem nematode	*Rotylenchus* spp., *Heliocotylenchus* spp.
stubby root nematode	*Trichodorus* spp., *Paratrichodorus* spp.
stunt nematode	*Tylenchorhynchus* spp.
ANIMAL PESTS	
canine heartworm	*Dirofilaria immitis*
filariasis nematode	*Wucheria bancrofti*
hookworm	*Ancylostoma duodenale*
pig lungworm	*Metastrongylus apri*
pinworm	*Enterobius vermicularis*

To identify plant pest nematodes, collect samples of soil, roots, and other affected plant parts. Send these samples to a laboratory for identification (see Sidebar 3). In agricultural situations, take samples randomly from several locations to provide information on distribution. Take samples from infected areas as well as those that appear normal. Place roots in the same bag with the soil to prevent the roots from drying. Keep aboveground plant parts separate from roots and soil. After working in areas infested with nematodes, always clean your boots, tools, and equipment thoroughly with hot water. This prevents spreading the organisms to other areas.

Plant Parasites. Most of the important nematode plant pests damage roots or other underground parts such as tubers or rhizomes. However, a few feed aboveground and damage stems, leaves, flowers, or seeds.

Root feeders impair the root system and prevent the plant from obtaining water and nutrients. Infected plants wilt under temperature and water stress, may become stunted or yellow, and are susceptible to infections by secondary pathogens such as fungi. The root-knot nematodes (*Meloidogyne* spp.) are pests of vegetable, field, and fruit and nut tree crops. These usually cause the formation of characteristic galls on roots of infested plants. Eggs and larvae of cyst nematodes (*Heterodera* spp.) develop within cysts that are the bodies of female parents. These nematodes survive inside these cysts for several years. Other root-feeding species do not cause characteristic growths on roots. Careful examination with a microscope reveals their damage.

Only a few California crops are subject to attack by nematodes that infest aboveground plant parts. Stem- and leaf-feeding species can cause leaf spots, deformities, and decay of plant parts and may kill growing buds. Some cause the formation of galls on stems, leaves, seeds, or in place of flowers. Their larvae may live many years inside galls.

Animal Parasites. Filaria are nematodes that are internal parasites of peo-

SIDEBAR 3

Sampling and Sending Plants for Identification of Plant-Infesting Nematodes

SAMPLING

1. Take random samples, but sample in a consistent manner. Mark off area to be sampled into grids. Randomly select areas to be sampled.

2. Keep samples from suspected diseased areas separated from samples taken in healthy areas.

3. Dig up and include roots and soil of diseased and healthy plants. Take root samples from below the level of surface feeder roots, because temperature and moisture fluctuations at the surface will affect the nematode species living there.

4. Include partially rotted or decayed roots.

5. Include aboveground plant parts if it is suspected that the nematodes are infesting these areas. Keep aboveground parts separate from root and soil samples.

PREPARATION

1. Place samples in clean plastic bags and keep them out of the sunlight. Keep samples in an insulated ice chest or refrigerator until they can be shipped. Do not freeze.

2. Pack samples in a well-insulated carton or disposable foam ice chest. Be sure container is sturdy enough to prevent damage to its contents.

LABELING

Attach a label to the outside of each sample bag. Include the following information on labels:

1. Name and address of grower or property owner.

2. Crop or plant types, including variety.

3. Location of field or property (names of nearby crossroads).

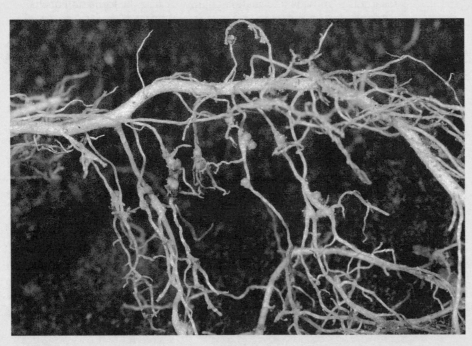

FIGURE 1-42

Nematode—Phylum Nemathelminthes, Class Nematoda. The photograph shows nematode galls on the roots of a plant.

4. Portion of planted area that sample represents. Include a map if necessary.

5. Brief description of the field's crop history (previous crops).

6. Observations by you and the owner or operator of previous problems and of when present problem was first detected.

7. Date samples were taken.

■ SHIPPING

1. Contact the person or laboratory who will receive samples to determine the best method of shipping and to inform them that samples will be arriving.

2. Mark package clearly and request shipper to keep it in a cool location.

3. Ship packages early in the week so they will arrive before a weekend.

ple and other vertebrates. Certain mosquito, tick, mite, fly, and flea species spread filaria from one infected animal to another. Elephantiasis and dog heartworm are nematode-caused diseases. Trichinosis, often transmitted to people through undercooked pork, is caused by the nematode *Trichinella spiralis*. The larvae of this nematode live in cysts in the muscle tissues of hosts, where they can survive for long periods of time.

Snails and Slugs

Snails and slugs belong to the phylum Mollusca. They are related to clams, scallops, abalone, octopi, and squid (Figure 1-43). Other pests that belong to this group are the shipworms and the pholads. Shipworms bore into wood that is in contact with salt or brackish water. Pholads are clamlike marine organisms that attack and destroy submerged wood. Snails have shells, which distinguishes them from slugs. Generally, identification of a snail or a slug species is not necessary for successful control. However, confirm that these pests are the actual cause of observed damage before starting control measures. In southern California, a predatory snail controls pest snails in citrus. Effective control of the pest includes identifying the predator.

Important Characteristics. Snails prefer cool, moist surroundings. However, their shells afford them protection from heat and dryness. This enables them to exploit many different environments. They seal themselves into their shells and become dormant for up to 4 years during dry periods. Slugs do not have shells and so are vulnerable to high temperatures and dry weather; they prefer cool, damp locations.

FIGURE 1-43

Snail—Phylum Mollusca.

Life Cycle. Snails and slugs lay between 10 and 200 eggs beneath the surface of the soil. They lay egg masses several times each year from spring through fall. In cooler areas, egg-laying activity stops during the winter. It takes from 1 to 3 years for newly hatched snails or slugs to reach maturity.

Where Found. Snails and slugs inhabit damp areas, soil litter, and foliage of plants. They are usually nocturnal and hide during the day under boards or stones, or among ivy, dense shrubbery, or damp refuse. At night and early in the morning, or during cool, damp periods, they forage for food. They often return to the same resting area each day unless the area becomes too dry or disturbed.

Damage. Snails and slugs feed on landscape plants, fruits, berries, and vegetables. Snails can be serious pests in citrus, where they feed on developing fruit. They are also pests in greenhouses. Besides feeding damage, both snails and slugs leave slime trails that detract from the appearance of produce and foliage. Some aquatic snails carry disease-causing organisms that can be transmitted to people.

Beneficial Aspects. Some species of snails are predaceous, making them useful in programs of biological control of pest snails.

Vertebrates

Vertebrates belong to the phylum Chordata and are animals with internal skeletons and backbones. They include fish, amphibians (frogs, toads, and salamanders), reptiles (turtles, lizards, and snakes), birds, and mammals. They become pests if they
- are reservoirs of pathogens that cause disease (such as plague and rabies)
- damage crops or stored products
- prey on livestock
- interfere with the activities or needs of people

Some of the most important vertebrate pests are rats and mice. These animals inhabit buildings and damage or soil furnishings and other items. They also consume and destroy stored food. They sometimes harbor disease organisms.

Identification of vertebrates is often easier than microorganisms, invertebrates, and weeds because there are fewer species involved. Endangered species, migrant species, or other wildlife laws protect many vertebrates. Therefore, it is important for you to know the species' identity before beginning any control program. Identify vertebrates by comparing them to photographs and drawings, such as those in the CDFA *Vertebrate Pest Control Handbook*. For help in identifying vertebrates, contact the U.S. Fish and Wildlife Service or the California Department of Fish and Game. These agencies require permits for control of some vertebrate species.

Besides observing the animals, another useful way to identify vertebrates is by recognizing certain characteristics. These include burrows, nests, tracks, and fecal droppings.

Fish

Some fish are pests because they eat other fish that are more important to people. Some also compete with important fish for limited food and space. Others occur in places where they are unwanted. Certain fish species may be undesirable because they serve as intermediate hosts for parasites, such as nematodes, that infect animals and people.

Amphibians and Reptiles

A few species of toads, frogs, snakes, lizards, and their relatives are poisonous to people and livestock. These species are pests if they occur in areas where people or livestock live. In addition, some people cannot tolerate the

FIGURE 1-44

Birds can be pests when they damage agricultural crops, nest on buildings, or interfere with aircraft operation.

FIGURE 1-45

Ground squirrels are often pests because they compete with people for agricultural products. Squirrels also damage levees and bridge foundations through their burrowing activities. Some vector diseases that fleas or other insects transmit to people and livestock.

presence of certain nonpoisonous species, requiring their control. Amphibians occasionally clog water outlets, filters, pipes, hoses, and other equipment associated with irrigation systems and drains.

Birds

People appreciate birds because of their song, beauty, or predaceous habits. Many birds catch insects and some kill snakes, rats, mice, and other pests. However, some pest birds harbor pathogens that insects or other organisms transmit to commercial poultry. Also, they eat or damage crops (Figure 1-44) and roost in massive numbers in trees or on window ledges. Some birds interfere with aircraft, cause damage to buildings, or make too much noise. Bird lice and mites associated with nesting areas can infest homes, hospitals, and offices.

Mammals

Pest mammals interfere with the activities of people or cause harm to their crops, livestock, or possessions (Figure 1-45). Rodents such as rats, mice, and squirrels compete with people and livestock for food. These animals often carry certain fleas and mites that harbor and transmit disease-causing organisms. Infected skunks and bats transmit rabies. Larger mammals, like foxes, coyotes, mountain lions, and bears, are occasional pests when they endanger people and their possessions or prey on pets or livestock. Foraging deer can be serious pests of agricultural crops and residential landscaping. Sea otters, seals, and sea lions are pests when they interfere with human activities or compete with people for food.

Disease-Causing Agents

Another important group of pests includes plant and animal disease-causing agents. Nonliving (*abiotic*) factors and living (*biotic*) pathogenic microorganisms cause diseases in plants and animals. Biotic and abiotic factors alter or interfere with the chemical processes that take place within an organism's cells. This produces disease symptoms or disorders. To avoid unnecessary pest management treatments, recognize abiotic factors that produce diseaselike symptoms in plants and animals.

Important Characteristics. Different plant or animal organisms have different susceptibilities to the effects of abiotic factors. An organism's susceptibility often depends on a combination of factors including its genetic makeup, nutritional state, and climatic conditions. Familiar signs of abiotic disorders in plants include

- poor growth
- yellow foliage
- deformed leaves
- poor fruit or seed production
- deformed or rotten fruit

Plants and animals exhibit symptoms resembling diseases as a result of physical factors. These include water stress or excess, nutrient deficiency or toxicity, and salt buildup. In addition, prolonged wind and other weather extremes, or exposure to toxic materials such as air pollutants or certain pesticides, produce disease symptoms (Table 1-5). Disorders caused by abiotic factors are a result of an organism's response to the conditions in its environment. These cannot be transmitted from one plant or animal to another. Pesticides do not correct or prevent abiotic diseases.

Biotic disease-causing factors are pathogens capable of spreading from one host to another and producing disease symptoms. The ability of the organism to spread and infect may depend on climatic factors. The host's genetic makeup or nutritional state also influence this ability. Several different types of microorganisms produce diseases in plants and animals. The most important are bacteria, fungi, viruses, viroids, and mycoplasmas.

TABLE 1-5.

Soil, Climatic, and Other Factors Contributing to Plant Growth Problems.

FACTOR	PROBLEM
TEMPERATURE	
freezing	May cause dieback, leaf scorch, frost nip, or bark split. Often causes separation of the epidermis from underlying tissues; use hand lens to see this.
cool temperatures	May reduce pollination or fertilization and lower crop production.
cool soil temperatures	Slows or shuts down water and nutrient uptake, resulting in wilting or nutrient deficiency symptoms even when soil contains adequate amounts.
inadequate chilling	Delays or interferes with normal breaking of dormancy; produces irregular bloom resulting in poor crop production.
high temperatures	Kills pollen, resulting in poor crop production. Causes sunburn of fruit and foliage. Results in sun scald, heat cankers, sunken lesions, pit burn, blossom end rot, and water core. May delay maturity of crops or reduce quality.
WATER	
too little water	Results in water stress, wilting, poor plant growth, leaf or fruit drop, leaf scorch, and nutrient deficiencies. Leaves may have dull coloration and may roll at edges.
too much water	Lowers oxygen available to roots; may cause flower, fruit, or leaf drop; lowers soil temperature; may kill roots. Plants may be more susceptible to soil fungi.
LIGHT	
too little light	Causes yellowing of leaves and elongation of stems. Plants become spindly. May cause twig or shoot dieback. Reduces fruit size and slows maturity.
too much light	Causes scalding or russeting of fruit or leaves; sunburn.
NUTRIENTS	
nutrient deficiencies	Causes leaf discoloration, leaf spotting, deformities of leaves and fruit; reduces growth, production, and shortens life of plant; makes plant unable to tolerate other stresses; causes leaf and fruit drop.
nutrient excess	Causes reduced fruit production, improper ripening, leaf burn or scald, fruit drop.
OTHER PHYSICAL FACTORS	
air pollution	Causes spotting and damaged foliage and fruit, discoloration, reduced growth and yield, and dieback.
pesticide injury	Causes leaf and fruit spotting, burning, or scorching; russeting of fruit; fruit and leaf drop; delayed maturity; and leaf deformity.
hail and rain	Causes physical injury to leaves and fruit, resulting in spotting and yield reduction; leaf and fruit drop, lodging of plants.
wind	Desiccates leaves. Results in spotting, burning, or scorching; improper pollination; and destruction of blossoms.
fire damage	Injures bark and nutrient transport system of plant; results in stunting and poor production and growth.
soil compaction	Limits root growth and nutrient availability, resulting in problems associated with water stress or excess and nutrient deficiencies.
potbound root system	Causes problems similar to soil compaction; plant exhibits weak growth, yellowed foliage, and may undergo leaf drop and twig dieback.
improper agricultural practices	Cause physical injury to roots or trunks of plants and reduces water and nutrient uptake; provides an entry point for disease infection and insect infestation.

Identifying Disease-Causing Pathogens. Many pathogens are submicroscopic, making identification difficult. Often only the use of electron microscopes or complex biochemical tests confirms the identity of a pathogen. It may even be necessary to grow the organism in the laboratory or inject plants or laboratory animals with the pathogen to make a positive identification. These types of tests require trained technicians and specialized laboratory equipment. Sidebar 4 contains information on using laboratory identification services and how to send material for analysis.

Another way to identify disease-causing microorganisms in plants and animals is by studying the observed symptoms. Each host plant or animal usually has specific diseases to which it is susceptible. These plants or animals produce specific symptoms or groups of symptoms. Learning to recognize disease symptoms helps you sort through and reject some pathogens as causes of the observed symptoms. In some cases, specific disease-causing pathogens are more prevalent in particular locations or under certain conditions. Knowing these limitations helps you to narrow the choices.

Fungi produce distinctive structures such as molds or spore-producing bodies that aid in identifying the organism. Also, lesions or rotted areas of infected plants may provide clues to the type of organism causing the damage. Inspect the plant's vascular system for damage. Be sure to dig up some infected plants and examine their root systems.

Check the disease symptom distribution throughout a population of plants or animals. Do many individuals show signs of infection, or only a few? Are the diseased plants distributed evenly, or are they confined to specific locations? Try to associate the distribution of infection with conditions that would favor specific diseases. This may provide valuable clues to the identity of the pathogen.

Bacteria

Disease-causing bacteria are small, usually single-celled organisms, although the *Streptomyces* species are many cells attached end-to-end. You cannot see bacteria without a microscope. Plant-infecting bacteria are rod shaped and most have threadlike structures called flagellae that propel them through liquids. Most bacteria require warmth and moisture to multiply. Some bacteria cause illness or death in animals and people. Only a few bacterial diseases are serious problems on plants in California. This is because of the semiarid climate and lack of significant summer rainfall.

Types of Bacteria. There are six genera of bacteria that have species capable of infecting plants and causing disease symptoms. These are *Pseudomonas, Xanthomonas, Agrobacterium, Erwinia, Corynebacterium*, and *Streptomyces.*

How Bacteria Are Spread. Anything that moves and comes in contact with bacteria may spread them to other areas. This includes farm equipment, rain or irrigation water, plant material, seeds, birds, insects, nematodes, and people.

Bacterial Infections. Bacteria invade plant tissues through natural openings and through wounds. They must enter tissues to infect the plant. Bacterial diseases show up as galls, leaf spots, soft rots, scabs, and systemic disorders. Table 1-6 lists examples of these diseases.

Fungi

Fungi are a diverse group of microscopic primitive plants. They must obtain their nutrients from some organic source such as living or dead plant material. Most fungi live off dead organic matter. These are called *saprophytes*. They are generally beneficial because they help break down organic materials and build up soil fertility. However, some fungi invade structural wood and other building materials. Certain species live off both dead and living plants, and some of these fungi cause plant diseases. A few fungi require living host plants to grow and reproduce. This group includes the major plant pest species.

SIDEBAR 4

Sampling and Sending Plants for Identification of Disease-Causing Pathogens

SAMPLING

1. Select plants that are most representative of the observed disease symptoms. Collect several plants.

2. Include roots by digging up plant and shaking off soil.

3. Place plants in plastic or paper bags. Keep plant materials cool. Put them in an ice chest while you are in the field. Store samples in a refrigerator until they can be shipped.

LABELING

Attach a label to the outside of each sample bag. Include the following information on labels:

1. Your name, address, and telephone number.

2. Crop or plant type, including variety.

3. Location of field or property (names of nearby crossroads).

4. Portion of planted area that sample represents. Include a map if necessary.

5. Brief description of the field's crop history (previous crops) or any information on what was planted in the area before diseased plants were grown there.

6. Observations by you and the owner or operator of the property of previous problems and of when present problem was first detected.

7. Date samples were taken.

SHIPPING

1. Contact the person or laboratory who will receive samples to determine the best method of shipping and to inform them that samples will be arriving.

2. Pack samples in a sturdy, well-insulated container to prevent crushing or heat damage.

3. Mark package clearly and request shipper to keep it in a cool location.

4. Ship packages early in the week so they will arrive before a weekend.

TABLE 1-6.

Examples of Bacterial Diseases in Plants.

SYMPTOM	DISEASE	PATHOGEN
galls	crown gall	*Agrobacterium* spp.
leaf spots	leaf spot of cucurbits	*Pseudomonas* spp.
	halo blight of beans	*Pseudomonas* spp.
	bacterial spot of tomato	*Xanthomonas* spp.
	bacterial blight of walnuts	*Xanthomonas* spp.
systemic infections	fire blight of apple, pear, and quince	*Erwinia* spp.
	bacterial wilt of cucurbits	*Erwinia* spp.
soft rot	blackleg of potato	*Erwinia* spp.
	vegetable soft rots	*Pseudomonas* spp.
scab	common potato scab	*Streptomyces* ssp.
	gladiolus scab	*Pseudomonas* spp.

Important Characteristics. Most pest fungi have a vegetative body (*mycelium*) that consists of tiny filamentous strands (*hyphae*). The mycelium grows through the tissues of an infected host. You can usually see this structure without magnification. Reproduction in fungi is primarily by means of spores. Many species of fungi produce more than one type of spore. One of these types of spores acts as a resting structure to carry the fungus through adverse conditions. Other spore types are responsible for the ongoing secondary spread of the organism.

Fungal identification usually depends on characteristics of the mycelium and structures known as *fruiting bodies* (because they produce spores). Diagnosis of a fungal infection involves looking for these structures on or in plant tissues or infected wood.

Disease Symptoms. Plants infected by fungi exhibit many different types of symptoms. Such symptoms are helpful in identifying the fungal organism. Powdery mildew, downy mildew, root and stem rot, sooty mold, and slime molds are types of fungi. Symptoms include

- soft, watery rots of fruits
- severe stunting of the plant
- profuse gumming
- smuts
- rusts
- leaf spots
- wilting
- malformation of plant parts, such as thickening and curling of leaves

How Fungi Spread. Spores of fungi spread by wind, rain, irrigation water, insects, and cultural practices. Any practice that moves infected plant material from one location to another can also spread fungal spores. Roots of noninfected plants may grow into areas where fungal organisms are present and become infected in this manner.

Fungal Infections. Fungi enter plant tissues through wounds and natural openings and by penetrating the outer surface of the host. Usually certain environmental conditions promote or accelerate fungal organism growth and infection. These include high humidity or presence of water and warm temperatures.

Viruses

Viruses are very small organisms that multiply in living cells to produce disease symptoms in plants and animals. Most can survive for only short periods of time outside host plant or animal cells. Viruses alter chemical activity (metabolism) within host cells, and these metabolic changes cause disease.

Important Characteristics. Viruses are very small and can only be seen with an electron microscope. They have different shapes depending on the type. Structurally, viruses are very simple compared with other living organisms. Viruses invade cells of plants or animals, then, using their own genetic information, alter these cells. Infected cells produce more viruses rather than the usual proteins or nucleic acid.

Symptoms of Virus Diseases. Almost all viruses reduce plant growth, resulting in stunting. Another common symptom is a change in coloration. This is most noticeable in the leaves and is often expressed as a mosaic pattern of light and dark blotches. Flowers also exhibit color variation. Sometimes the veins of leaves become lighter, producing a netlike appearance. Russeting is a color change that appears on fruit. Viruses also produce malformations or abnormal growth in various parts of affected plants, including leaves, fruits, stems, or roots. Some viruses cause parts of infected plants to die, a condition called *necrosis*. Severe necrosis results in complete death of the plant.

Identifying Viruses. Virus identification involves three different methods. The simplest is to compare the infected plant and its symptoms with photographs and written descriptions. A method called *indexing* involves inoculating a series of indicator plants with extracts from the diseased plant. Researchers compare disease symptoms with the results obtained from similar plants inoculated with known viruses. If symptoms from the unknown pathogen match any of the plants inoculated with a known virus, you can assume the unknown pathogen is that virus. A third method, known as *serological testing*, involves testing plant extracts for the presence of virus proteins. The tests use antibodies specific to known viruses.

How Viruses Are Spread. Mites and several plant-feeding insects, such as aphids, leafhoppers, and whiteflies, move viruses from plant to plant. Nematodes and fungi, cultivation practices, pollination, and pruning and grafting are also ways of transmitting disease-producing viruses. The seeds of infected plants transmit some viruses. Each virus usually is transmitted in only one or a few of these ways.

Viroids

Although viroids differ from viruses in several ways, they are most distinguishable microscopically. Viroids are much smaller and do not have a protein coat. So far, researchers have identified only a few viroid-caused plant diseases. However, researchers suspect that viroids cause many other plant and animal disorders. Potato spindle tuber, citrus exocortis, chrysanthemum stunt, and chrysanthemum chlorotic mottle are viroid diseases. Viroids spread primarily through infected stock. Infected plant sap can be carried on hands or tools during propagation and cultural practices. Some viroids transmit through pollen and seeds; insect transmission is unknown.

Mycoplasmas

Mycoplasmas are intermediate in size between viruses and bacteria. They survive for extended periods outside plant cells and are the smallest known independently living organisms. Mycoplasmas are responsible for several insect-transmitted plant diseases. These include pear decline, aster yellows, X disease of peach, and stubborn disease of citrus. Insects (usually leafhoppers) transmit most mycoplasma-caused diseases. Mites may also transmit mycoplasmas. Grafting woody crop plants also accounts for mycoplasma transmission.

REVIEW QUESTIONS

1. **A disadvantage of using common names for identifying organisms is:**
   - ☐ a. Often, they do not provide any information about the relationship of one organism to another
   - ☐ b. Common names usually describe some characteristic of the pest
   - ☐ c. Pesticide labels list common names of pests
   - ☐ d. Pesticide use reports require scientific names of pests

2. **Which of the following *is not* a characteristic of weeds?**
   - ☐ a. Some weeds are noxious and endanger livestock
   - ☐ b. Weeds interfere with the safety or use of roads, utilities, and waterways
   - ☐ c. Most weeds produce large quantities of seeds, even under adverse conditions
   - ☐ d. Weeds enhance the growth of agricultural crops

3. **Plants that are capable of reproducing from overwintering storage organs such as bulbs, tubers, and rhizomes are called:**
   - ☐ a. Monocots
   - ☐ b. Biennials
   - ☐ c. Perennials
   - ☐ d. Dicots

4. **Perennial weeds are generally the most difficult to control because:**
   - ☐ a. They produce more seeds than other types of plants
   - ☐ b. They can reproduce and spread from storage organs such as rhizomes and tubers
   - ☐ c. Their seeds remain viable for more years than those of annual and biennial plants
   - ☐ d. They produce deep taproots that resist mechanical control as well as herbicides

5. **Which of the following insect orders includes species known to transmit diseases in humans?**
   - ☐ a. Orthoptera (crickets and grasshoppers)
   - ☐ b. Thysanura (firebrats and silverfish)
   - ☐ c. Blattodea (cockroaches)
   - ☐ d. Thysanoptera (thrips)

6. **Which organism is *not* an invertebrate pest?**
   - ☐ a. Snail
   - ☐ b. Caterpillar
   - ☐ c. House mouse
   - ☐ d. Garden spider

7. **Which of the following orders of insects includes several species of agricultural pests?**
   - ☐ a. Isoptera (termites)
   - ☐ b. Thysanura (firebrats and silverfish)
   - ☐ c. Blattodea (cockroaches)
   - ☐ d. Heteroptera (true bugs)

8. **The various immature stages of an insect are known as:**
   - ☐ a. Instars
   - ☐ b. Metamorphoses
   - ☐ c. Juveniles
   - ☐ d. Pre-adults

9. **Which of the following groups of insect orders includes both pests and beneficials that attack pest insect species?**
   - ☐ a. Hymenoptera (wasps and bees), thysanoptera (thrips), and heteroptera (true bugs)
   - ☐ b. Thysanura (firebrats and silverfish), blattodea (cockroaches), and dermaptera (earwigs)
   - ☐ c. Isoptera (termites), mallophaga (chewing lice), and anoplura (sucking lice)
   - ☐ d. Homoptera (aphids and whiteflies), lepidoptera (moths and butterflies), and siphonaptera (fleas)

10. **Which of the following insect orders includes important livestock pests?**
    - ☐ a. Dermaptera (earwigs)
    - ☐ b. Homoptera (aphids and whiteflies)
    - ☐ c. Heteroptera (true bugs)
    - ☐ d. Orthoptera (crickets and locust)

11. **Which part of a plant do nematodes most commonly attack?**
    - ☐ a. Tender young foliage
    - ☐ b. Roots and underground plant parts
    - ☐ c. Germinating seeds
    - ☐ d. Flowers

12. **Pest nematode species damage plants by:**
    - ☐ a. Sucking plant sap
    - ☐ b. Preventing flower and fruit formation
    - ☐ c. Impairing water and nutrient uptake capacity
    - ☐ d. Transmitting several bacterial diseases

13. **Which one of the following types of plant disorders cannot be transmitted?**
    - ☐ a. Bacterial diseases such as Pseudomonas
    - ☐ b. Fungal diseases such as downy mildew
    - ☐ c. Diseases caused by viruses, viroids, and mycoplasmas
    - ☐ d. Water stress and other abiotic problems

14. **Which one of the following types of disease-causing organisms is easily seen without a microscope?**
    - ☐ a. Bacteria
    - ☐ b. Viruses
    - ☐ c. Fungi
    - ☐ d. Mycoplasmas

15. **Honey bees belong to the insect order:**
    - ☐ a. Coleoptera
    - ☐ b. Diptera
    - ☐ c. Hymenoptera
    - ☐ d. Lepidoptera

2 Pest Management

Pest managers use pheromone traps to monitor the activities of some insects.

*P*EST MANAGEMENT is the science of safely preventing, suppressing, or eliminating unwanted organisms. Carrying out a successful pest management program involves choosing the right prevention or control methods. It also involves knowing how to use these techniques to reduce pest populations to acceptable levels.

Besides knowing the identity of a pest, you must learn its importance. There are key pests, occasional pests, and secondary pests:

Key pests are those that cause major damage on a regular basis unless you successfully control them. Many weeds are key pests because they compete with crop or ornamental plants for resources. These weeds require regular control efforts to prevent damage.

Occasional pests are those that become pests once in a while. This may be due to their life cycles, environmental conditions, or as a result of people's activities. For instance, ants become pests when sanitation practices change, providing them with food where none previously existed. They also move into buildings after a rainfall or another event destroys their outdoor food source.

Secondary pests become problems after controlling a key pest. Some weed species become pests only after key weeds have been controlled. Particular species of fleas, ticks, and blood-feeding bugs attack people only after their natural hosts are eliminated. Certain secondary plant-feeding pests begin to cause damage when the key plant pests are under control.

APPROACHES TO PEST MANAGEMENT

A pest management program *prevents*, *suppresses*, or *eradicates* pest populations. Often pest management programs combine prevention and suppression techniques.

Prevention

Usually there are economical and environmentally sound ways to prevent pest infestation or buildup. Such techniques include planting weed- and disease-free seed and growing varieties of plants that resist diseases or insects. Other control options include using cultural methods to prevent weedy plants from seeding or choosing planting and harvesting times that minimize pest problems. Often, sanitation practices reduce pest buildup. Some preventive methods involve excluding pests from the target area or host. An important preventive measure uses pest management practices that conserve natural enemies. In addition, plants, poultry, and livestock that receive adequate water and nutrients are less susceptible to diseases or pests.

There are also preventive practices that use pesticides. These include

- using preplant or preemergence herbicides on areas where weed seeds are present
- using fungicides to protect plants from disease when environmental conditions favor infection
- applying preservatives to structural lumber before construction to protect it from insects, fungi, or marine borers

Suppression

Common pest control methods suppress pest populations but usually do not eliminate them. These methods reduce pest numbers below an *economic injury threshold* or to a tolerable level. Suppression sometimes lowers pest populations so that natural enemies are able to maintain control. Suppression is the goal of most pesticide applications used to manage weeds, insects and mites, and microorganisms. Examples of other suppression techniques include cultivating or mowing weeds and releasing biological control agents.

Eradication

Eradication is the total elimination of a pest from a designated area. This is a common objective of pest control efforts in buildings or other small, confined spaces. Over larger areas, however, eradication is a radical approach to pest control. Eradication can be very expensive and often has limited success. Government agencies conduct large-scale eradication programs to eliminate exotic or introduced pests that pose area-wide public health or economic threats. Mediterranean fruit fly and hydrilla eradication efforts in California and Florida are examples of this type of pest management approach.

Which pest control strategy you choose depends on the nature of the pest, the environment of the pest, and economic considerations. Combining prevention and suppression techniques usually enhances a pest management program. Objectives might differ, however, for the same pest in different situations. For example, the Mediterranean fruit fly is an established pest in Hawaii, so the emphasis there is both prevention and suppression to reduce crop damage. Regulatory agencies in California and Florida, however, use eradication measures to keep the Mediterranean fruit fly from becoming permanently established. The states' goal is to prevent severe economic losses to their agricultural industries.

SETTING UP A PEST MANAGEMENT PROGRAM

To begin a management program that controls an identified pest you must

- know what control methods are available
- evaluate the benefits and risks of each method
- select methods that are most effective and least harmful to people and the environment
- use several methods whenever possible
- use each method correctly
- observe local, state, and federal regulations
- evaluate the success of your pest management efforts

Pest Management Methods

Once you anticipate or identify a pest, begin planning your management program. Learn what management techniques are available and evaluate the benefits and limitations of each. Select methods that are most effective but least harmful to people and the environment. There are usually several ways to manage pests or pest complexes. Whenever possible, combine several compatible methods into an integrated pest management program.

Biological Control

Most arthropod pests have one or more natural enemies, and biological control pest management programs depend on these natural enemies. Pest managers successfully use natural enemies and pathogens as biological control agents to manage certain insect, mite, fish, and weed pests.

Classical Biological Control.

Researchers and pest managers use *classical biological control* to manage pests that are not native to a geographical area. These introduced pests are often problems in their new location because there are no natural enemies to help control them. Classical biological con-

FIGURE 2-1.

Classical biological control involves locating the native home of a pest (usually outside of the United States), finding and rearing one or more of its natural enemies, and releasing these natural enemies into the pest-infested area. In this photo the parasitic wasp Hyposoter exiguae *is laying an egg inside a beet armyworm larva.*

trol involves locating the native home of an introduced pest and finding suitable natural enemies there. After extensive testing and evaluation, researchers select certain natural enemies and import, rear, and release them (Figure 2-1). If successful, the introduced natural enemies become established within large areas and effectively lower target pest populations. The control lasts for long periods of time without further intervention. This is a difficult process because the native homes of some pests are hard to locate. Also, researchers must prove that the natural enemies will not become pests. Laws strictly control importation of all organisms, including biological control agents, into the United States. Other countries have similar restrictions.

Augmentation. Augmentation involves rearing and releasing large numbers of certain natural enemies. These are organisms that probably already occur in an area. However, their natural populations are too low to be effective in controlling the target pest. Augmentation usually does not have long-term results because environmental or other conditions do not favor these natural enemies. Therefore, pest managers must make periodic releases to maintain sufficient population levels.

Commercial insectaries raise many different natural enemies. These include predatory mites to control plant-infesting spider mites, and parasitic wasps and lacewings to control various insect pests. Researchers are studying nematodes as biological control agents for certain weeds and some insects. A spray-on rust pathogen is under development as an early nutsedge control. Some companies sell general predators with claims made for biological control. These include insects such as praying mantids and lady beetles. In many cases, however, researchers have not established the effectiveness of these predators.

Naturally Occurring Control. Many factors influence pests, including natural enemies, environmental and geographical features, and climatic conditions. Maintaining populations of natural enemies can be one of the most economical means of control. Do this by avoiding damaging cultural practices or indiscriminate pesticide use. If pesticides are part of your control program, select types that are less toxic to natural enemies. Otherwise, consider applying pesticides at lower-than-label rates so as not to lower natural enemy populations. Sometimes it is possible to modify certain parts of the environment to maintain or enhance natural enemies. Examples include planting flowering plants that produce nectar for parasitic wasps or planting groundcovers to compete with weeds.

FIGURE 2-2.

Pesticides provide an effective way to control pests. Usually pest damage stops within a few hours to a few days after a pesticide application. This photo shows a fungicide being applied to carnation plants in a greenhouse.

Pesticides

Pesticides often have a key role in pest management and occasionally may be the only control method available. Major benefits associated with the use of pesticides are

- their effectiveness
- the speed and ease of controlling pests
- their reasonable cost compared to other control options (in many instances)

Pest damage usually stops within a few hours (for arthropods) to a few days (for weeds) after applying a pesticide. Fungicides provide plants with immediate, short-term protection against microorganisms (Figure 2-2).

According to the Federal Insecticide, Fungicide, and Rodenticide Act (FIFRA), a pesticide is "any material applied to plants, the soil, water, harvested crops, structures, clothing and furnishings, or animals to kill, attract, repel, or regulate or interrupt growth and mating of pests." Some pesticides also regulate plant growth. Herbicides, insecticides, fungicides, rodenticides, nematicides, and miticides are common types of pesticides. Chapter 3 describes pesticide types and classification.

Mechanical and Cultural Control

An important way to control pests or protect crops, livestock and poultry, people, and manufactured products is by using mechanical and cultural control methods. Use mechanical devices and cultural techniques separately or together to

- exclude or trap pests
- destroy pests
- alter pest life cycles
- encourage natural enemies
- change the environment so that it is not suitable for pest survival

Exclusion. Exclusion consists of using barriers to prevent pests from getting into an area. Window screens, for example, exclude flies, mosquitoes, and other flying insects (Figure 2-3). Patching or sealing cracks, crevices, and small openings in buildings excludes insects, rodents, bats, birds, and other pests. Fences and ditches make effective barriers against many vertebrate pests. Wire or cloth mesh excludes birds from fruit trees. Sticky material painted onto tree trunks, posts, wires, and other objects prevents crawling insects from crossing.

FIGURE 2-3.

Window screens and paper tree protectors are mechanical devices that exclude certain pests.

Trapping. Traps physically catch pests within an area or building. There are several types of traps. Some, such as gopher traps, kill the animals. Others snare animals for relocation. Traps are either mechanical devices or sticky surfaces.

Cultivation. Cultivation is one of the most important methods of controlling weeds. It also controls some insects and other soil-inhabiting pests. Mechanical devices such as plows, discs, mowers, cultivators, and bed conditioners physically destroy weeds or control their growth. They disrupt conditions suitable for the survival of some microorganisms and insects.

Other Cultural Practices. Many different cultural practices influence the survival of pests. In turf, mowing, irrigation, aeration, and fertilization are all important ways to prevent pest buildup and damage. In agricultural crops, you can reduce populations of weeds, microorganisms, insects, mites, and other pests by
- selecting pest-resistant crop plant varieties
- timing planting and harvesting to avoid pests
- managing the amount and timing of irrigation water
- using crop rotations
- using trap crops

Mulching (using plastic, straw, or other materials), flooding, solarization, and flaming (a process of exposing weeds to high-temperature flames) are effective weed management methods.

Modifying the Environment. Altering environmental conditions, such as temperature, light, and humidity, sometimes suppresses pests in enclosed areas. Refrigeration, for example, protects stored food products, furs, and other items from insect pests. Lowered temperatures either kill the insects, cause them to stop feeding, or prevent egg hatch or development. Installing bright lights in attics sometimes discourages bats from roosting there. Lowering the humidity of stored grains and other food products reduces damage from molds and some insects.

Sanitation. Sanitation practices control pests in many locations. Sanitation, or *source reduction*, involves eliminating food, water, shelter, or other necessities important to the pest's survival. In agriculture, sanitation includes removing weeds that harbor pest insects or rodents and removing weed plants before they produce seed. Sanitation also involves destroying diseased plant material and removing and destroying unharvested produce and crop residues. It includes keeping field borders or surrounding areas free of pests and pest breeding sites.

Animal manure management is an effective sanitation practice used for preventing or reducing fly problems in

FIGURE 2-4.

Draining standing water is an important cultural practice that reduces mosquito populations.

FIGURE 2-5.

Sanitation around homes, restaurants, and businesses reduces populations of cockroaches, ants, and rodents. Garbage and trash containers must have tight lids to keep out pests.

poultry and livestock operations. Properly storing feeds and preventing feed waste reduces rodent problems in these locations. In nonagricultural areas, draining standing water (Figure 2-4) and managing wastes controls certain pests. Waste management is very important—closed garbage containers and frequent garbage pickup eliminate food sources for flies, cockroaches, and rodents (Figure 2-5). Removing soil, trash, and other debris from around and under buildings reduces termite and fungal rot damage. It also prevents rodent nesting.

Host Resistance

Breeding or selecting plants and animals to resist specific pest problems is another method of pest control. For example, breeders select livestock for physical characteristics that prevent attack by some pests. They also select for physiological resistance to disease or parasitic organisms. The host's health and nutritional needs also influence resistance. Certain plant varieties are naturally resistant to insects, pathogens, or nematodes. All plants actually repel different types of pests and some contain toxic substances.

FIGURE 2-6.

When using an integrated pest management approach, use pesticides only in situations when decision-making guidelines and field-collected data indicate that pesticides are economically and environmentally justified.

Pests, however, often adapt to the toxins or repellents. This enables them to feed on these plants.

Inoculating growing plants with certain microorganisms sometimes induces resistance. Genetic engineering research demonstrates that it is possible to build pest resistance into the genetic makeup of some plants. Future generations then have this resistance.

Integrated Pest Management

Integrated pest management (IPM) is an ecological approach to managing pests that often provides economical, long-term protection from pest damage or competition. Before control decisions are made, pest managers consider

- prior pest history
- crop growth and development
- weather
- visual observations
- pest monitoring information
- cultural practices

Integrated pest management programs emphasize preventing weed competition and other types of pest damage by anticipating these problems whenever possible. Goals include conserving natural enemies and avoiding secondary pest problems. You can accomplish this by using nondisruptive and mutually compatible biological, cultural, and chemical methods. Decision-making guidelines and field-collected data must indicate that using a pesticide is economically and environmentally justified (Figure 2-6).

Concern about pesticides in the environment and their potential harm to users and consumers continues to increase. Integrated pest management addresses many of the problems associated with chemical pest control because IPM relies on careful and continual pest monitoring. Sometimes pesticide applications are not needed or can be timed more accurately. Generally, growers use less pesticide, resulting in a lower risk to people and to elements of the environment. Ongoing programs in many locations have proven IPM techniques to be economical and effective. Through IPM, long-term pest control reduces reliance on more expensive, short-term pest treatments.

FIGURE 2-7.

This border inspection station located in Truckee is part of the effort to control the movement of pests into California. Inspection stations are in operation on all major highways into the state from Oregon, Nevada, Arizona, and Mexico.

Regulatory Pest Control

Individuals cannot control some types of pests at the local level. These pests include those that seriously endanger or harm the health of the public. These pests are also likely to cause widespread damage to agricultural crops or animals, forests, or ornamental plants. State and federal quarantine, eradication, and abatement programs prevent the introduction and spread of such pests.

Quarantine. Quarantine is a pest control process designed to prevent entry of pests into areas free of that pest. The state of California maintains inspection stations at all major entry points into the state. The goal of the inspection stations is to intercept pests or materials that might harbor pests. There are 16 border stations for inspecting vehicles entering the state from Oregon, Nevada, Arizona, and Mexico (Figure 2-7). The California Department of Pesticide Regulation, in cooperation with the U.S. Department of Agriculture and local offices of county agricultural commissioners, also monitors airports and ocean ports.

Quarantine is also used to prevent movement of designated pests within the state. Fumigation of produce and other identified items to destroy pests is required by law before these items leave a quarantine area.

Nursery stock, plant cuttings, and budding and grafting material are regulated to prevent spreading pests. As part of this program the State of California maintains a registry of certified pest-free plant material that can be shipped throughout the state.

Eradication. For pests that are unacceptable at any level, eradication is generally the only option. These pests are usually also under quarantine restrictions. State or federal agencies supervise eradication programs. Once monitoring information confirms the need for eradication, state agencies determine the geographical extent of pest infestation. They then begin control measures to eliminate this pest from the defined area. Procedures may include

- an area-wide spray program
- releasing sterile insects
- using mechanical and cultural practices
- intensively monitoring for pests within and around the borders of the infested area

Regulations prohibiting planting or growing certain host plants (host-free areas) or prohibiting the planting and growing of these plants during certain periods (host-free periods) may also be part of eradication programs.

Abatement. Weedy areas and neglected or abandoned crops create fire hazards and may harbor vertebrate, invertebrate, or microorganism pests. They also provide a reservoir of weed seeds that threaten adjoining areas or crops. Specific host plants attract or promote the buildup of certain pest invertebrates or disease-causing organisms. Some weedy plants are noxious to people or livestock. Government agencies destroy weeds and plants that cause fire hazards, harbor harmful pathogens or animals, or are noxious to people or livestock in and around agricultural areas. Similar authority applies to diseased or infected livestock or poultry and also extends to weeds and nuisance plants in residential, commercial, and industrial areas.

Mosquito abatement is an important pest control function undertaken to protect public health. Under the authority of mosquito abatement laws, state agencies drain or treat standing water that serves as breeding sites for mosquitoes.

Other. Certain other activities can spread pest organisms to areas where they do not presently exist. These pests may cause injury or disease in people, high-value crops, or livestock and poultry. As a result, regulatory activities play a role in

- protecting native plants and preventing them from being transported out of their native habitat
- regulating and protecting the honey bee industry
- regulating the production and sale of seeds within California
- regulating predatory animals that damage livestock, agricultural crops, or standing timber
- regulating the disposal of vessel and aircraft garbage

Due to the migratory or dispersal nature of some pests and the susceptibility of California to infestations of pests from other areas, the State of California has entered into a pest control compact. This is an agreement with other participating states to share in managing mutual pest problems. Cooperating states contribute money to help finance pest control programs included within the compact.

REVIEW QUESTIONS

1. **Efforts to completely eliminate a pest species such as the Mediterranean fruit fly are known as:**
   - ☐ a. Eradication
   - ☐ b. Suppression
   - ☐ c. Sanitation
   - ☐ d. Biological control

2. **A *key pest* is one that:**
   - ☐ a. Causes damage only after other pests have been eliminated
   - ☐ b. Hardly ever needs to be controlled by pesticides
   - ☐ c. Causes damage on a regular basis unless you successfully control it
   - ☐ d. Becomes a pest once in a while

3. **Applying a preemergence herbicide to an area where weed seeds are present is an example of what kind of pesticide use?**
   - ☐ a. Preventative
   - ☐ b. Suppressive
   - ☐ c. Augmentative
   - ☐ d. Casual

4. **Suppressing a pest population involves:**
   - ☐ a. Completely eliminating the pest
   - ☐ b. Treating to control a pest before it appears
   - ☐ c. Keeping a pest population below a certain level
   - ☐ d. Using only nonchemical control techniques

5. **Which of the following is *not* an example of biological control?**
   - ☐ a. Predatory wasps on spider mites
   - ☐ b. Parasitic wasps on certain insects
   - ☐ c. Disease-carrying fleas on rodents
   - ☐ d. Nematodes for weed control

6. **The effectiveness of augmentation (the release of natural enemies) as a biological control technique is limited because the released organisms:**
   - ☐ a. Are quickly destroyed by the pest population
   - ☐ b. Soon become a pest species
   - ☐ c. Upset the ecological balance by killing the pest population
   - ☐ d. Tend to leave the area soon after release

7. **Which of the following is an example of cultural control?**
   - ☐ a. Discing weeds
   - ☐ b. Applying an herbicide
   - ☐ c. Releasing imported natural enemies
   - ☐ d. Fumigating a field prior to planting

8. **The use of barriers such as screens, fences, and cloth mesh is known as:**
   - ☐ a. Eradication
   - ☐ b. Elimination
   - ☐ c. Ecology
   - ☐ d. Exclusion

9. **Sanitation is important in order to control:**
   - ☐ a. Insects and rodents only
   - ☐ b. All types of pest and disease organisms
   - ☐ c. Upsurges in natural enemy populations
   - ☐ d. Beneficial insects

10. **Integrated pest management is an important pest control strategy because it strives to:**
    - ☐ a. Control pests without disrupting the ecological balance
    - ☐ b. Completely eliminate pest species
    - ☐ c. Control pests without the use of pesticides
    - ☐ d. Eliminate the need for constant pest monitoring

11. **One of the primary goals of integrated pest management is to:**
    - ☐ a. Eliminate all uses of pesticides
    - ☐ b. Change the ecological balance
    - ☐ c. Conserve natural enemies
    - ☐ d. Eradicate all pest species

12. **Quarantine is a pest management practice that is used to:**
    - ☐ a. Maintain a population of a pest species
    - ☐ b. Prevent the entry of pests into new areas
    - ☐ c. Assure the uniform establishment of pest species in all parts of the state
    - ☐ d. Eliminate pests in areas where they have become established

13. **One of the main purposes of government abatement programs is to:**
    - ☐ a. Eliminate areas where pests may breed and seek shelter
    - ☐ b. Prevent exotic pests from entering the state
    - ☐ c. Maintain mosquito breeding areas
    - ☐ d. Provide areas where endangered pest species can seek shelter and breed

3 Pesticides

Pesticides are an important part of many pest management programs.

THE FEDERAL INSECTICIDE, Fungicide, and Rodenticide Act (FIFRA) defines a pesticide as "any substance or mixture of substances intended for preventing, destroying, repelling, or mitigating any insects, rodents, nematodes, fungi, or weeds, or any other forms of life declared to be pests; and any substance or mixture of substances intended for use as a plant regulator, defoliant, or desiccant."

Certain pesticides are synthetically produced *organic* chemicals. Others include naturally occurring organic chemicals, naturally occurring *inorganic* chemicals, or microbial agents. An organic chemical is one that contains carbon and hydrogen in its basic structure. Do not confuse organic chemicals with the pesticides approved for use in *organic agriculture*. Microbial agents include naturally occurring organisms and those made through genetic manipulation. A few pesticides are chemicals not commonly thought of as pest control agents. For instance, chlorine added to swimming pools for algae control is a pesticide. So are household disinfectants, insect repellents, and plant growth regulators.

Pesticides represent a broad range of hazardous and unique chemical compounds. Many are toxic and present risks to users as well as the environment. As a result, selecting, using, and handling pesticides requires that you have special skills and training. You must understand the different ways in which pesticides control pests. Also, you need to recognize how different pesticide formulations react with target pests, nontarget organisms, and the environment.

To help you learn more about them, this chapter describes various types of pesticides and their formulations. It explains pesticide toxicity and how certain factors alter toxicity. It shows you ways to prevent and resolve problems with pesticide incompatibility. The final section summarizes the types of pesticides suitable for organic agriculture.

PESTICIDE TOXICITY

Toxicity, just like color or boiling point, is one of the characteristics used to describe chemicals. Toxicity is the capacity of a chemical to cause injury, sometimes referred to as *potency*. Most pesticides, by their nature, are toxic in order to destroy pests. Like other toxic chemicals, pesticides are hazardous because they have a potential for causing injury. Not all pesticides present the same hazard—some are more toxic or potent than others. The highly toxic pesticides cause injury at smaller doses and therefore are more hazardous.

Plant and Animal Testing

One way to measure the toxicity of pesticides is to give known doses to laboratory animals and observe the results. This is the way researchers find out the lethal dose or lethal concentration of each pesticide. Through animal testing, researchers also decide the maximum dose to which organisms can be exposed without causing injury. They use the results from these types of tests to predict hazards to people and nontarget organisms.

Animal testing establishes exposure risks and provides information on *mode of action* (see page 80). Researchers conduct different types of tests depending on what kind of information they need. In some cases, they feed the laboratory animals small *sublethal* doses of a pesticide on a daily basis. Such studies establish *no observable effect levels* (NOEL) and give information on the long-term, or *chronic*, effects of pesticides. An array of special studies assesses the potential for causing sterility, birth defects, cancer, or other problems in people.

Short-term toxicity testing predicts the *acute* (or immediate) health effects of pesticides. During a study, researchers give groups of laboratory animals single, high doses of a certain pesticide. They measure immediate responses and study the pesticide's mode of action. Exposing animals for short periods to large doses of a pesticide predicts human hazards from exposure to small doses over longer periods.

Research workers test pesticides on mice, rats, rabbits, and dogs. They also perform toxicity tests on nontarget plants and animals when these organisms are at risk from pesticide exposure. Nontarget animals may include insects (such as bees), fish, amphibians (frogs, toads, salamanders), deer, birds, and other wildlife. Researchers also test the pesticides on target pests to set the dosage rates listed on pesticide labels. These tests also tell how well the pesticide works under different conditions. The effectiveness of a pesticide on its target pest is its *efficacy*.

Lethal Dose and Lethal Concentration. Researchers divide laboratory animals into several groups and test different *routes of exposure*. They rate a pesticide's toxicity by determining the amount, or *lethal dose* (LD_{50}), that kills 50% of a test population (Figure 3-1). LD_{50} is expressed as the milligrams (mg) of pesticide per kilogram (kg) of body weight of test animal (mg/kg). Research workers also determine how much pesticide vapor or dust in the air or what amount of pesticide diluted in

FIGURE 3-1.

The amount of pesticide that will kill half of the group is the LD_{50}. The smaller the LD_{50} the more toxic or hazardous a pesticide is. LD_{50} values are established for both oral and dermal (skin) exposure. In this illustration the LD_{50} is 10 mg of pesticide per kg of body weight of test animal.

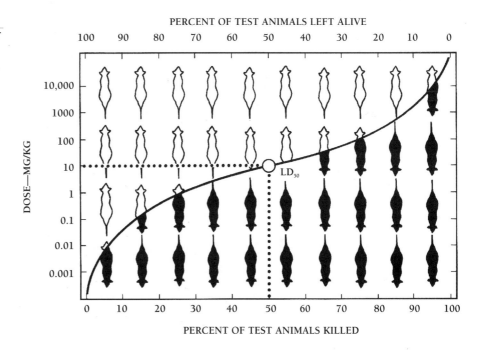

rivers, streams, or lake water causes death in 50% of test animal populations. This is the *lethal concentration or LC_{50}*, which is expressed as micrograms (1/1,000,000g) per liter of air or water (µg/l).

Different animals react differently to the same toxic chemicals, however. Even animals of the same species sometimes respond differently. This may be due to their age, life stage, health, or influences of environmental surroundings.

The more toxic pesticides present higher hazards, or risks of injury, to people and the environment (Table 3-1). Besides toxicity, pesticide hazards also vary according to the way they enter the body. Normal routes of entry include the mouth, skin, eyes, and lungs. Researchers usually determine the LD_{50} of a pesticide for exposures to skin (dermal exposure) and by swallowing (oral exposure).

Lethal dose or lethal concentration classifications do not provide information about chronic, long-term toxic effects. A pesticide that has a high LD_{50} (relatively nontoxic) may not necessarily be harmless. Low exposure to some pesticides may cause health problems that only appear months or even years later.

No Observable Effect Level. The no observable effect level (NOEL) is the maximum dose or exposure level of a pesticide that produces no noticeable toxic effect on test animals. NOEL is a guide for establishing maximum exposure levels for people and residue tolerance levels on pesticide-treated produce. Usually, the U.S. Environmental Protection Agency (EPA) sets exposure levels and residue tolerances at 100 to 1,000 times less than the NOEL. This provides a wide margin of safety.

Threshold Limit Value. The *threshold limit value* (TLV) for a chemical is its airborne concentration in parts per million that produces no adverse effects over time. The TLV applies to pesticides used as *fumigants*. The most common TLV protects workers who are exposed

TABLE 3-1.

Oral LD_{50} Values for Some Pesticides*

CHEMICAL	BRAND NAME	LD_{50}	TYPE OF PESTICIDE
aldicarb	Temik	0.79	insecticide
methyl parathion	Penncap-M	3	insecticide
azinphos-methyl	Guthion	11	insecticide
paraquat	Gramoxone Extra	150	herbicide
diazinon	D•z•n diazinon	300	insecticide
2,4-D	Weedone	375	herbicide
carbaryl	Sevin	500	insecticide
copper hydroxide	C-O-C-S	1,000	fungicide
pendimethalin	Prowl	1,250	herbicide
malathion	Cythion	1,375	insecticide
ziram	Ziram	1,400	fungicide
propargite	Omite	2,200	acaricide
iprodione	Rovral	3,500	fungicide
trifluralin	Treflan	3,700	herbicide
glyphosate	Roundup	4,300	herbicide
simazine	Princep	5,000	herbicide
capatafol	Difolatan	6,200	fungicide
benomyl	Benlate	>10,000	fungicide
chlorothalonil	Bravo	>10,000	fungicide
oryzalin	Surflan	>10,000	herbicide
B. thuringiensis	Dipel	15,000	insecticide
methoprene	Precor	34,600	insect growth regulator

*LD_{50} values may vary due to formulation types. These values are shown for comparative purposes only. Some chemicals listed may no longer be in use as pesticides.

to low-level concentrations of a toxic chemical for 8 hours per day for 5 consecutive days. Sometimes regulations set a TLV for *short-term* exposure to protect workers who must briefly enter recently treated areas. Although this concentration of airborne chemical is higher than the long-term TLV, injury will not result because of the limited exposure period. Researchers establish safe TLVs by exposing laboratory animals to different airborne concentrations and analyzing the results.

Factors that Influence Pesticide Toxicity

Certain conditions increase or decrease the ability of a pesticide to control a pest. Some of these are temperature, humidity, and exposure to sunlight, wind, or rain. Even genetic variations cause some plants or animals to respond differently. Also, the age and general health of a pest often control how well pesticides work. For instance, weeds that are water stressed or not growing vigorously may be more tolerant to some herbicides.

Once applied, pesticides usually break down into different chemicals or chemical compounds after a while. These new chemicals may be less toxic or more toxic than the original pesticide. The time it takes for a chemical to break down in the environment or change from its original form is its *half-life*. Soil microbes, ultraviolet light, temperature, quality of the water used in mixing, or impurities combined with the pesticide increase or decrease the half-life. Sometimes impurities contaminate pesticides during manufacture, formulation, storage, or while you are mixing them. Besides the environment, the chemical nature of the pesticide and its formulation affect its half-life.

Combining pesticides with other pesticides can also change toxicity or alter the half-life. *Persistent* pesticides are those that remain in their active state in the environment for long periods. Chapter 5 discusses pesticide persistence.

Pesticide Toxicity Classification

Federal regulations group pesticides into three categories according to their toxicity and potential to injure people or the environment (Table 3-2). Pesticide labels indicate these categories by the following signal words:
- Danger
- Warning
- Caution

TABLE 3-2.

Signal Words of Pesticide Toxicity Categories.

PESTICIDE LABEL SIGNAL WORDS			
HAZARD INDICATORS:	*DANGER*	*WARNING*	*CAUTION*
oral LD_{50}*	up to and including 50 mg/kg	from 50 to 500 mg/kg	greater than 500 mg/kg
inhalation LC_{50}*	up to and including 0.2 mg/liter (0–2,000 ppm)	from 0.2 to 2 mg/liter (2,000–20,000 ppm)	greater than 2 mg/liter (greater than 20,000 ppm)
dermal LD_{50}*	up to and including 200 mg/kg	from 200 to 2,000 mg/kg	greater than 2,000 mg/kg
eye effects	corrosive; corneal opacity not reversible within 7 days	corneal opacity reversible within 7 days; irritation persisting for 7 days	no corneal opacity; irritation reversible within 7 days
skin effects	corrosive	severe irritation at 72 hours	moderate irritation at 72 hours

*LD_{50} values represent milligrams (mg) of the pesticide per kilogram (kg) of body weight of the test animals. LC_{50} values represent the milligrams of pesticide per liter of air inhaled by the test animals.

The most hazardous pesticides are recognized by the signal word Danger *and a skull and crossbones with the word "Poison" on the label. A few drops to a teaspoonful of these pesticides, taken internally, would probably cause death. These pesticides have an oral LD$_{50}$ of 50 mg/kg or less and dermal LD$_{50}$ of 200 mg/kg or less.*

Danger pesticides are the most toxic or hazardous, and regulations normally restrict their use. *Caution* pesticides are the least toxic to people and are generally less hazardous. Different label and regulatory requirements apply to each category. For example, you must use a closed mixing system and other safety equipment when mixing liquid *Danger* pesticides. In California you need permits to buy, possess, and use most *Danger* pesticides. To get a permit you must be a certified applicator.

Danger Pesticides

Danger pesticides have an oral LD$_{50}$ up to 50 mg/kg or a dermal LD$_{50}$ up to 200 mg/kg. Some of these also have the word *Poison* and a skull and crossbones on their labels (Figure 3-2). *Danger* pesticides with the skull and crossbones are the most hazardous because they are the most toxic. A few drops to a teaspoonful of some of these pesticides could possibly cause death if swallowed. Less toxic pesticides may still have the signal word *Danger* on their labels if they cause specific hazards. These hazards include severe skin or eye injury or a particular hazard to the environment. For those, the signal word *Danger* appears on the label, but not the word *Poison* or the skull and crossbones.

Warning Pesticides

Warning pesticides have an oral LD$_{50}$ between 50 and 500 mg/kg or a dermal LD$_{50}$ between 200 and 2,000 mg/kg. These are moderately hazardous (Figure 3-3). If swallowed, from 1 teaspoonful to 1 ounce (6 teaspoons) of many pesticides in this group would probably kill an adult.

Caution Pesticides

Caution pesticides have an oral LD$_{50}$ over 500 mg/kg and a dermal LD$_{50}$ greater than 2,000 mg/kg (Figure 3-4). The signal word *Caution* indicates they may be slightly hazardous. An adult would probably need to swallow over 1 ounce of these types of pesticides to cause death or serious injury.

HOW PESTICIDES ARE CLASSIFIED

Experts classify pesticides according to their function (Table 3-3). For example, *insecticides* control insects and *herbicides* control weeds. Many *plant growth regulators* enhance growth or fruiting of cultivated plants. *Attractants* and *repellents* are pesticides because of their use in pest control.

Some specific pesticides control more than one group of pests and are therefore in more than one pesticide class.

Moderately hazardous pesticides have the signal word Warning *on their labels. One teaspoonful to 1 ounce of pesticide in this category would probably kill a person if taken internally. These pesticides have an oral LD$_{50}$ in the range of 50 to 500 mg/kg and a dermal LD$_{50}$ in the range of 200 to 2,000 mg/kg.*

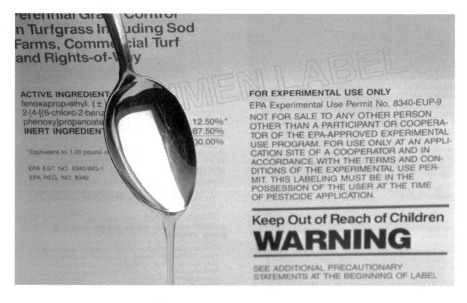

FIGURE 3-4.

The least hazardous pesticides are recognized by the signal word Caution on their labels. It would probably take more than 1 ounce of material in this category, taken internally, to kill an adult. These pesticides have an oral LD$_{50}$ greater than 500 mg/kg and a dermal LD$_{50}$ greater than 2,000 mg/kg.

TABLE 3-3.

Pesticide Classification Based on Target Pests and Pesticide Functions.

PESTICIDE TYPE	FUNCTION	PESTICIDE CHEMICAL* (BRAND NAME)
acaricide	kills mites	propargite (Omite) fenbutatin-oxide (Vendex)
algaecide	kills algae	copper sulfate dichlone endothall (Hydrothol 191)
attractant	attracts pests	pheromones baits miscellaneous chemicals
avicide	kills birds	aminopyridine (Avitrol) starlicide Ornitrol
bactericide	kills bacteria	oxytetracycline (Mycoshield) copper compounds
defoliant	removes plant foliage	endothall (Accelerate) thidiazuran (Dropp) tributyl phosphorotrithioite (Folex)
desiccant	removes water from arthropod pests	boric acid powder silica gel diatomaceous earth
fungicide	kills (or suppresses) fungi	benomyl (Benlate) copper sulfate chlorothalonil (Bravo)
growth regulator	regulates plant or animal growth	gibberellic acid (Pro-Gibb) chlorocarbanilate (Sprout Nip) methoprene (Precor)
herbicide	kills weeds	atrazine bromoxynil (Buctril) trifluralin (Treflan) paraquat (Gramoxone) petroleum oil

*Some chemicals listed here may not be currently registered as pesticides.

(continued)

PESTICIDE TYPE	FUNCTION	PESTICIDE CHEMICAL* (BRAND NAME)
insecticide	kills insects	diazinon permethrin (Ambush) azinphos-methyl (Guthion) methyl parathion petroleum oils
molluscicide	kills snails or slugs	Snarol mesurol triphenmorph (Frescon) clonitralid (Bayluscide)
nematicide	kills nematodes	carbofuran (Furadan) phosphoramidate (Nemacur) dicloropropene (Telone)
piscicide	kills fish	rotenone Lamprecide antimycin (Fintrol)
predacide	kills mammal predators	strychnine zinc phosphide compound 1080
repellent	repels animals or invertebrates	DEET methiocarb (Mesurol) avitrol thiram
rodenticide	kills rodents	chlorophacinone strychnine hydroxycoumarin (Warfarin) diphacinone (Diphacin) brodifacoum (Talon) bromadiolone (Maki)
silvicide	kills trees and woody shrubs	tebuthiuron (Spike) petroleum oils

*Some chemicals listed here may not be currently registered as pesticides.

The compound 2,4-D, for instance, when used at low rates, regulates plant growth. However, it is an effective broadleaf herbicide when applied at higher concentrations. Oxythioquinox (Morestan) works as an *acaricide, fungicide,* and *insecticide.*

Pesticide Chemical Groups

Experts also group pesticides according to chemical origin. This type of classification often reveals common characteristics such as mode of action, chemical structure, and types of formulations possible. There may also be similarities in environmental persistence and how related pesticides break down through biological processes. Table 3-4 lists the chemical groups for most commonly used pesticides and their modes of action.

Insecticides

Materials used as insecticides come from various chemical groups, such as those listed in Table 3-4. Three of the most common insecticide groups are the organochlorines, organophosphates, and N-methyl carbamates.

Organochlorines. Organochlorines (also known as chlorinated hydrocarbons) were one of the original types of synthetic chemicals used as pesticides. They became the mainstay for controlling insects and mites in the early years of chemical pest management. Some of these materials are highly poisonous to mammals, including people, while

TABLE 3-4.

Pesticide Chemical Groups.

CHEMICAL TYPE	EXAMPLE*	MODE OF ACTON**
INSECTICIDES		
petroleum oils	supreme oil, superior oil	physical toxicants

organochlorines	DDT, methoxychlor
	hexachlorocyclohexanes
	cyclodienes (chlordane,
	    thiodan)
	polychloroterpenes (toxaphene)
		axonic poisons
		axonic poisons
		central nervous system
		    synaptic poisons
		axonic poisons

organophosphates
    aliphatic derivatives
	malathion, dimethoate,
	    disulfoton (Di-Syston)
		central nervous system
		    synaptic poisons

phenyl derivatives	ethyl parathion, methyl parathion,
	    sulprofos (Bolstar)
		central nervous system
		    synaptic poisons

heterocyclic
    derivatives
	diazinon, azinphos-methyl
	    (Guthion), chlorpyrifos
	    (Lorsban, Dursban),
	    phosmet (Imidan)
		central nervous system
		    synaptic poisons

organosulfurs	propargite (Omite)	axonic poisons (also
		    inhibit metabolism
		    and respiration)

carbamates	carbaryl (Sevin), methomyl
	    (Lannate), aldicarb (Temik),
	    propoxur (Baygon),
	    bendiocarb (Ficam)
		central nervous system
		    synaptic poisons

formamidines	chlordimeform (Galecron), amitraz (Baam)	adrenergic insecticides

thiocyanates	thanite	interferes with cellular
		    respiration and
		    metabolism

dinitrophenols	dinoseb, dinocap (Karathane)	metabolic inhibitors
organotins	cyhexatin (Plictran), fenbutatin-oxide (Vendex)	metabolic inhibitors

botanicals	nicotine
	rotenone
	sabadilla
	ryania
	pyrethrum
		postsynaptic poison
		metabolic inhibitor
		muscle poison
		muscle poison
		axonic poison (also inhibits
		    mixed function oxidase
		    when mixed with
		    a synergist)

pyrethroids	permethrin (Ambush and
	    Pounce), fenvalerate (Pydrin),
	    allethrin (Pynamin),
	    resmethrin (Synthrin)
		axonic poisons (also inhibit
		    mixed function oxidase
		    when mixed with
		    a synergist)

inorganics	silica gel, boric acid
	sulfur
	
	arsenic
		physical toxicants
		interferes with electron
		    transport, also a cellular
		    poison
		inhibits respiration

fumigants	methyl bromide
	ethylene dibromide
	hydrogen cyanide
	
	chloropicrin, vapam,
	    telone, naphthalene
		narcotic and alkylating agent
		narcotic
		narcotic and alkylating
		    agent
		narcotic

* Some of the materials listed on this table may no longer be registered for use as pesticides in the United States.

** See the Glossary for definitions of the modes of action.

(continued)

CHEMICAL TYPE	EXAMPLE*	MODE OF ACTON**
INSECTICIDES *(continued)*		
microbials	*Bacillus thuringiensis* viruses fungi	various various various
insect growth regulators	methoprene, diflubenzuron (Dimilin), other chitin synthesis inhibitors	influence growth and development
HERBICIDES		
inorganics	sodium chlorate	desiccant
petroleum oils	summer oil, dormant oil	physical toxicants
organic arsenicals	MSMA, DSMA, cacodylic acid	interfere with cellular respiration and metabolism and other functions
phenoxyaliphatic acid	2,4-D, 2,4,5-T, diclofob methyl (Hoelon)	multiple actions
amides	propanil (Kerb), napropamide (Devrinol), alachlor (Lasso), metolachlor (Dual)	inhibit root and shoot growth
substituted anilines	trifluralin (Treflan), oryzalin (Surflan), pendimethalin (Prowl)	inhibit root and shoot growth
substituted ureas	tebuthiuron (Spike), diuron (Karmex), fenuron (Dybar)	block photosynthesis
carbamates	propham (Chem Hoe), barban, asulam (Asulox)	block photosynthesis and interfere with cell division
thiocarbamates	molinate (Ordram), cycloate (Ro-Neet), butylate (Sutan)	interfere with cellular respiration and metabolism, block photosynthesis, and inhibit root and shoot growth
triazines	atrazine (Aatrex), simazine (Princep), metribuzin (Lexone), cyanazine (Bladex)	block photosynthesis
aliphatic acids	TCA, dalapon	unknown
substituted benzoic acids	dicamba (Banvel), DCPA, chloramben (Amiben)	unknown
phenol derivatives	dinoseb	destroy cell membranes, also a desiccant
nitriles	dichlobenil (Casoron), bromoxynil (Buctril)	interfere with cellular respiration and metabolism and inhibit carbon dioxide fixation
bipyridyliums	diquat, paraquat	destroy cell membranes, desiccant, and block photosynthesis
microbials	*Phytophthora palmivora* (Devine)	destroy plant cells
uracils	bromacil (Hyvar-X), terbacil (Sinbar)	block photosynthesis

*   Some of the materials listed on this table may no longer be registered for use as pesticides in the United States.

** See the Glossary for definitions of the modes of action.

(continued)

CHEMICAL TYPE	EXAMPLE*	MODE OF ACTON**
HERBICIDES *(continued)*		
sulfonylureas	chlorsulfuron (Glean), sulfomethuron-methyl (Oust)	interfere with cell division
miscellaneous herbicides	endothall, glyphosate (Roundup), oxyfluorfen (Goal)	inhibit metabolism and protein synthesis
PLANT GROWTH REGULATORS		
auxins	IAA, 2,4-D, VAR	act on DNA-RNA protein system to increase or retard growth rate
gibberellins	ProGibb, Release	important in shoot elongation control of dormancy, and fruit maturation
cytokinins	zeatin, kinetin	promote cell division, bud growth; used to prolong storage of fresh produce
ethylene generators	ethephon (Ethrel)	stimulate seed germination and sprouting; regulate flower, leaf, and fruit drop
FUNGICIDES inorganic fungicides	copper sulfur	enzyme inhibitor metabolic inhibitor
dithiocarbamates	thiram, maneb, ferbam, ziram, Vapam, zineb	enzyme inhibitors
thiazoles	ethazol (Terrazole)	enzyme inhibitors
triazines	anilazine	inhibits metabolism and protein synthesis
substituted aromatics	hexachlorobenzene, chlorothalonil (Bravo), chloroneb	enzyme inhibitors
dicarboximides	captan, folpet, captafol (Difolatan)	enzyme inhibitors
oxathiins	carboxin, oxycarboxin	metabolic inhibitors
benzimidazoles	benomyl (Benlate), thiabendazol, thiophantate (Topsin)	inhibit metabolism and protein synthesis
acylalanines	metalaxyl (Dual)	
triazole	tridimefon (Bayleton)	
piperazine	triforine	
imides	iprodione (Rovral), vinclozolin (Ronilan)	
quinones	chloranil, dichlone	enzyme inhibitors
aliphatic nitrogen compounds	dodine	inhibit metabolism and protein synthesis
fumigants	chloropicrin, methyl bromide	
antibiotics	streptomycin, cycloheximide	

* Some of the materials listed on this table may no longer be registered for use as pesticides in the United States.

** See the Glossary for definitions of the modes of action.

others are reasonably harmless. Many are fat-soluble, so traces of organochlorine pesticides frequently appear in animal tissues. Most organochlorines do not break down rapidly in the environment. This made them attractive for structural pest control and public health applications.

The U.S. EPA has now banned most of the early organochlorines due to environmental persistence, impact on wildlife, or other concerns. DDT, chlordane, toxaphene, and dieldrin are some of these earlier organochlorine insecticides. Newer, less persistent types of organochlorines are used today for controlling certain insects and rodents.

Organophosphates. Organophosphates are an important group of pesticides widely used to manage insect and mite pests. These pesticides are derivatives of phosphorous compounds and some are among the most acutely toxic chemicals known. Many organophosphates are absorbed through the skin, lungs, or digestive tract. They interfere with animal and human nervous systems, effects that are shared by some of the carbamates. Organophosphate pesticides usually break down rapidly in the environment. Well-known organophosphate insecticides include parathion, malathion, phosdrin, diazinon, chlorpyrifos, and azinphos-methyl.

Carbamates. Carbamates are a widely used group of synthetic organic pesticides. They are highly effective, moderately priced, and, under normal conditions, short-lived in the environment. Derivatives of carbamic acid, they include the sulfur-containing subgroups of *dithiocarbamates* and *thiocarbamates*. Besides being used as insecticides, some types of carbamates have uses as fungicides, herbicides, *molluscicides*, and *nematicides*. In animals, one group, the n-methyl carbamate insecticides, impairs nerve function and is highly toxic to mammals, including human beings. N-methyl carbamate insecticides do not build up in animal tissue, so their toxic effects are often short-lived and reversible. Examples of n-methyl carbamate insecticides include carbaryl (Sevin), aldicarb (Temik), and methomyl (Lannate).

Herbicides

Table 3-4 lists many of the chemical groups that have compounds used to control weeds. Early herbicides were generally broad-spectrum contact materials. These are now being replaced by more unique chemicals that destroy weeds through many varied and specific modes of action.

Fungicides

Fungicides include compounds such as inorganic metals and sulfur and a wide range of synthetic organic chemicals. Table 3-4 lists these various chemical groups.

Special Types of Pesticides

A few pesticides do not belong to specific chemical groups. Some occur naturally, some are produced by living organisms, and others are manufactured. These special types of pesticides include antibiotics, anticoagulants, botanicals, insect growth regulators, inert dusts, microbials, petroleum oils, pheromones, plant hormones, and soaps. The following sections describe these unique materials.

Antibiotics

An antibiotic is a substance produced by one organism that kills or inhibits another organism. The antibiotic *penicillin*, used to control bacterial infections in people and animals, comes from a fungus. *Streptomycin*, used to treat bacterial diseases in people, animals, and plants, occurs naturally and is also a synthetically produced antibiotic. *Terramycin* and other similar synthetic antibiotics resemble naturally

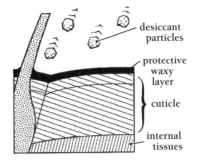

DESICCANT BEING APPLIED

- desiccant particles
- protective waxy layer
- cuticle
- internal tissues

AFTER APPLICATION

- moisture escaping
- wax adsorbed by desiccant particle

FIGURE 3-5.

Desiccants (inert dusts and sorptive powders) destroy insects and mites by removing or disrupting their protective outer body covering. This causes the organism to lose body fluids.

FIGURE 3-6.

Microbial pesticides contain microorganisms that kill other living organisms. The insecticide shown here contains spores of the bacterium Bacillus thuringiensis.

occurring antibiotics. These control several plant diseases caused by fungi, viruses, and bacteria.

Anticoagulants

Anticoagulants interfere with the blood-clotting mechanism of mammals, causing them to die of blood loss after an injury. Pest managers use anticoagulants to control rodents such as rats and mice. Rodents must feed on some types of anticoagulants several times before accumulating enough toxic material to cause death. Other anticoagulants are effective after a single feeding.

Botanicals

Certain plants contain substances that are naturally poisonous to insects and other animals. These include species of chrysanthemum flowers from which manufacturers extract pyrethrum. The roots of the cube plant supply rotenone. Species of lily plants provide sabadilla and hellebore. Ryania comes from a tropical South American plant. Nicotine, extracted from tobacco, had extensive uses as an insecticide in the past; its use, however, has declined since the introduction of newer synthetic pesticides. Strychnine comes from the dried seeds of a small tree found in India, Sri Lanka, Australia, Cambodia, Laos, and Vietnam. Table 3-5 lists insecticidal chemicals derived from plants.

Inert Dusts

Inert dusts, also called *desiccants* or sorptive dusts, are fine powders with low toxicity. Pest managers use them to control various insects and other invertebrates. These dusts kill pests through a physical, rather than chemical, action. Some are abrasive and scratch the pests' waxy body coverings, causing them to lose water. Other dusts remove (or *adsorb*) this protective waxy coating (Figure 3-5). Manufacturers sometimes combine inert dusts with aluminum fluosilicate. This gives the mixture an

electrostatic charge and causes it to cling to surfaces, including the pest's outer body covering.

Because some inert dusts are low in toxicity, pest managers use them in locations where other pesticides are unsafe. Since the killing action is physical rather than chemical, these dusts do not lose their effectiveness over time. However, inert dusts are not effective once they become wet.

Diatomaceous earth, silica gel, and boric acid powder are some of the materials used as desiccants. These pesticides leave highly visible residues on all treated surfaces. Boric acid powder is toxic to people if ingested, so do not use it around young children. Although most inert dusts are low in toxicity, avoid inhaling them because they can cause serious lung irritation.

Insect Growth Regulators

Insect growth regulators (IGRs) are chemicals that control insects by altering their normal development (Table 3-6). Natural growth hormones produced by insects regulate how long individuals remain in each of their larval or nymphal stages. They also control when the insects become reproductive adults. Synthetically produced IGRs mimic or interrupt the action of natural growth hormones. Some prevent insects from changing into adults while others force insects to change into adults before they are physically able to reproduce.

Microbials

Manufacturers produce microbial pesticides by combining certain microorganisms with other ingredients. Various strains of the bacterium *Bacillus thuringiensis* control species of moth larvae, mosquito larvae, and black fly larvae (Figure 3-6). *Agrobacterium radiobacter* controls the bacterium that produces crown gall in trees, shrubs, and vines. Certain fungi kill some pest mites; other strains control the north-

TABLE 3-5.

Insecticidal Chemicals Derived from Plants.

INSECTICIDE	SOURCE	USES/COMMENTS
pyrethrum	Extract from dried flowers of certain chrysanthemum species.	Has contact, stomach, and fumigant poisoning action on insects. Is also toxic to cold-blooded animals. Kills aphids, mosquitoes, flies, fleas, mealybugs, cabbageworms, thrips, beetles, leafhoppers, lice, loopers, and many others. Insecticidal action is degraded rapidly by sunlight. Action is often enhanced by addition of piperonyl butoxide, a synergist.
pyrethrins	Chemical extracts of naturally occurring pyrethrum.	Similar uses as for pyrethrum. Many different pyrethrins are derived from pyrethrum. Some may have more specific action to certain insect pests and are safer to nontarget insects.
rotenone	Derived by grinding roots of of certain legume plants (68 different species). The United States supplies come primarily from roots of the cube plant.	Contact and stomach poison. Used to control beetles, weevils, slugs, loopers, mosquitoes, thrips, fleas, lice, and flies. Also used to control unwanted fish. Acts as a repellent and acaricide—nontoxic to honey bees. Rotenone is slow acting and has a short residual.
nicotine	An extract from several species of tobacco, usually used as the sulfate.	Registered for use on many types of crops. Used in greenhouses and household applications for control of aphids, thrips, leafhoppers, and other sucking insects. Kills by contact and fumigation poison activity. Toxic to people and domestic animals if used improperly. Used also to repel dogs and rabbits.
sabadilla	Obtained from the dried ripe seed of a South American lily plant.	Has contact and stomach poison action against cockroaches, several species of bugs, potato leafhopper, imported cabbageworm, house fly, thrips, and the cattle louse. Is toxic to honey bees but not highly toxic to mammals. Used on many types of tree and vine fruits, forage crops, and vegetables.
hellebore	Made from the dried rhizomes of several species of lily plants, many of which occur naturally in the United States.	Controls several types of insects but does not have high insecticidal activity. Hellebore is rapidly broken down by sunlight.
ryania	Made from the powdered roots, leaves, and stems of a native South American plant. A synergist is often used to enhance its activity.	This compound is effective against corn earworm, codling moth, German cockroach, house fly, mosquitoes, European corn borer, oriental fruit moth, and the imported cabbage worm. Ryania has low toxicity to mammals.

ern jointvetch weed in rice and soybeans. Some viruses effectively control several moth pests, including the codling moth. The plant disease caused by *Phytophthora palmivora* controls milkweed vine in citrus.

The use of microbial pesticides is growing in popularity. This is due to their extremely low hazards to people and nontarget organisms and their specificity to target pests. Besides naturally occurring microbial organisms,

TABLE 3-6.

Insect Growth Regulators.

COMPOUND	BRAND NAME(S)	USES
hydroprene	Gencor	Used for control of cockroaches.
methoprene	Altosid, Diacon, Pharoid, Precor	Controls ants, cigarette beetles, fleas, flies, leafhoppers, lice, mosquitoes, moths, stored product pests, and others.

TABLE 3-7.

Characteristics of Petroleum Oils Used as Insecticides and Acaricides.

CLASSIFIED OILS			
Grade	Minimum UR*	50% Point °F**	Percent Distilled at 636° F and Atmospheric Pressure
heavy	94	671	10-25
heavy-medium	92	656	28-37
medium	92	645	40-49
light-medium	92	628	52-61
light	90	617	64-79

UNCLASSIFIED OILS				
Type	Minimum UR*	50% Point °F**	10–90% Range***	Minimum %Cp****
supreme	92	490	100–110	60
NR 440	92	440 + 8	80	60
NR 415	92	415 + 3	60	60

* UR = Unsulfonated Residue.
** The temperature at which half of the oil distills under a vacuum of 10 mm of mercury.
*** Distillation temperature range.
**** The percent of paraffin-based molecules in the oil.

manufacturers are researching uses for genetically altered organisms as pest control products.

Petroleum Oils

Some highly refined petroleum oils are lethal to certain invertebrates. Pest managers use them to control aphids, scales, mealybugs, eggs of these insects, and mites and mite eggs. Petroleum oils destroy these plant-feeding pests through suffocation. Lesser-refined petroleum oils have uses as nonselective herbicides. They destroy weeds by injuring cell membranes.

Refined oils used as insecticides and acaricides consist of five grades of *classified* oil: light, light-medium, medium, heavy-medium, and heavy. They also include two types of *unclassified* oils: supreme and narrow-range. Oils in these groups include types commonly referred to as dormant oils, summer oils, supreme oils, superior oils, and narrow-range oils. Each type has certain features important for controlling pests and reducing injury to treated plants (Table 3-7). Materials that injure plants are *phytotoxic*.

Characteristics that influence the safety and effectiveness of insecticidal oils are the

- unsulfonated residue (UR) rating
- distillation temperature and range
- hydrocarbon composition

Pheromones

Pheromones are unique chemicals produced by animals that stimulate behavior in other animals of the same species. Many insects depend on pheromones to locate mates. Synthetic insect pheromones are useful tools for monitoring insect activity, timing insec-

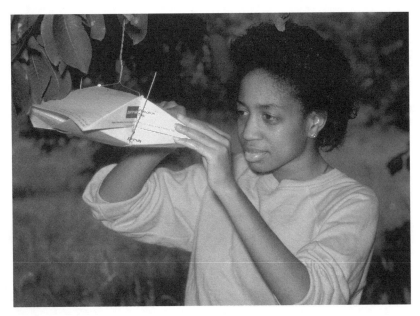

FIGURE 3-7.

Pheromones are unique chemicals that attract certain species of insects. Use them in your pest management program to monitor pest insect activity. This allows you to know when to make an insecticide application. This photograph shows codling moths being monitored in a walnut orchard.

ticide applications, and attracting insects to poisoned sprays. For monitoring, pest managers use synthetic pheromones with sticky insect traps (Figure 3-7). Pest managers use certain pheromones to disrupt mating activity of some insects and reduce these pest populations.

Plant Growth Regulators and Plant Hormones

In nature, hormones and growth regulators produced by plants control functions such as flowering, fruit development, nutrient storage, and dormancy. Manufacturers either derive plant growth regulators and plant hormones from plants or synthesize them. These synthesized materials mimic naturally occurring plant chemicals or induce abnormal growth changes in plants. They regulate plant growth, enhance fruit production, remove foliage for ease in harvesting a crop, or destroy undesirable plants. Table 3-8 lists some of the chemicals that have hormonelike action.

Soaps

Pesticide soaps control insects, mites, mosses, liverworts, algae, and lichens by interfering with cellular metabolism of the target pest. Insecticidal soaps are most effective on soft-bodied insects such as aphids, scales, psyllids, and some larval stages of other insects. Pesticide soaps have the advantage of being nearly nontoxic to vertebrates, including people. Soap sprays might damage some nontarget plants, so before using them, check the label for any restrictions. Use only soaps labeled for pest control.

MODE OF ACTION

The way a pesticide destroys or controls a target organism is its *mode of action*. Table 3-4 (page 73) lists different modes of action. Understanding modes of action makes it easier to select the right pesticide. It also helps you predict which pesticide works best in a particular situation. If pests show resistance to one pesticide, select a material with a different mode of action.

Usually, pesticides within a chemical class have the same mode of action on specific types of pests. They may also have similar characteristics such as chemical structure, persistence in the environment, and types of formulations possible.

The type of injury caused by a pesticide may be local, systemic, or both. Local injury usually involves damage to tissues that initially contact the pesticide, such as leaves. Pesticides with systemic action move, after application, to other tissues where damage occurs. For instance, some leaf-applied herbicides move through the plant to growing points (roots and shoots). Ingested anticoagulant rodenticides move from the intestines into the blood of rodents where they interrupt the normal clotting mechanism. Organophosphate and n-methyl carbamate insecticides interfere with nerve transmission at specific sites within the insects' central nervous system.

TABLE 3-8.

Materials Having Plant Growth Regulator and Plant Hormone Activity.

COMPOUND	BRAND NAME	USES*
carbaryl	Sevin	A thinning agent on apples. (Also used as an insecticide.)
chlorpropham	Sprout Nip	Inhibits potato sprouting.
cytokinin	Cytex	Increases cell elongation, improves fruit set, and enhances color.
daminozide	Alar	Controls height, retards growth, promotes early budding of ornamentals. Hastens ripening and concentrates maturity of cherries, peaches, and nectarines. Controls premature ripening and prevents drop in pears. Many other uses.
dimethipin	Harvade	A desiccant, defoliant, and abscission agent for improving cotton harvest.
ethephon	Ethrel, Florel, Prep	Hastens yellowing of tobacco. Promotes and concentrates maturity of berries, tree fruits, grapes, tomatoes, and other crops. Loosens walnuts to improve harvest. Used to eliminate unwanted fruit and leaves. Promotes flowering in certain ornamentals. Accelerates opening of mature unopened cotton bolls and enhances defoliation to improve early harvest.
gibberellic acid	Pro-Gib, Gibrel	Increases fruit set, size, and yield. Controls lemon maturity. Breaks dormancy in potatoes. Produces larger and more profuse flowers in ornamentals. Many other uses in vegetable, grain, and fruit crops.
gibberellic acid and N-[phenylmethyl]-1H-purine-6-amine	Promalin	Improves shape, size, firmness, color, and yield in apples.
mefluidide	Embark	Regulates growth of turfgrass, broadleaf vegetation, and ornamentals in landscaped areas.
mepiquat-chloride	Pix	Improves yield, shortens plant height, accelerates maturity, and opens canopy of cotton plants.
nephthaleneacetic acid (NAA)	Fruitone N, NAA-800, Stik, Tre-Hold	Controls drop in apples and pears. Used as apple thinning agent. As wound dressing, suppresses sprouting from pruning cuts.
N-[phenylmethyl]-1H-purine-6-amine	Pro-Shear	Improves growth and fullness of white pine grown for Christmas trees.
N-[phenylmethyl]-9-[tetrahydro-2H-pyran-2-yl]-9H-purine-6-amine	Accel	Increases number of lateral branches of roses, carnations, and other ornamental flowers.
pyridazinedione	Royal MH-30, Royal Slo-Gro, Sprout Stop, Sucker-Stuff	Controls sprouting of potatoes and onions.
2,4-D	2,4-D	Increases fruit size and reduces drop in citrus. Intensifies color and improves skin appearance in potatoes. (Also used as an herbicide.)

*Some materials listed here may not be registered for use as plant growth regulators or plant hormones. Check current labels before use.

Applying systemic insecticides to host plants or animals sometimes protects them from damage by pest organisms. For example, growing plants pick up soil-applied systemic insecticides and transport them to the leaves. This makes the plants toxic to foliage-feeding insects. Veterinarians give pets and livestock low doses of systemic insecticides to control internal and external parasites. Pest managers inject trees with insecticides or antibiotics to protect them from pest organisms.

The mode of action of certain herbicides destroys weeds by damaging leaf cells and causing plants to dry out. Others alter the uptake of nutrients or interfere with the plant's ability to grow normally or convert light into food. The mode of action often dictates when and how to use an herbicide. Apply those that inhibit seed germination or seedling growth as *preemergent* herbicides. Incorporate them into the soil to control weed seedlings before they break through the soil surface. Apply *postemergent* herbicides to the foliage or soil of growing weeds. Some postemergents have contact activity, meaning they kill the plant by destroying leaf and stem tissues. Other postemergents are moved within the tissues of the plant (*translocated*) from leaves and other green parts to growing points.

Various insecticides act as nerve poisons, muscle poisons, desiccants, growth regulators, or sterilants. Others have purely physical effects such as clogging air passages. Often an insecticide will have more than one mode of action.

Some fungicides are *eradicants* because they destroy fungi that have already invaded and begun to damage plant tissues. Their mode of action is to inhibit the metabolic processes of the growing fungal organisms. Others are *protectants* that prevent fungal infections. Their mode of action retards fungal growth or prevents the organisms from entering treated plants.

Factors Influencing Reactions to Pesticides

Several factors influence how a pest reacts to a pesticide, and two of these factors are very important. First, the target pest must be in a susceptible life stage. Second, the pesticide must be able to reach the active site within the organism (pesticide uptake).

Life Stage

The life stage of a target organism influences its response to a pesticide. For instance, young plants are generally more susceptible to herbicides than older ones. Some herbicides are most effective on perennial plants just beginning to flower. These same herbicides are less effective on plants that have not yet begun to flower or have completed their flowering stage. Perennial weeds are more difficult to control once they have developed rhizomes or nutlets. Insects go through several life stages including eggs, nymphs or larvae, pupae (in some orders), and finally adults. Each insect life stage has different susceptibilities to insecticides. Differences are due to biological and physical characteristics, feeding habits, and the physical location of the organism. Similarly, the success of rodent control with toxic baits depends on the rodent's life stage. Food preference at different times of year influences the acceptability of the baits.

Pesticide Uptake

Most pesticides have specific sites of action. Before they can act they must move into the tissues of intended target organisms and reach these sites. Structural differences, protective coatings, and habits of the pest influence pesticide uptake. Types of pesticide formulations as well as environmental conditions also influence uptake.

Various terms describe methods and routes of pesticide uptake. Pesticides with *contact* activity pass through the target organism's outer covering (for example, plant cuticle, arthropod cuticle, or vertebrate skin). Some insecticides and rodenticides are *stomach poisons*—the target organism must ingest the toxin. The toxin absorbs through linings of the pest's mouth or intestinal tract. Other pesticides have *fumigant* activity and pass as vapors into the tissues of the target plant or animal. The fumigant enters through respiration or breathing channels, or by passing through skin or cuticle. Certain pesticides exhibit all these types of uptake.

PESTICIDE FORMULATIONS

Pesticide chemicals in their "raw" or unformulated state are not usually suitable for pest control. These concentrated chemicals (*active ingredients*) may not mix well with water and may be chemically unstable. For these reasons, manufacturers add substances to improve application effectiveness, safety, handling, and storage. The final product is a *pesticide formulation*. This formulation consists of

- the pesticide active ingredient
- the carrier, such as an organic solvent or mineral clay
- surface-active ingredients, often including stickers and spreaders
- other ingredients, such as stabilizers, dyes, and chemicals that improve or enhance pesticidal activity

Some liquid pesticides have antifreeze added to protect them against freezing. *Inert ingredients* are all the additives that manufacturers add to the active ingredient in the pesticide formulation.

Usually you need to mix a formulation with water or oil for final application. However, baits, granules, and dusts are ready for use without additional dilution. Manufacturers package specialized pesticides, such as products for households, in ready-to-use formulations.

The label lists the amount of actual pesticide in a dry formulation as percentage of *active ingredient* (a.i.). For instance, a 50-W wettable powder contains 50% by weight of actual pesticide. Ten pounds of "D•z•n diazinon 50W" contains 5 pounds of diazinon and 5 pounds of inert ingredients. With liquid formulations, the label lists the pounds of active ingredient in 1 gallon of formulated pesticide. For example, in "Lorsban 4E," the "4" indicates that there are 4 pounds per gallon of the active ingredient *chlorpyrifos*.

Labels usually indicate formulation type by letters that follow or are a part of the brand name of the pesticide (Table 3-9). In the examples above, the "W" represents a wettable powder. The "E" indicates that the pesticide is an emulsifiable concentrate. Sometimes these codes describe what the pesticide is used for or how it is used (for example "SD" indicates the pesticide is used as a side dressing). They may describe some special characteristics of the formulation, such as "LO" for low odor. In some cases, they indicate a use for a specific location, such as "PNW" for Pacific Northwest.

Selecting a Formulation

Sometimes you must choose between two or more formulations of the same pesticide to control a target pest. When possible, make your selection based on the type of control desired, safety, cost, and other factors such as those listed in Table 3-10. For example, emulsifiable formulations of insecticides usually provide quick control but have shorter residual action compared to wettable powders. Whenever you have a choice, consider the safety of pesticide applicators and helpers. Select the formulation that is less hazardous to people working or living in the application area. Consider the potential impact on pets, livestock, and poultry.

TABLE 3-9.

Suffixes of Chemical Brand Names.

SUFFIX	MEANING
TYPE OF FORMULATION	
AF	aqueous flowable
AS	aqueous suspension
D	dust
DF	dry flowable
E	emulsifiable concentrate
EC	emulsifiable concentrate
ES	emulsifiable solution
F	flowable
FL	flowable
G	granular
OL	oil-soluble liquid
P	pelleted
PS	pelleted
S	soluble powder
SG	sand granules
SL	slurry
SP	soluble powder
ULV	ultra-low-volume concentrate
W	wettable powder
WDG	water-dispersible granules
WP	wettable powder
HOW A PESTICIDE IS USED	
GS	for treatment of grass seed
LSR	for leaf spot and rust
PM	for powdery mildew
RP	for range and pasture
RTU	ready to use
SD	for use as a side dressing
TC	termiticide concentrate
TGF	turf grass fungicide
WK	to be used with weed killers
CHARACTERISTICS OF THE FORMULATION	
BE	the butyl ester of 2,4-D
D	an ester of 2,4-D
K	a potassium salt of the active ingredient
LO	low odor
LV	low volatility
MF	modified formulation
T	a triazole
2X	double strength
LABEL FOR USE IN SPECIAL LOCATIONS	
PNW	for use in the Pacific Northwest (i.e., Benlate PNW)
TVA	for use in the waterways of the Tennessee Valley Authority (i.e., Aqua-Kleen TVA)

Evaluate the habits and growth patterns of each pest. Be sure the formulation is suitable for the pest's life stage. Pick a formulation that causes the least impact on the environment. Consider drift, runoff, wind, and rainfall along with soil type and characteristics of the surrounding area. Cost also influences your selection. Finally, choose a formulation that is compatible with available application equipment.

Common Pesticide Formulations

A few pesticides consist of undiluted, technical-grade liquids that pest managers apply in small quantities as aerosol sprays. These are primarily used for residential, industrial, and institutional pest control situations. They are safer to use around open flames, electric motors, and electrical outlets than formulations containing

TABLE 3-10.

Comparisons of Pesticide Formulations.

FORMULATION	MIXING/ LOADING HAZARDS	PHYTO- TOXICITY	EFFECT ON APPLICATION EQUIPMENT	AGITATION REQUIRED	VISIBLE RESIDUES	COMPATIBLE WITH OTHER FORMULATIONS
wettable powders	dust inhalation	safe	abrasive	yes	yes	highly
dry flowables/ water-dispersible granules	safe	safe	abrasive	yes	yes	good
soluble powders	dust inhalation	usually safe	nonabrasive	no	some	fair
emulsifiable concentrates	spills and splashes	maybe	may affect rubber pump parts	yes	no	fair
flowables	spills and splashes	maybe	may affect rubber pump parts; also abrasive	yes	yes	fair
solutions	spills and splashes	safe	nonabrasive	no	no	fair
dusts	severe inhalation hazards	safe	—	yes	yes	—
granules and pellets	safe	safe	—	no	no	—
microencapsulated formulations	spills and splashes	safe	—	yes	—	fair

petroleum solvents or water. This is because these undiluted pesticides are usually not flammable and will not conduct electricity.

You cannot use most pesticides in their pure, undiluted form. Except for dusts and granules and the special uses described above, you must dilute and mix almost all pesticides with water or oil before applying them as liquid sprays.

Occasionally, pest control problems lend themselves better to dry pesticide formulations. Three dry formulations—dusts, granules, and pellets— are available. Manufacturers package some pesticide formulations in ways that increase their safety or make them easier to use. Water-soluble bags are an example of packaging that increases the safety to the handler. The following section describes dry and liquid formulations.

Wettable Powders (W or WP)

Wettable powder formulations do not dissolve in water. Instead, they form a milky suspension similar to mixing chocolate drink mix with water. Wettable powder formulations consist of the pesticide and a finely ground dry carrier, usually mineral clay. Manufacturers combine these with other ingredients that enhance the ability of the powder to remain *suspended* in water. Most wettable powder formulations contain between 15% and 75% active ingredient.

Choose formulations with the highest percentage of active ingredient if visible residues are a concern. Carriers and other inert ingredients are the most common source of unsightly residues on sprayed surfaces. Also, the cost per unit of active ingredient is usually less in formulations with a high percentage of active ingredient. However, a higher percentage of active ingredient in the formulation makes the wettable powder more hazardous. These require more care in handling and mixing and often require special personal protective equipment.

Wettable powders are among the safest formulations to use if plant injury (*phytotoxicity*) is a concern. This is because the carriers are inert minerals. These formulations are compatible with many other pesticides (especially other wettable powders) and fertilizers. A disadvantage is the abrasiveness of the inert carrier, which contributes to pump and nozzle wear. Wettable powders *always* require agitation during application to keep the mixture suspended. When you apply wettable powders to porous materials, water in the mixture penetrates, but the pesticide remains on the surface. On nonporous surfaces, water evaporates and leaves the pesticide as a residue.

A serious problem with wettable powders is the potential hazard of inhaling dust during handling and mixing. Dust particles usually contain high concentrations of pesticide active ingredient. These particles are very fine and can remain suspended in the atmosphere for several hours. To overcome this hazard, some manufacturers package wettable powders in water-soluble bags. If you choose a formulation packaged in water-soluble bags, do not open the bags during mixing. Calibrate your equipment so you can use one or more whole bags. Drop these premeasured *unopened* bags into a filled spray tank. With agitation, the bags dissolve and release the wettable powder into the tank's water.

Dry Flowables or Water-Dispersible Granules (DF or WDG)

Dry flowables (also called *water-dispersible granules*) are similar to wettable powders. However, rather than being a powder, the formulated pesticide consists of small granules. These require

mixing with water before use. The granules have a higher percentage of active ingredient per unit of weight because manufacturers use less carrier.

Dry flowables do not have the dust problems associated with wettable powders, so they are safer to handle. Measuring and mixing granules is simple because manufacturers package them in easy-to-pour plastic containers. Measure these out by volume, similar to liquids, rather than by weight. Like wettable powders, dry flowables require constant agitation during application and are abrasive to application equipment.

Soluble Powders (S or SP)

A soluble powder formulation is similar to a wettable powder. However, the pesticide, its carrier, and all other formulation ingredients completely *dissolve* in water to form a true solution. In this manner, they are similar to dissolving sugar or salt in water. Once dissolved, soluble powders require no additional mixing or agitation. They are not abrasive to spray nozzles or pumps. Only a few pesticides are available in this formulation because most pesticide active ingredients do not dissolve in water. While mixing, inhalation of soluble powders is a potential hazard.

Emulsifiable Concentrates (E or EC)

Many pesticides are not soluble in water but dissolve completely in petroleum solvents. Emulsifiable concentrates are petroleum-soluble pesticides formulated with emulsifying agents (soaplike materials) and other enhancers. When you add emulsifiable concentrates to water, they form an emulsion (milky liquid), similar to mixing certain household disinfectants in water. After mixing, the emulsified pesticide disperses evenly in the water. Agitation during application is important to keep this emulsion uniform.

Emulsifiable concentrates are among the most versatile of all formulations and have many applications. They penetrate porous materials such as soil, fabrics, paper, and wood better than wettable powders. Since they are liquid, they pour easily for mixing. However, using emulsifiable concentrates introduces several handler hazards:

- If spilled they spread easily and are difficult to clean up.
- Porous protective clothing and leather boots readily absorb them.
- They pass through the skin more readily than powders.
- They may cause serious injury if splashed into the eyes.

Emulsifiable concentrates are more risky to use (potentially *phytotoxic*) on sensitive plants than wettable powders because they contain petroleum solvents. These solvents also contribute to the deterioration of rubber and plastic hoses and gaskets. The solvents may damage some pump parts and corrode painted surfaces.

Flowables (F)

A flowable formulation combines many of the characteristics of emulsifiable concentrates and wettable powders. Manufacturers use this formulation when the active ingredient is an insoluble solid and will not dissolve in either water or oil. They combine finely ground pesticide particles with a liquid carrier and emulsifiers to form a concentrated emulsion (similar to liquid antacids). Flowables share the features of liquid emulsifiable concentrates, and they have similar disadvantages. They require agitation to keep them in suspension and leave visible residues, similar to wettable powders.

Flowables are easy to handle and apply. Because they are liquids, they are subject to spilling and splashing like emulsifiable concentrates. They contain solid particles, so they contribute to abrasive wear of nozzles and pumps. Flowable suspensions settle out in their containers, so always shake them thoroughly before mixing. Because flowables tend to settle, manufacturers package them in containers of 5 gallons or less to make remixing easier.

Water-Soluble Concentrates or Solutions (S)

Water-soluble concentrates or solutions are formulations that dissolve in water, similar to sugar-based syrups. Once dissolved, they require no further mixing or agitation. The same handler hazards are present with water-soluble concentrates as with other liquids, but they are nonabrasive to application equipment. Only a limited number of pesticide liquids dissolve in water.

Low-Concentrate Solutions (S)

Low-concentrate formulations are ready to use and require no dilution. They consist of a small amount of active ingredient dissolved in an organic solvent. They usually do not stain fabrics or have unpleasant odors. They are especially useful for structural and institutional pests as well as for household use. Major disadvantages to low-concentrate formulations include limited availability and high cost per unit of active ingredient. Many organic solvents are harmful to foliage, so they cannot be used as plant sprays.

Ultra-Low-Volume Concentrates (ULV)

Ultra-low-volume concentrates have high concentrations (between 80% and 100%) of active ingredient. These formulations require little or no dilution. However, they require application equipment suited to applying very small quantities of pesticide over a large area. This results in less frequent refilling of spraying equipment, a major advantage when treating large areas. You usually dilute ULV formulations with vegetable oil rather than water when dilution is needed. Droplets of ULV formulations do not evaporate as rapidly as those from emulsions. Because of the high concentration of active ingredient, you must be extremely accurate with your equipment calibration.

Slurry (SL)

A slurry is a thin, watery, paste-like mixture of finely ground dusts. Because they are dusts before mixing, slurries have similar respiratory hazards to the handler as other powdered formulations. Usually, a slurry is first mixed in a small container. Combine water with the powder and stir to form a paste. Slowly add this mixture to water in a partially filled spray tank. Be sure to agitate the mixture constantly to prevent settling. After adding the paste, fill the tank with water. Allow it to mix thoroughly before applying. Pest managers apply slurries to seeds and plants to protect them against insects or fungi. After application, slurries dry and leave thick residues on treated surfaces, similar to paint. Usually these residues are highly visible. Slurries are abrasive and contribute to pump and nozzle wear.

A common slurry formulation is the Bordeaux mixture applied to plants as a fungicide. People who use a Bordeaux mixture combine hydrated lime and copper sulfate in various proportions with water to produce a slurry. They usually combine the dry materials just before application, although some premixed dry formulations are commercially available.

Fumigants

Fumigants have many uses because they penetrate hard-to-reach areas. They control insect pests of stored products as well as soil pests such as weeds, insects, nematodes, and microorganisms. Some fumigants control vertebrates such as ground squirrels and gophers. Fumigants are used in ships, boxcars, aircraft, trucks, dwellings, warehouses, greenhouses, and commercial buildings. Fumigants may be either solid, liquid, or gas. Solids and liquids evaporate (volatilize) into a gas after or during application.

Many fumigants are gases at room temperature. Manufacturers package these in steel cylinders for metering into treatment areas.

Fumigants introduce a serious inhalation hazard to applicators and other people in or near the treated area. Applicators often must wear supplied-air breathing equipment and protective clothing. When applying, they use atmosphere-monitoring equipment to detect fumigant concentration. Atmosphere monitoring enables them to determine when people can safely enter the area without protective equipment.

Pest managers apply many soil fumigants through irrigation systems or inject them directly into the soil. Usually soil moisture needs to be high to prevent fumigants from volatilizing into the atmosphere. For example, high soil moisture contributes to the effectiveness of rodent burrow fumigation. Tarping the soil with plastic sheeting also confines the fumigant and maintains its concentration. Texture, soil type, amount of organic material, and soil condition affect how well soil fumigants work. Soil temperature and weather during and after application also influence the effectiveness of soil fumigants.

People who fumigate structures seal the structures with tarps or make them airtight in some other way. They often use fans to circulate the air in the area and mix the fumigant uniformly. Treated areas must be thoroughly ventilated after fumigation and before they are reoccupied. Stored products are fumigated in airtight containers or specially designed rooms or buildings.

Invert Emulsions

Invert emulsions are liquid formulations of small water droplets suspended in oil. Pesticides dissolve in either oil or water (Figure 3-8). Invert emulsion concentrates have the consistency of mayonnaise and usually require continuous agitation. Uses of invert emulsions

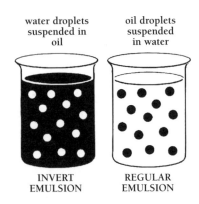

water droplets suspended in oil

oil droplets suspended in water

INVERT EMULSION

REGULAR EMULSION

FIGURE 3-8.

An invert emulsion consists of small water droplets suspended in oil. Compare this to the regular emulsion where oil droplets suspend in water.

FIGURE 3-9.

One type of pesticide formulation consists of a finely ground powder containing active and inert ingredients. This is applied dry as a dust. A common use of dust formulations is to control external parasites on livestock and pets. For example, this dog is being dusted with an insecticide to control fleas and ticks.

are limited, and regulations prohibit some uses.

Invert emulsions aid in reducing drift. With other formulations, some drift results when water droplets begin to evaporate before reaching target surfaces. As a result, they become very small and light. Because oil evaporates more slowly than water, invert emulsion droplets shrink less, therefore more pesticide reaches the target. The oil helps to reduce runoff and improves rain resistance. It also serves as a sticker-spreader by improving surface coverage and absorption. Since droplets are larger and heavier, it is difficult to get thorough coverage on the undersides of foliage.

Dusts (D)

Dust formulations consist of finely ground pesticide combined with an inert dry carrier (Figure 3-9). Most dust formulations contain between 1 and 10% active ingredient. Some, such as sulfur dust, may be pure active ingredient. Dusts are more appropriate in situations where moisture from liquid sprays would damage crops, foliage, or sprayed surfaces. You can apply dusts to many surfaces without harm, although they do leave visible residues. Depending on the pesticide being used, dust formulations often provide long-term protection of treated surfaces.

Because of drift hazards, most pest managers prefer liquid sprays to dusts in agricultural applications. However, they work well in hard-to-reach indoor areas and for treating pests in home gardens. Pesticidal dusts control parasites on pets, livestock, and poultry. They also protect seeds. Fungicides, herbicides, insecticides, and rodenticides are available in dust formulations.

Other problems associated with dust applications include

- Dusts present serious inhalation hazards to applicators—to prevent poisoning, wear respirators whenever using dust formulations.
- Regulations restrict outdoor applications of dusts to periods when the air is still.
- Application equipment is difficult to calibrate, and dusts require agitation during application to prevent settling and caking in the hopper.

Tracking Powders. Special dusts known as *tracking powders* are used for rodent and insect monitoring and control. For rodent control, the tracking powder consists of finely ground dust combined with a stomach poison rodenticide. Rodents walk through the dust, pick it up on their feet and fur, and ingest it when they clean themselves. Tracking powders are useful when bait acceptance is poor due to an abundant, readily available food supply. Use nonpoisonous powders, such as talc or flour, to monitor and track the activity of rodents in buildings.

You can control some insects, such as cockroaches, by using poisoned tracking powders. The insects ingest the poisonous dusts during grooming or absorb the dusts through their outer body covering. Desiccants or sorptive dusts remove or disrupt the waxy protective coatings of insects. This causes death by loss of water (desiccation) rather than by a toxic reaction. Desiccants include boric acid powder, diatomaceous earth, and silica gel.

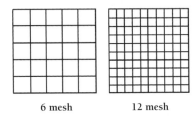

6 mesh   12 mesh

FIGURE 3-10.

The size of dust and granule particles is measured by passing the material through screens with different sizes of mesh. Mesh is the number of wires per inch of screen. As seen here, the larger the mesh number, the finer the screen. Granules range in size between 4 and 80 mesh, while dusts are 80 mesh and finer.

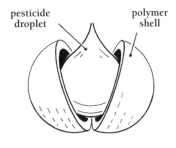

pesticide droplet   polymer shell

FIGURE 3-11.

Microencapsulated formulations consist of pesticides enclosed in tiny plastic capsules. This often makes them safer to use and increases their effectiveness.

Granules (G)

Granules consist of a pesticide and carrier combined with a binding agent. They range in size between 4 and 80 mesh. The most common formulations are in the range of 15 to 30 mesh. *Mesh* is the term used to describe the number of wires in an inch of screen (Figure 3-10). Larger numbers indicate more wires, therefore a finer screen. (Dusts pass through 80 mesh and finer screens.) The larger size and weight of granules helps eliminate drift. You can minimize dust and spray mist hazards to the applicator and environment by using granular formulations. Granular formulations are more persistent in the environment than other formulations because the pesticide active ingredient releases slowly.

Some granular pesticide formulations that dissolve in water control aquatic pests such as algae, aquatic weeds, or fish. These have advantages over liquids in aquatic situations because liquids are hard to disperse. When sprayed, liquids may dry on plants or floating debris. Also, liquids may not pass through the surface film of the water. Granules bounce off vegetation and easily penetrate the surface film. Some aquatic granular formulations offer sustained, controlled release of the pesticide because they dissolve slowly. However, slow-dissolving granules may be hazardous to waterfowl because they mistake them for food.

Pest managers apply granules to soil to control weeds, nematodes, and soil insects. Manufacturers formulate some systemic insecticides as granules. The granules dissolve in the soil, and plants absorb the active ingredients through their roots. These materials control leaf- and stem-feeding insects. Some granular formulations require mechanical incorporation into the soil and often need moisture for activation. Granules are not suitable for conventional foliar application since they do not stick to leaves. However, when applied to plants

like corn, the granules lodge in the leaf whorls. This provides effective control for some corn insect pests. For this type of application, manufacturers weight granules with sand.

Pellets (P or PS)

Pellets are identical to granules, except manufacturers mold them into specific uniform weights and shapes. Pest managers apply pellets with equipment such as precision planters to achieve uniformity that is normally difficult to accomplish with granules.

Microencapsulated Materials

Manufacturers cover liquid or dry pesticide particles in a plastic coating, producing a microencapsulated formulation (Figure 3-11). You mix microencapsulated pesticides with water and spray them in the same manner as other sprayable formulations. After spraying, the plastic coating breaks down and slowly releases the active ingredient. There are several advantages to microencapsulated formulations:

- Highly toxic materials are safer for applicators to mix and apply.
- Delayed or slow release of the active ingredient prolongs its effectiveness, allowing for fewer and less-precisely-timed applications.
- The pesticide volatilizes more slowly, so less drifts away from the application site.
- These formulations reduce phytotoxicity problems.

In residential, industrial, and institutional applications, microencapsulated formulations offer several advantages. These include reduced odor, release of small quantities of pesticide over a long time, and greater safety. Microcapsules offer less hazard to the skin than do ordinary formulations. Microcapsules pose a special hazard to bees, however. Because microcapsules are about the same size as pollen grains, bees may carry them back to their hives. As the capsules break down,

FIGURE 3-12.

Water-soluble bags protect handlers during the mixing of some types of highly toxic or hazardous pesticides. A preweighed amount of formulated pesticide powder is in a plastic bag inside this paper envelope. Remove the bag from the envelope and drop it into your water-filled spray tank. The plastic bag dissolves in the water and releases the powder.

they release the pesticide, poisoning the adults and brood.

Breakdown of the microcapsules to release the pesticide sometimes depends on weather conditions. Under certain conditions, the microcapsules may break down more slowly than expected. This could leave higher residues of pesticide active ingredient in treated areas beyond normal restricted-entry or harvest intervals with the potential to injure fieldworkers. For this reason, regulations require long restricted-entry intervals for some microencapsulated formulations.

Water-Soluble Packets

Water-soluble packets reduce the mixing and handling hazards of some highly toxic pesticides (Figure 3-12). Manufacturers package preweighed amounts of wettable powder or soluble powder formulations in a special type of plastic bag. As you drop these bags into a filled spray tank, they dissolve and release their contents to mix with the water. There are no risks of inhaling or contacting the undiluted pesticide as long as you do not open the packets. Once mixed with water, pesticides packaged in water-soluble packets are no safer than other mixtures.

Baits

Baits are pesticides combined with food, attractants, or feeding stimulants. Because baits attract target pests to a pesticide, they eliminate the need for widespread pesticide application. Sometimes target pests, such as ants, carry baits back to their nestbound young. Use baits indoors to control rodents, ants, roaches, and flies. Use them outdoors to control slugs, snails, insects, and vertebrates such as birds, rodents, and larger mammals. Dangers associated with baits include their attractiveness to nontarget animals and to children. When children or pets are present, place baits in special pet- or child-proof bait stations. Manufacturers color some baits to distinguish them as being poisonous and to make them less attractive to birds.

Attractants

Attractants include pheromones, sugar and protein hydrolysate syrups, yeasts, and rotting meat. Pest managers use these attractants in sticky traps. You can also combine them with pesticides and spray them onto foliage or other items in the treatment area.

Aerosol Containers

Manufacturers package some insecticides and other pesticides in small aerosol cans (Figure 3-13). The pesticide combines under pressure with a chemical propellant in the can. Some aerosol containers emit pesticides as a fine airborne mist or fog (aerosol foggers). Usually, you use the aerosol foggers as one-time, total release units.

FIGURE 3-13.

This aerosol container offers greater convenience without waste. It contains a low-concentration insecticide solution.

Other aerosol containers produce a coarse spray of liquid or powder (pressure spray applicators). With pressure spray applicators, you apply a pesticide film directly onto surfaces.

Residential, industrial, and institutional pest control operators frequently use refillable aerosol applicators. In structural pest control, aerosol containers are convenient because they require no mixing or special application equipment. They are handy for situations when you apply only small amounts of pesticide at any one time. The remaining pesticide in the container does not lose its potency during storage.

Hazards from aerosol containers include risks of inhalation injury from breathing the spray or dust. Also, it is difficult to confine the spray, fog, or dust emitted from aerosol containers. Because of the flammable petroleum oil carriers, do not use pressure spray applicators around open flames or other sources of ignition.

Impregnates

Manufacturers *impregnate* pet collars, livestock ear tags, adhesive tapes, plastic pest strips, and other products with pesticides (Figure 3-14). These pesticides evaporate over time, and the vapors provide control of nearby pests. Some paints and wood finishes have pesticides incorporated into them to kill insects or retard fungus growth. Special paint formulations control cockroaches in residences and commercial buildings. These consist of certain insecticides incorporated into clear plastic or lacquer paint. Surfaces painted with this material provide 6 to 12 months of residual control. Sometimes manufacturers impregnate carpeting, furniture, bedding, fabrics, and clothing with pesticides to prevent damage from insects and fungi. Adhesive-backed impregnated strips provide long-term protection against insect damage when placed inside electrical boxes, electronic equipment, and appliances.

FIGURE 3-14.

Manufacturers impregnate flea collars with an insecticide that kills fleas. A low level of this insecticide is slowly released by the collar.

Repellents

Various types of insect repellents are available in aerosol and lotion formulations. People apply these to their skin, clothing, or to plant foliage to repel biting and nuisance insects. You can mix other types of repellents with water and spray these onto ornamental plants and agricultural crops. Use these to prevent damage from deer, dogs, and other animals.

Animal Systemics

Systemic pesticides protect animals against fleas and other external blood-feeding insects as well as against worms and other internal parasites. These pesticides enter the animals' tissues after being applied orally or externally. Oral applications include food additives and premeasured capsules and liquids. External applications involve pour-on liquids, liquid sprays, and dusts. Most animal systemics are used under the supervision of veterinarians.

Fertilizer Combinations

Pest managers frequently combine insecticides, fungicides, and herbicides with fertilizers. This provides a convenient way of controlling pests while fertilizing crops or ornamental plants. Homeowners commonly use these combinations, although the unit cost of pesticide in these preparations is usually high. In commercial applications, dealers or growers custom-mix pesticides with fertilizers to meet specific crop requirements.

PESTICIDE MIXTURES

Combining two or more pesticides and applying them at the same time is convenient and cost effective. Only a few pesticide manufactures sell their product as premixed combinations. Usually you must combine the pesticides at the time of application. When you combine mixtures of two or more pesticides or pesticides and fertilizers at the time of application, you create a *tank mix*. A common tank mix involves combining fungicides with insecticides as a dormant spray in deciduous tree crops. Another involves combining two or more herbicides to increase the number of species of weeds controlled. Some people mix pesticides with micronutrients or fertilizers. This saves money by reducing the time, labor, and fuel required for multiple applications. Tank mixes reduce equipment wear and decrease labor costs. They lessen the mechanical damage done to crops and soil by heavy application equipment.

If you mix *Danger* pesticides with *Warning* or *Caution* pesticides, treat the mixture as a *Danger* pesticide. Required safety equipment and all other label restrictions must comply with the label having the greater restrictions.

Incompatibility

Incompatibility is a physical condition that prevents pesticides from mixing properly to form a uniform solution or suspension. Precipitation of flakes, crystals, or oily clumps—or severe separation—are unacceptable (Figure 3-15). Such incompatible mixtures clog application equipment and limit even distribution of the active ingredient in the spray tank. This prevents good pesticide coverage. However, if you can mix the incompatible mixture thoroughly and keep it in that condition with agitation, the mixture is probably suitable to use.

The cause of incompatibility may relate to the chemical nature of the materials you are mixing. Impurities in the spray tank or water may also affect compatibility. Even the order in which you mix pesticides in the spray tank is important. Sometimes the types of formulations being mixed influence compatibility. Pesticide formulations of the same type are rarely incompatible with each other because they usually contain the same inert ingredients and solvents.

Before preparing a tank mix, be sure the spray tank is thoroughly clean and contains no sediments or residues. Evaluate the tank mixture by performing the compatibility test described below.

Testing for Incompatibility. Before preparing a full tank, mix small quantities of the same pesticides to test for incompatibility problems. Sidebar 5 provides instructions for a simple compatibility test that requires only a small investment of time. This test will not help you determine if the mixture has changed the chemical effectiveness of any or all the pesticides, however.

When combining chemicals for either the compatibility test or for mixing in the spray tank, add formulations in the following order:
(1) wettable powders
(2) flowables
(3) water-soluble concentrates
(4) emulsifiable concentrates
For example, when combining a water-soluble concentrate with a wettable powder, always add the wettable powder first. When mixing an emulsifiable concentrate with a flowable, add the flowable first.

Field Incompatibility. Sometimes tank mixes seem compatible during testing and after mixing in the spray tank, but problems arise during application. This is *field incompatibility*. The temperature of the water in the tank can cause this problem. It could also be due to water impurities. Sometimes the amount of time the spray mixture has been in the tank causes field incompatibility. Occasionally there are variations among different lots of pesticide chemicals that are great enough to cause an incompatibility. In this case, increased agitation is usually sufficient to recombine the mixture.

Resolving Compatibility Problems in the Spray Tank. There are several things you should try if pesticide incompatibility develops in the spray tank. First,

SIDEBAR 5

Compatibility Test for Pesticide Mixtures

WARNING: Always wear the label-required personal protective equipment when pouring or mixing pesticides. Perform this test in a safe area away from food and sources of ignition. Pesticides used in this test should be put into the spray tank when completed. Rinse all utensils and jars and pour rinsate into the spray tank. Do not use utensils or jars for any other purpose after they have contacted pesticides.

1. Measure one pint of the intended spray water into a clear quart glass jar.

2. Adjust pH if necessary (see Sidebar 6).

3. Add ingredients in the following order. Stir well each time an ingredient has been added.

   ☐ Surfactants, compatibility agents, and activators: add 1 teaspoon for each pint per 100 gallons of planned final spray mixture.
   ☐ Wettable powders and dry flowable formulations: add 1 tablespoon for each pound per 100 gallons of planned final spray mixture.
   ☐ Water-soluble concentrates or solutions: add 1 teaspoon for each pint per 100 gallons of planned final spray mixture.
   ☐ Emulsifiable concentrate and flowable formulations: add 1 teaspoon for each pint per 100 gallons of planned final spray mixture.
   ☐ Soluble powder formulations: add 1 teaspoon for each pint per 100 gallons of planned final spray mixture.
   ☐ Remaining adjuvants: add 1 teaspoon for each pint per 100 gallons of planned final spray mixture.

4. After mixing, let the solution stand for 15 minutes. Stir well and observe the results.

■ COMPATIBLE

Smooth mixture, combines well after stirring. Chemicals can be used together in the spray tank.

■ INCOMPATIBLE

Separation, clumps, grainy appearance. Settles out quickly after stirring. Follow instructions below to try to resolve incompatibility, otherwise do not mix this combination in the spray tank.

■ RESOLVING INCOMPATIBILITY

1. Add 6 drops of compatibility agent and stir well. If mixture appears compatible, allow it to stand for 1 hour, stir well, and check it again. If the mixture appears incompatible, repeat one or two more times, using 6 drops of compatibility agent each time.

2. If incompatibility still persists, dispose of this mixture, clean the jar, and repeat the above steps, but add 6 drops of compatibility agent to the water before anything else is added.

3. If the mixture is still incompatible, do not mix the chemicals in the spray tank. To overcome this problem you might consider the following alternatives:

   ☐ Use a different water supply.
   ☐ Change brands or formulations of chemicals.
   ☐ Change the order of mixing.

4. Make only one change at a time, and perform a complete test, as described above, before making another change. Do not mix the chemicals in the spray tank if incompatibility cannot be resolved.

FIGURE 3-15.

Sometimes mixtures of pesticides are incompatible and may separate or curdle. This clogs spray equipment and wastes the pesticide material.

increase agitation and try to break up the aggregates with a water stream to get the mixture recirculating. If the material still separates, contact your pest control dealer for an appropriate compatibility extender. Add the extender to the tank and continue agitation.

Changing filter screens to a larger size and cleaning them frequently may help eliminate some of the clumping. When these steps do not resolve the problem, dilute the mixture with additional water and filter off larger particles. If you cannot spray the mixture onto an application site, place it into an appropriate container for disposal. Follow the same procedures you would use to dispose of any other unused pesticide.

Chemical Changes with Pesticides and Pesticide Combinations

In some tank mixes, pesticides may mix properly in solution but the effectiveness or toxicity of the pesticides in the mixture changes. These changes are due to chemical, rather than physical, reactions between combined pesticides, impurities, or the water used for mixing. Such changes are difficult to recognize because you cannot see them.

Additive Effect

Combining two or more pesticides may result in an additive effect: the toxicity of the combination is no greater than if you used an equal amount of only one of the materials. For example, you apply two insecticides—Compound A and Compound B—at the rate of ½ pound of each per acre. The result on the target insect is no different than if you applied 1 pound of Compound A *or* 1 pound of Compound B. The results are greater, however, than if you applied just ½ pound of Compound A or ½ pound of Compound B (Figure 3-16).

Greater than Additive Effect

Sometimes the toxicity of pesticides being mixed increases above what you expected through an additive effect. You may notice three types of changes: *potentiation* or *synergism*, illustrated in Figure 3-17, or a *coalescent* effect.

Potentiation. Potentiation increases the toxicity of a pesticide because something mixed with it lowers the pest's tolerance to that chemical. Impurities in malathion, for example, can make malathion more toxic because the impurities inactivate enzymes produced by the pest that normally detoxify malathion. In mixtures of two or more pesticides, one compound may potentiate another in the same way. The result is an effect greater than the expected additive effect.

POTENCY

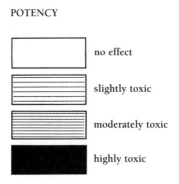

no effect

slightly toxic

moderately toxic

highly toxic

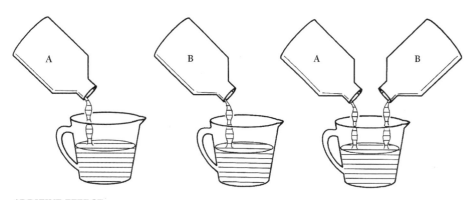

ADDITIVE EFFECT

FIGURE 3-16.

If you combine two or more pesticides and toxicity increases proportionally to the total amount of pesticide being used, the effect is additive.

FIGURE 3-17.

When combined pesticides produce a response greater than what would be expected by the additive effect, the response may be due to potentiation *or* synergism, *as illustrated here.*

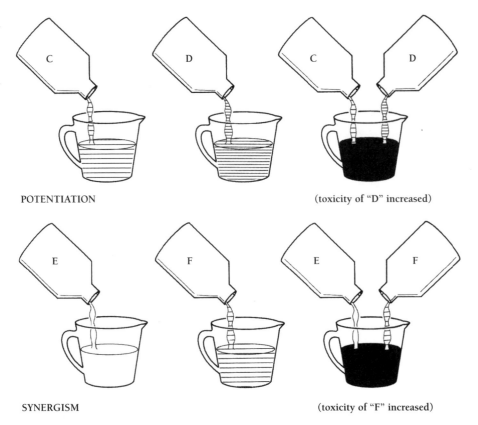

POTENTIATION   (toxicity of "D" increased)

SYNERGISM   (toxicity of "F" increased)

Synergism. Synergism is another way pesticides increase in toxicity. The chemical you mix with the pesticide may or may not have pesticidal properties but is a *synergist.* The synergistic chemical may slow the breakdown of the pesticide or increase its uptake by the pest. For example, *piperonyl butoxide* has no insecticidal properties, but it is commonly used to increase the toxicity of pyrethrum insecticides. By using this synergist, less of the expensive active ingredient is needed.

Coalescent Effect. A coalescent effect occurs when the toxic response from a pesticide mixture is unlike the expected response from either pesticide alone. The combined materials have formed a chemical with a different mode of action.

Antagonistic Effect

Antagonism occurs when a mixture reduces the toxic effect of one or more of the pesticides. For example, if you combine two pesticides, one pesticide may allow the target organism to resist, slow down, or degrade the toxic action of the other (Figure 3-18).

Deactivation

Deactivation may take place before a spray reaches the intended destination. This usually happens in the spray tank when you mix the pesticides. The quality of the water being used in the spray mixture may cause breakdown, or *hydrolysis,* of some pesticides. Water with a high pH (alkaline water) commonly shortens pesticide half-life. Sometimes one of the pesticide compounds changes the pH of the spray mixture. Also, one compound may alter or neutralize an electrical charge of the other to reduce its effectiveness. This problem is especially important when using herbicides.

Delayed Mixtures

If two pesticides are interactive, problems can occur even when you apply one of them several weeks after the other. An earlier spray may cause

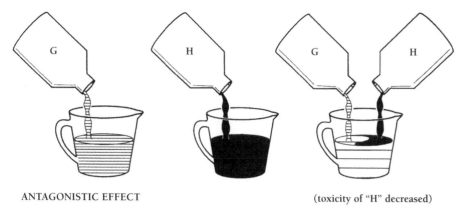

ANTAGONISTIC EFFECT   (toxicity of "H" decreased)

deactivation of the second spray. The combination of the two sprays may injure treated plants (phytotoxic). Check pesticide labels for this type of incompatibility.

Damage to Treated Plants or Surfaces

Pesticide combinations may work well to control target organisms but still create problems. The interaction between the chemicals may cause spotting or staining of sprayed surfaces. They may even damage plant foliage or produce. To avoid this problem, test the mixture on a small area first and observe the results. Chemicals affect some surfaces less than others. Similarly, some species of plants are more sensitive than others. Plant phytotoxicity, however, may not be apparent until several weeks after application.

Sources of Information on Compatibility

Although there are many good reasons to use tank mixes, it is important to avoid combinations that could damage sprayed surfaces or cause problems with the application equipment. There are several ways to get information on pesticide mixtures.

Labels

Pesticide labels provide compatibility information on tank mixes. For instance, tank-mixing herbicides is a common practice. Many herbicide labels list other herbicides that can be mixed with them. Labels sometimes list pesticides or materials that are incompatible with one of the pesticides being used. These may be specific compounds or general classes of chemicals, such as sulfur containing compounds or alkaline materials. When making tank mixes, be sure to follow all the instructions on *all labels*.

Pesticide Manufacturers

You can get specific information on compatibility by calling or writing to the main office, district office, or field representative of a pesticide manufacturer. Pesticide labels provide manufacturers' addresses. Chemical dealers usually have the names and telephone numbers of local field representatives. Most public libraries can also assist you in locating the nearest district office or corporate headquarters of a particular company.

ADJUVANTS

Adjuvants are materials you can add to the spray tank to improve mixing and application or enhance pesticide performance. Manufacturers formulate pesticides to be suitable to many types of application conditions. However, they cannot formulate them for all possible situations. Use adjuvants to customize the formulation to specific needs and compensate for local conditions. Adjuvants are used to

- improve the wetting ability of spray solutions
- control evaporation of spray droplets
- improve weatherability of pesticides
- increase the penetration of pesticides through plant or insect cuticles
- adjust the pH of spray solutions
- improve spray droplet deposition
- increase safety to target plants
- correct incompatibility problems
- reduce spray drift

Familiarize yourself with adjuvant types to understand where and how to use them (Table 3-11). When selecting adjuvants, outline the effect you wish the adjuvant to have. Next, check pesticide and adjuvant labels to make sure these materials are suitable to the application site, target pest, and application equipment.

Often a single chemical will accomplish two or more separate adjuvant functions. Examples of these are spreader-stickers, spreader-*activators*, or spreader-sticker-drift retardants. Some manufacturers also produce blends of chemicals to accomplish multiple functions. The effectiveness of most adjuvants is proportional to their concentration in the spray tank mixture, however. Therefore, ready-mixed blends may limit your ability to achieve the proper concentration of some component for your application requirements unless the requirements are identical to the ratio of components in the adjuvant mixture. It is often better to use several single-active-ingredient adjuvants rather than one multiple-function adjuvant. Add these at the appropriate concentrations for your specific needs.

Surfactants

Surfactants are *surface active agents*, also known as wetting agents or spread-

TABLE 3-11.

Comparisons of Adjuvants.

FUNCTION	TYPE OF ADJUVANT											
	Surfactant	Sticker	Spreader-Sticker	Extender	Activator	Compatibility Agent	Buffer	Acidifier	Deposition Aid	Defoamer	Thickener	Attractant
reduce surface tension	■		■		■							
improve ability to get into small cracks	■		■									
increase uptake by target	■		■		■			■				
improve sticking	■	■	■									
protect against wash-off/abrasion	■	■	■	■								
reduce sunlight degradation		■	■	■								
reduce volatilization	■	■	■									
increase persistence			■	■					■		■	
improve mixing						■	■	■				
lower pH							■	■				
slow breakdown							■	■				
reduce drift									■	■	■	
eliminate foam										■		
increase viscosity									■		■	
increase droplet size									■		■	
attract pests to pesticide												■

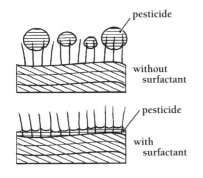

FIGURE 3-19.

Spray droplets will not spread out over waxy or hairy leaf or insect surfaces because of surface tension. Adding a surfactant, however, lowers surface tension. This causes droplets to spread out and come in contact with the cuticle of the leaf or insect.

ers. They enhance spray coverage by reducing the surface tension of spray droplets. Sometimes vegetable oils such as cottonseed oil and soy oil are used as surfactants. Surfactants allow better coverage on waxy or hairy surfaces, such as leaves of many plants or the outer coverings of insects and mites (Figure 3-19). They also help to get sprays into small cracks or openings.

The amount of surface tension reduction is proportional, to an extent, to the amount of surfactant used. Surface tension is measured in dynes/cm. Water has a normal surface tension of about 72 dynes/cm. Optimal spreading occurs by lowering this to about 30 dynes/cm. At this point, spray droplets are able to penetrate the small openings in leaf surfaces or insect cuticles. Increasing surfactant concentration any more than this usually causes spray materials to run off treated surfaces. This results in reduced effectiveness and a waste of materials. Mix surfactants according to directions on their labels to achieve the appropriate surface tension reduction.

Three types of surfactants are available. *Nonionic* surfactants do not react in water. *Anionic* surfactants ionize into negatively charged ions in water. *Cationic* surfactants ionize into positively charged ions in water. The surfactant's charge or lack of charge is important to pesticide applications. The charge affects how the spray material will react after application, drying, and exposure to environmental conditions. Emulsifiers used in the formulation of many pesticides are usually a blend of anionic and nonionic surfactants. This enables petroleum or other solvent-based chemicals to break up into droplets and suspend in water.

Anionic surfactants (negative electrical charge) help prevent pesticides from washing off sprayed plants due to rain, dew, or irrigation. They prevent pesticides from being readily absorbed through plant cuticle because plant surfaces have a negative charge, and like charges repel each other. Use anionic surfactants when it is important for the pesticide to remain on the outer surface of plants, even during adverse weather or environmental conditions. Also use them to increase the effectiveness of insecticides and miticides that are stomach or contact poisons. These surfactants keep more active ingredient on leaf surfaces rather than allowing them to be absorbed by the plant.

Nonionic surfactants (no electrical charge) increase pesticide penetration through plant cuticles. Labels recommend their use with systemic herbicides such as glyphosate and oxyfluorfen to improve target plant uptake. They also work with insecticides and fungicides that have systemic action. They improve the absorption of translocated pesticides into plant tissues. Rainfall, dew, or irrigation may wash pesticides mixed with nonionic surfactants off treated surfaces.

Cationic surfactants (positively charged) are strongly attracted to plant surfaces. Although they aid in getting pesticides through cuticles, they are highly phytotoxic when not blended with other types of surfactants. Pure cationic surfactants are not used as pesticide adjuvants.

Some surfactants are a blend of anionic and nonionic surfactants and may also contain cationic surfactants. Blends are general-purpose surfactants and usually have a wider range of application.

Selecting Surfactants. When selecting surfactants for pesticide application, consider several factors:

- the nature of the target surface (waxy layers or fine, hairlike structures are difficult to penetrate)
- the physical and chemical nature of the pesticide (some pesticides dissolve in water, while others are not soluble)
- the site of action of the pesticide (some must be absorbed by the

target and translocated, while other types must remain on the surface)

- weather conditions and cultural practices, such as irrigation, that may wash pesticides off treated surfaces or influence application methods and timing
- the biology or habits of the pest

Consider also the cost of the surfactant compared to the cost per unit area of treatment. Surfactants are not always pure active ingredient; most contain an alcohol solvent. The percentage of alcohol varies from one brand of surfactant to another. You will need to use more surfactant if it contains a high percentage of alcohol.

Stickers

Stickers are substances such as latex or other adhesives that improve pesticide attachment to sprayed surfaces. They protect pesticides from washing off due to rainfall, heavy dew, or irrigation. They also help prevent pesticide loss from wind or leaf abrasion. Many stickers incorporate ultraviolet inhibitors to slow pesticide breakdown by sunlight. Follow label directions carefully to avoid using too much sticker. Excess sticker binds the pesticide so well that it may be unavailable to react with target organisms. If the pesticide formulation already contains stickers, do not use additional amounts. Always read the pesticide label in case there are recommendations against using a sticker.

Spreader-Stickers

Spreader-stickers are mixtures of surfactants and latex or other adhesive stickers. These are general-purpose adjuvants used for many types of pesticide applications. When using a spreader-sticker, be certain that the surfactant is compatible with the type of pesticide being used. Also, check the pesticide formulation to see if it already contains a sticker.

Extenders

Extenders are chemicals that enhance the effectiveness or effective life of a pesticide. Some extenders function by screening out ultraviolet light that decomposes many pesticides; others slow down pesticide volatilization. Use stickers as extenders to slow down the loss of pesticide from surfaces due to irrigation, rainfall, and abrasion. Remember that extenders may make sprayed areas toxic longer than expected. This is because they slow the pesticide breakdown or natural degradation process.

Activators

Activators increase the activity of a pesticide. Some surfactants are activators because they reduce surface tension and allow greater pesticide contact. Activators also include chemicals that speed up pesticide penetration through insect or plant cuticles. Use activators carefully because they may increase risk to nontarget organisms by making pesticides more toxic.

Compatibility Agents

When physical incompatibility occurs among pesticides, compatibility agents may reduce or eliminate separating or clumping. For example, one type of compatibility agent, an emulsifier, is a soaplike material that combines with oil to make the oil disperse in a water solution. When trying to correct an incompatibility problem with a compatibility agent, mix small quantities of the pesticides and compatibility agent in a jar. Add all components in your test in the same order that you mix them in the spray tank. Unless pesticide or compatibility labels specify the mixing order, follow the technique described in Sidebar 5 on page 94.

Buffers and Acidifiers

The term *pH* is a measure of the acidity or alkalinity of a solution. A neutral solution has a pH of 7. A solution with a pH of 6 is slightly acid, while one with a pH of 8 is slightly alkaline. Many pesticides are unstable in alkaline solutions but quite stable if the solution is slightly acid. The optimal pH for most pesticides is about 6, although solutions in the range of pH 6 to 7 are usually satisfactory. Some pesticides are most effective when the solution is acidified to a pH of 3 to 3.5. High pH (alkalinity) often causes accelerated pesticide breakdown. Table 3-12 shows some of the effects that water pH has on the activity of pesticides. Sidebar 6 describes how to measure and alter the pH of the spray solution should this be necessary.

Buffers. *Buffers* are substances capable of changing the pH of a water solution to a prescribed level. They keep this level relatively constant, even though conditions such as water alkalinity may change.

Acidifiers. *Acidifiers* (also called *acidulators*) are acids that neutralize alkaline solutions and lower the pH. Acidifiers do not have a buffering action like buffers. Therefore alkaline or acid compounds added to the spray solution *after* the acidifier may change the pH of the solution.

Deposition Aids

Deposition aids are adjuvants that improve the ability of pesticide sprays to reach surfaces in a treatment area. Different types of products work as deposition aids. Inverting agents, for instance, encapsulate the pesticide, forming oil droplets of uniform size. These suspend in larger water droplets to form an invert suspension. Encapsulation prevents evaporation or volatilization of the pesticide before it reaches the target surface. Drift control agents increase droplet size by altering shear forces of the liquid spray emitted from a nozzle. Because larger droplets have more momentum, they travel far-

ther and are influenced less by wind. The result is that more pesticide reaches target surfaces in the treatment area. Surfactants that alter the surface tension of the spray solution also improve deposition. They do this because they influence droplet size as well as distribution on sprayed surfaces.

Defoaming Agents

Many pesticide mixtures produce copious amounts of foam as a result of the action of hydraulic or mechanical agitators. Foaming in the spray tank introduces air into the pressure system. This makes it difficult to maintain the even pressure required for proper mixing and uniform pesticide application. Defoaming agents eliminate foam in the spray tank.

Thickeners

Thickeners increase the viscosity of spray mixtures. Although thickeners work as drift retardants, they also assist in keeping spray mixtures in suspension. In addition, they slow the separation process once these materials reach the target. They help to slow the water evaporation, therefore extending pesticide activity and reducing drift. Sometimes regulations require the use of a thickener as a drift control agent when applying phenoxy herbicides such as 2,4-D.

Attractants

Attractants are food or bait, such as sugar, molasses, protein hydrolysates, or insect pheromones, that attract specific pests, usually insects. These combine with a pesticide to form a lethal mixture. Attractants allow spot applications of pesticides to localized areas within the treatment site rather than the entire site. They often enhance pesticide specificity to target pests.

Spray Colorants

Spray colorants are dyes you add to the spray tank to be able to see areas

SIDEBAR 6

Testing and Adjusting pH of Water Used for Mixing Pesticides

You can measure pH with an electronic pH meter, a pH test kit such as those used for testing swimming pool water, or pH test paper available from a chemical supply dealer.

▮ TEST WATER

1. Using a clean container, obtain a sample of water from the same source that will be used to fill the spray tank.

2. Measure exactly 1 pint of this water into a clean quart jar.

3. Check the pH of the water using a pH meter, test kit, or test paper.

pH level	
3.5–6.0	Satisfactory for spraying and short-term (12 to 24 hours) storage of most spray mixtures in the spray tank.
6.1–7.0	Adequate for immediate spraying of most pesticides. Do not leave the spray mixture in the tank for over 1 to 2 hours to prevent loss of effectiveness.
Above 7.0	Add buffer or acidifier.

▮ ADJUST pH

1. Using a standard eyedropper, add 3 drops of buffer or acidifier to the measured pint of water.

2. Stir well with a clean glass rod or other clean, nonporous utensil.

3. Check pH as above.

4. If further adjustment is needed, add 3 drops of buffer or acidifier, stir well, then recheck pH. Repeat until pH is satisfactory. Remember how many times 3 drops were added to bring the solution to the proper pH.

▮ CORRECT pH IN SPRAY TANK

1. Before adding pesticides to the sprayer, fill the tank with water.

2. For every 100 gallons of water in the spray tank, add 2 ounces of buffer or acidifier for each time 3 drops were used in the jar test above. Add buffer or acidifier to water while agitators are running. If tank is not equipped with an agitator, stir or mix well.

3. Check pH of the water in the spray tank to be certain it is correct. Adjust if necessary.

4. Add pesticides to spray tank.

TABLE 3-12.

Effect of Water pH on the Chemical Stability of Pesticides.

COMPOUND	BRAND NAME	HALF-LIFE AT DIFFERENT pH VALUES*
azinphosmethyl	Guthion	12 hours at pH 9.0, 17.3 days at pH 5.0.
benomyl	Benlate	Very stable in mildly acid to slightly alkaline solutions.
carbaryl	Sevin	24 hours at pH 9.0, 2.5 days at pH 8.0, 24 days at pH 7.0.
chlorothalonil	Bravo	38.1 days at pH 9.0. Stable below pH 7.0.
chlorpyrifos	Dursban Lorsban	1.5 days at pH 8.0. 35 days at pH 7.0.
diazinon	Knox-Out	37 hours at pH 6.0. Hydrolysis is very rapid in strong acid or strong alkaline solutions.
dimethoate	Cygon	12 hours at pH 6.0. Maximum stability is between pH 4.0 and pH 7.0. Unstable in alkaline water.
EPN	EPN	8.2 hours at pH 9.0, 10 years at pH 6.0.
ethoprop	Mocap	Stable in acid solutions, but hydrolyzes rapidly in alkaline solutions.
formetanate	Carzol	3 hours at pH 9.0, 14 hours at pH 7.0, 4 days at pH 5.0.
malathion	Cythion Carbophos others	Stable in neutral or moderately acid solutions, but undergoes hydrolysis rapidly at pH values above 7.0 or below 3.0.
methomyl	Lannate	Stable in slightly acid water. Slight hydrolysis after 6 hours in pH 9.1 solution.
monocrotophos	Azodrin	22–23 days at pH below 7.0. Hydrolysis increases rapidly at pH above 7.0.
naled	Dibrom	Undergoes 90 to 100% hydrolysis in 48 hours in alkaline water.
phosmet	Imidan	4 hours at pH 8.0, 12 hours at pH 7.0, 13 days at pH 4.5.
phosphamidon	Dimecron	30 hours at pH 10.0, 13.5 days at pH 7.0, 74 days at pH 4.0.
trichlorfon	Dylox	Rapid hydrolysis under conditions greater than pH 8.5. Most stable at pH 5.0.

*These figures are generalized estimates and reflect trends, but half-life periods may vary considerably. Hydrolysis depends on other factors besides the pH of the solution, including temperature, other pesticides and adjuvants in the spray tank, and formulation of the pesticide.

you have sprayed. Use colorants in backpack sprayers when applying herbicides to turf or a landscaped area. Also use them in rangeland areas and when spraying fencerows. Spray colorants are not suitable for use on food crops. The dyes may remain on produce and there may not be an established residue tolerance.

ORGANIC PEST CONTROL MATERIALS

In 1979, the Organic Foods Act became part of the California Health and Safety Code. (A proposed federal law similar to this is going through the legislative process.) This law specifies the types of pesticides people can use in agriculture. It covers crops, livestock, poultry, and dairy products sold as *organic*. The law applies to any labeling using the terms organically grown, naturally grown, wild, ecologically grown, or biologically grown (Figure 3-20). In the case of perennial crops, it requires that in fields where commodities are grown no synthetically compounded fertilizers, pesticides, or growth regulators be applied for 12 months before the appearance of flower buds. In addition, none can be applied throughout the growing and harvest season. In the case of annual and two-year crops, no synthetically compounded fertilizers, pesticides, or growth regulators can be applied for 12 months before seed planting and throughout the entire growing and harvest season.

Organically grown animals used for food (including poultry and fish) may not receive pesticides in any form except for treatment of a specific disease or malady. Animal growers cannot under any circumstances administer or introduce pesticides within 90 days of slaughter. Feed given to livestock or poultry must be produced using only approved pesticides. The law imposes similar restrictions on milk-producing animals.

Pesticides allowed for use on organically produced foods include microorganisms, microbiological products, and materials derived or extracted from plant, animal, or mineral-bearing rock substances. Permitted pesticides include Bordeaux mixes, trace elements, soluble aquatic plant products, botanical lime sulfur, naturally mined gypsum, dormant oils, summer oils, fish emulsion, and insecticidal soaps. All materials used as pesticides must have current labels for such use. Table 3-13 lists many of the materials that currently are allowable or have been used as organic pesticides.

FIGURE 3-20.

Organic produce must be grown without the use of synthetic pesticides or synthetic soil amendments. Only microorganisms, microbiological products, and materials derived or extracted from plants, animals, or mineral-bearing rock substances may be used to control the pests.

TABLE 3-13.

Pesticides Accepted for Use on or around Some Types of Organically Grown Produce. *

COMPOUND	TYPE	USE/COMMENTS
INSECTICIDES *Bacillus thuringiensis*	microbial	Controls many species of lepidopteran larvae and mosquito larvae (depending on the variety of the *B. thuringiensis* used).
boric acid	inorganic	A sorptive dust having a desiccant action. Controls cockroaches, ants, other household pests. Ineffective if dust gets wet.
cryolite	inorganic	Controls mites, moth larvae, beetles, weevils, and thrips.
diatomaceous earth	inorganic	A sorptive dust derived from the skeletons of microscopic marine organisms. As a desiccant, controls household pests such as cockroaches and ants. Also controls some plant pests.
granulosis virus	microbial	Controls codling moth.
lime	inorganic	Controls mites, some plant-sucking insects.
lime sulfur	inorganic	Controls mites and psylla.
nicotine sulfate	plant derivative	Controls aphids, thrips, leafhoppers, other sucking insects. Toxic to mammals.
petroleum oils	hydrocarbon	Controls aphids, psylla, scale insects, mites, aphid and mite eggs. May provide some control of other overwintering insects.
pheromones	attractants	Used mainly for monitoring to time other control measures. Sometimes used to confuse insects in localized area to disrupt mating. Occasionally used to catch large numbers of specific insects to reduce future generations.
pyrethrum	plant derivative	Broad spectrum of pests is controlled, including mosquitoes, flies, aphids, beetles, moth larvae, thrips, and mealybugs. Provides rapid knockdown of flying pests.
rotenone	plant derivative	Contact and stomach poison. Controls beetles, weevils, slugs, loopers, mosquitoes, thrips, fleas, lice, and flies. Also used for control of unwanted fish. Acts as a repellent and acaricide. Rotenone is slow acting and has a short residual. It is nontoxic to honey bees.
ryania	plant derivative	Controls codling moth, thrips, and the European corn borer.
sabadilla	plant derivative	Has contact and stomach poison action against cockroaches, several species of bugs, potato leafhopper, imported cabbage worm, house fly, citrus thrips, and the cattle louse. Is toxic to honey bees. Not highly toxic to mammals.
soaps	soap	Controls mites, aphids, and other plant-sucking arthropods. Can be phytotoxic under certain conditions. Soap must be specifically labeled for use as an insecticide.
sulfur	inorganic	Controls mites.
vegetable oils	plant derivative	As a contact spray, controls scale insects, aphids, and mites.

*Some pesticides on this list may not be currently approved for use on organically grown produce. Many materials listed in this table may no longer be registered as pesticides or their labels may restrict their use to specific pests, crops, or sites. Use all pesticides only in accordance with current federal and state labels.

(continued)

COMPOUND	TYPE	USE/COMMENTS
FUNGICIDES basic copper sulfate	inorganic	Controls early and late blight, scab, blotch, bitter rot, fire blight, downy mildew, black rot, leaf spot, melanose, greasy spot, brown rot, anthracnose, angular leaf spot, and others.
Bordeaux mix	inorganic	A slurry made of hydrated lime and copper sulfate. Controls brown rot and shot hole diseases in tree fruits. Controls some grape diseases. Also controls apple scab, blotch, apple black rot, melanose, anthracnose, early and late blight of potatoes and tomatoes, downy mildew, fire blight, leaf spot, peach leaf curl, and many other fungal diseases.
copper ammonium carbonate	inorganic	Controls angular leaf spot, alternaria leaf spot, cercospora leaf spot, early and late blight, bacterial blight, common blight, anthracnose, melanose, powdery mildew, downy mildew, and others.
copper hydroxide	inorganic	Controls cercospora leaf spot, bacterial blight, septoria, leaf blotch, anthracnose, halo blight, helminthosporum, downy mildew, leaf curl, early and late blight, angular leaf spot, melanose, scab, walnut blight, and others.
copper oxychloride sulfate	inorganic	Controls peach blight, peach leaf curl, damp-off, anthracnose, fire blight, shot hole fungus, pear blight, bacterial spot, walnut blight, brown rot, celery blight, downy mildew, early and late blight of vegetables, cherry leaf spot, septoria leaf spot, powdery mildew, melanose, scab, and others.
copper sulfate	inorganic	Suppresses development of fungal and bacterial organisms such as fire blight, cercospora leaf spot, early and late blight, bacterial blight, and others.
lime sulfur	inorganic	Controls powdery mildew, anthracnose, apple scab, brown rot, peach leaf curl, and others.
sulfur	inorganic	Controls brown rot, peach scab, apple scab, powdery mildew, downy mildew, rose black spot, and others.
terramycin	antibiotic derived from a fungus	Controls certain bacterial diseases in plants.

*Some pesticides on this list may not be currently approved for use on organically grown produce. Many materials listed in this table may no longer be registered as pesticides or their labels may restrict their use to specific pests, crops, or sites. Use all pesticides only in accordance with current federal and state labels.

In general, pesticides approved for use on organically grown produce break down rapidly. These materials are often less disruptive to natural enemies and other organisms in the environment. However, the modes of action of many chemicals acceptable under the Organic Foods Act are similar to some synthetically manufactured pesticides. For example, copper materials and rotenone interfere with cell respiration, and pyrethrins interfere with nerve transmission, similar to DDT. Nicotine blocks nerve and nerve-muscle connections; petroleum oils interfere with cell membrane activity; and ryania affects the nervous system. These pesticides have LD_{50} values similar to *Warning* and *Caution* organophosphate and carbamate pesticides (Table 3-14).

TABLE 3-14.

Oral LD$_{50}$ Values for Some Pesticides Used to Control Pests on Organically Grown Produce.

CHEMICAL*	BRAND NAME	LD$_{50}$	TYPE OF PESTICIDE
nicotine	Black Leaf 40	55	insecticide
rotenone	—	132	insecticide
Bordeaux mix	—	300	fungicide
copper hydroxide	Kocide	1,000	fungicide
copper oxychloride sulfate	C-O-C-S	1,000	fungicide
ryania	—	1,200	insecticide
pyrethrum	—	1,500	insecticide
silica aerogel	Dri-Die	3,160	insecticide
sabadilla	—	4,000	insecticide
cryolite	Kryocide	10,000	insecticide

*Some of the materials on this list may not currently be registered as pesticides or be acceptable for use on organically grown produce.

REVIEW QUESTIONS

1. **Which part of the label gives you an indication of the toxicity of the pesticide?**
   - ☐ a. The *Statement of Use Classification*
   - ☐ b. The *Signal Word*
   - ☐ c. The *Directions for Use*
   - ☐ d. The *EPA Registration Number*

2. **The LD$_{50}$ of a pesticide tells you:**
   - ☐ a. The toxicity of the pesticide
   - ☐ b. The level of possibility for long-term health effects
   - ☐ c. Its effectiveness as a pest control agent
   - ☐ d. The likelihood of it causing plant injury

3. **The toxicity of a pesticide is usually measured by its:**
   - ☐ a. No observable effect level (NOEL)
   - ☐ b. Long-term health effects
   - ☐ c. LD$_{50}$
   - ☐ d. Half-life

4. **Which signal word indicates the *least* hazardous pesticide?**
   - ☐ a. Poison
   - ☐ b. Danger
   - ☐ c. Warning
   - ☐ d. Caution

5. **The toxicity of a pesticide is:**
   - ☐ a. The length of time it remains active in the environment
   - ☐ b. The potential for reaching groundwater
   - ☐ c. Its boiling point
   - ☐ d. Its capacity to cause injury

6. **Which of the following chemical families contains pesticides that are typically persistent in the environment?**
   - ☐ a. Organophosphates
   - ☐ b. Carbamates
   - ☐ c. Botanicals
   - ☐ d. Organochlorines

7. **A postemergent contact herbicide:**
   - ☐ a. Is applied before weeds germinate
   - ☐ b. Must be translocated in the plant to be effective
   - ☐ c. Causes injury to any part of the plant it touches
   - ☐ d. Provides a crop with systemic weed protection

8. **How much active ingredient would be found in a 20-pound bag of a 25W formulation?**
   - ☐ a. 4 pounds
   - ☐ b. 5 pounds
   - ☐ c. 10 pounds
   - ☐ d. 20 pounds

9. **How much active ingredient would there be in a 5-gallon bottle of a 4E formulation?**
   - ☐ a. 4 pounds
   - ☐ b. 20 pounds
   - ☐ c. 4 quarts
   - ☐ d. 20 gallons

10. **Which of the following formulation is *least* likely to cause plant injury?**
    - ☐ a. Emulsifiable concentrate (EC)
    - ☐ b. Soluble powder (SP)
    - ☐ c. Wettable powder (W or WP)
    - ☐ d. Fumigant

11. **Which of the following formulations requires no further agitation once it is fully mixed with water?**
    - ☐ a. Emulsifiable concentrate (EC)
    - ☐ b. Soluble powder (SP)
    - ☐ c. Wettable powder (W or WP)
    - ☐ d. Flowable (F)

12. **The tendency of ants to take poisoned bait back to the nest:**
    - ☐ a. Makes ant bait too dangerous for home use
    - ☐ b. Contributes to the effectiveness of ant baits
    - ☐ c. Can cause ant populations to grow rapidly
    - ☐ d. Makes ant baits illegal for agricultural use

13. **The way a pesticide destroys or controls a target organism is its:**
    - ☐ a. Half-life
    - ☐ b. Toxicity
    - ☐ c. Mode of action
    - ☐ d. Phytotoxicity

14. **When combining a wettable powder, a water soluble concentrate, and an emulsifiable concentrate in a tank mix:**
    - ☐ a. The emulsifiable concentrate should go in first
    - ☐ b. The order in which the formulations are added does not matter
    - ☐ c. The wettable powder should go in last
    - ☐ d. The emulsifiable concentrate should go in last

15. **If a mixture of two pesticides in the spray tank results in clumping and the spray nozzles clog up, the mixture is:**
    - ☐ a. Synergistic
    - ☐ b. Antagonistic
    - ☐ c. Surface active
    - ☐ d. Incompatible

4 Pesticide Laws and Regulations

Laws and regulations governing the use of pesticides are made by federal and state agencies.

STATE AND FEDERAL laws regulate the manufacture, sale, transportation, and use of pesticides. At the national level, the U.S. EPA is the pesticide regulatory agency. In California the Department of Pesticide Regulation (DPR) assumes this role. EPA's authority is a mandate from the Federal Insecticide, Fungicide, and Rodenticide Act (FIFRA). Originally passed in 1947, this law has undergone several amendments and updates, including the 1992 *Worker Protection Standard*. Based on this federal law, EPA establishes regulations for pesticide registration and labeling and pesticide residue tolerance levels on or in foods. These regulations also set standards for using restricted-use pesticides and certifying pesticide applicators. Other federal agencies, including the Department of Agriculture (USDA), the National Institute of Occupational Safety and Health (NIOSH), and the Fish and Wildlife Service (FWS), monitor and regulate some types of pesticide uses.

Pesticide applicators in all states must comply with federal laws. California has enacted additional laws that strive to make pesticide use safer under the special conditions existing here (see Sidebar 7). California laws are sometimes more restrictive than federal laws but cannot permit uses or activities prohibited by the federal laws. California laws require reporting the uses of all pesticides in many application locations, such as production agriculture. Each year, managers of agricultural operations and certain other nonagricultural operations must obtain site and operation identification numbers before buying or using pesticides. This chapter describes the requirements for obtaining identification numbers and reporting pesticide uses.

California's pesticide laws are part of the California Food and Agricultural Code. The California legislature passes these laws in response to needs arising within the state or from federal mandates. *Regulations* are the working rules needed to interpret and carry out these laws. Regulations pertaining to pest control and pesticide use are part of the California Code of Regulations. The California DPR develops and proposes pesticide regulations. After receiving comments by mail and from public hearings concerning a proposed regulation, the DPR writes its final *Statement of Reasons* and forwards it to the Office of Administrative Law for approval. If approved, it is forwarded to the Secretary of State's office to be filed. At this point the new regulation is implemented by the DPR.

Several other state agencies in California monitor and regulate pesticide use. These include the Department of Health Services, Air Resources Board, Department of Fish and Game, Department of Forestry, Occupational Safety and Health Administration, Waste Management Board, Department of Water Resources, Water Resources Control Board and Regional Water Control Board, and Structural Pest Control Board. In addition, agricultural commissioners in each county develop pesticide use policies or conditions. These are specific to the needs of their counties. The DPR director must approve county agricultural commissioner policies before they become operative, however. Counties and local governments also may create ordinances governing the use and storage of pesticides within their jurisdictions.

Laws or regulations change when new situations arise that are not covered by existing laws and regulations. For example, pesticides and pesticide application equipment are constantly being improved or modified. These improvements often require people to use pesticides differently. In addition,

pest problems and pest management techniques usually differ from year to year. This also affects how people use pesticides. Also, as regulators identify new health and environmental problems, they create or modify laws to deal with them. For instance, the Worker Protection Standard was a change in FIFRA that strengthened requirements to protect people who work in pesticide-treated areas.

For current pesticide laws and regulations information, obtain a copy of the publication *Laws and Regulations Study Guide for Agricultural Pest Control*

SIDEBAR 7

Reasons for Pesticide Laws and Regulations

1. To provide for the proper, safe, and efficient use of pesticides essential for the production of food and fiber and for protection of public health and safety.

2. To protect the environment from environmentally harmful pesticides by prohibiting, regulating, or controlling uses of these pesticides.

3. To assure the agricultural and pest control workers of safe working conditions where pesticides are present.

4. To permit agricultural pest control by competent and responsible licensees and permittees under strict control of the Director of the California Department of Pesticide Regulation and local agricultural commissioners.

5. To assure the users that economic poisons are properly labeled and are appropriate for the use designated by the label.

6. To encourage the development and implementation of pest management systems, stressing application of biological and cultural pest control techniques with selective

pesticides when necessary to achieve acceptable levels of control with the least possible harm to nontarget organisms and the environment.

United States
Environmental Protection
Agency
Office of Pesticide Programs

730L97001
March 1997

⊕EPA
The Federal Insecticide, Fungicide, and Rodenticide Act (FIFRA) and Federal Food, Drug, and Cosmetic Act (FFDCA) As Amended by the Food Quality Protection Act (FQPA) of August 3,1996

Adviser, Pest Control Business, Pest Control Dealer, Pest Control Aircraft Pilot Examinations. Order this booklet from the California Department of Pesticide Regulation, Pesticide Enforcement Branch, 830 K Street, Sacramento, California 95814.

ENFORCEMENT

The DPR director and county agricultural commissioners enforce state pesticide laws and regulations. Applicators who fail to comply with federal and state pesticide laws and regulations are subject to fines and/or imprisonment. They also face the possible loss or suspension of their DPR-issued licenses or certificates. The offices of the state attorney general or local district attorneys prosecute violators. In addition, county agricultural commissioners may issue citations and levy fines on violators of certain pesticide-use regulations. Table 4-1 summarizes the responsibilities of the DPR, county agricultural commissioners, and other state and federal government agencies.

PESTICIDE REGISTRATION AND LABELING

Manufacturers must register pesticides with the U.S. EPA and DPR before anyone can buy or use them in California. These agencies register individual pesticide *products*, not generic pesticides. The registration procedure protects people and the environment from ineffective or harmful chemicals. Sidebar 8 lists the information that a manufacturer provides to register a pesticide.

The registration procedure includes an evaluation of each chemical. This evaluation establishes how EPA classifies the material at the federal level. Pesticides are either *general-use* or *restricted-use*. A general-use pesticide is one that can be sold without a permit and can be used by the general public. However, only certified pesticide applicators can buy, use, or supervise the use of a federal restricted-use pesticide. California designates certain general-use pesticides as restricted-use due to local hazards or specific health concerns. With few exceptions, you must obtain a permit from the county agricultural commissioner to buy any California restricted-use pesticide. The last section of this chapter contains information on permits for buying and using restricted-use pesticides.

As part of California's pesticide registration procedure, several state agencies review registration information. These include the California Departments of Food and Agriculture, Fish and Game, Health Services, and Industrial Relations. The Air Resources Board and Water Resources Control Board also review this information. In addition, there is a 45-day public review and comment period. This takes place before DPR makes a decision to register, renew, or reevaluate a pesticide. The public review provides opportunities for interested or concerned people to contribute to registration decisions.

To complete registration, manufacturers supply labels meeting all federal and state requirements. These labels become legal documents and contain important information for users. Some labels refer to other documents, such as endangered species range maps. Agricultural-use pesticide labels also refer to the Worker Protection Standard provisions of the Code of Federal Regulations (40 CFR part 170). These and other documents referred to on pesticide labels become part of the pesticide *labeling*.

Emergency Exemptions and Special Local Need

Occasionally pest problems arise that you cannot control with currently registered pesticides. Sometimes the commodity, target, or site are not on the registered pesticide label. In some situations, you can request an emergency

TABLE 4-1.

Responsibilities of Government Agencies in California's Pesticide Regulatory Program.

REGULATORY PROGRAM	WHO ADMINISTERS IT	WHAT IT DOES
registering pesticides	EPA, DPR	Refuse or accept registration; suspend, cancel, or reregister pesticides.
classifying pesticides	EPA, DPR	EPA classifies pesticides as restricted-use or general-use in the United States; DPR may impose more stringent restrictions for California, based on special conditions existing in the state.
permitting	CAC, DPR	Issue, revoke, or refuse restricted-use pesticide permits (with use conditions) to growers, other private applicators, or certified applicators.
licensing commercial applicators, advisers, pest control businesses, pesticide dealers, and maintenance gardeners	DPR*	Issue licenses and administer tests to commercial applicator license applicants; revoke, suspend, or refuse licenses upon violation of pesticide laws.
registering applicators and advisers, certifying private applicators	CAC	Register pest control businesses, aerial pest control operators, licensed pest control advisers, and maintenance gardeners. Through written examination, certify private applicators. Provide applicators and advisers with information on local pesticide use conditions. Inspect pesticide use records and pest control recommendations to verify proper pesticide use.
monitoring pesticide residues on food and feed	EPA, USDA, DPR, CAC**	Test food and feed for pesticide residues; quarantine or destroy illegally contaminated commodities; bring cases of violation to county district attorney or state attorney general for prosecution.
regulating pesticide use and worker safety	EPA, DPR, CAC, DHS	General authority to regulate pest control operations, including restrictions on the time, place, and manner of application; inspect training programs and records; various warning and enforcement powers.
pesticide illness investigation	DPR, CAC, DHS	Participate in pesticide illness investigations and in development of worker safety regulations; confirmation of compliance with worker training requirements.
pesticide disposal and storage	DPR, DHS, WRCB, WQCB, ARB, CAC	Regulate hazardous waste storage and disposal, pesticide container disposal sites, and water quality standards.
protecting wildlife	EPA, FWS, DFG, CAC, DPR	Investigate fish and wildlife losses. Identify and monitor endangered species. Restrict pesticide use to protect endangered species and other wildlife.
citing or prosecuting violators	EPA, DPR, CAC, SPCB, state attorney general, local district attorneys	Agricultural commissioner may levy civil penalties with fines. DPR may request attorney general to take civil action. Attorney general may file accusation. DPR may suspend or revoke applicator's certificate. CAC may suspend, revoke, or refuse permits and county registration.

Abbreviations:

ARB: California Air Resources Board

CAC: County Agricultural Commissioner

DPR: California Department of Pesticide Regulation

DFG: California Department of Fish and Game

DHS: California Department of Health Services

EPA: U.S. Environmental Protection Agency

FWS: U.S. Fish and Wildlife Service

SPCB: Structural Pest Control Board, California Department of Consumer Affairs

USDA: U.S. Department of Agriculture

WRCB: California Water Resources Control Board

WQCB: California Water Quality Control Board

*In California, Structural Pest Control Operators are licensed by the Structural Pest Control Board, California Department of Consumer Affairs. Vector Control Certificates are issued by the Department of Health Services.

**13 other state and 5 federal agencies monitor various parts of the environment for pesticides and other substances.

SIDEBAR 8

Information Manufacturers Must Provide to DPR to Register a Pesticide in California

1. Exposure information: data on risks of exposure and how people can be protected

   ☐ Safety related to exposure
   ☐ Mixer, loader, applicator exposure
   ☐ Management of poisoning
   ☐ Toxicology of adjuvants and other components of the formulation
   ☐ Indoor exposure information
   ☐ If material is a rodenticide, metabolic pathway and mode of action
   ☐ Foliar residue and field restricted-entry data

2. Residue test method

3. Residue data

4. Efficacy

5. Hazard to bees

6. Closed-system compatibility

7. Effects on pest management

8. Inert ingredient hazard

9. Volatile organic compounds: their relationship to air quality

10. Other data as requested by the director of DPR, such as

    ☐ Information on drift potential
    ☐ Phytotoxicity
    ☐ Contaminants or impurities in the product
    ☐ Analytical and environmental chemistry
    ☐ Effects of tank mixes on the product (compatibility)

exemption or a special local need (SLN) registration.

Emergency Exemptions from Registration. Emergency exemptions from registration address pest problems for which there are no pesticides registered. The U.S. EPA can issue an emergency exemption from registration at the request of the DPR. First, DPR must acknowledge the need and consider it appropriate. Usually these needs are based on specific public health quarantine or crisis emergencies that require the use of an unregistered pesticide. There must be no feasible alternative to the exemption. Known as *Section 18 Exemptions*, they allow the sale and use of a certain pesticide product for a specific nonregistered purpose during a specified period of time.

Regulations impose strict controls and require recordkeeping for all emer-

gency uses. You must understand the special requirements and responsibilities involved whenever you use pesticides with emergency exemptions. The Department of Pesticide Regulation prescribes application rates, safety precautions, and other vital application information.

Special Local Need Registrations. Special Local Need (SLN) registrations are categorized as *24(c) registrations*. They allow states to expand or limit the uses of certain registered pesticides within their jurisdictions. For instance, some SLNs allow uses of pesticides for crops or sites not listed on the label. Others add limitations to the uses of a federally registered pesticide to accommodate area-specific conditions. Manufacturers must provide *supplemental labeling* for each SLN registration.

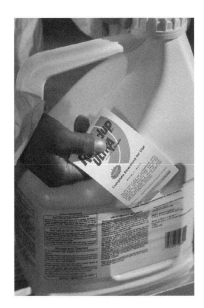

FIGURE 4-1.

Supplemental labels are often attached to pesticide packages. Before purchasing a pesticide, make sure you have a complete set of labels.

You must have the SLN labeling in your possession to use the pesticide for that purpose. The registration numbers of Special Local Need labeling include *SLN* and the code for the state issuing the registration (CA). These registrations are legal only in the region, state, or local area specified in the labeling. Applying a pesticide having an SLN from another state or region subjects you to civil and criminal penalties.

To find out which SLN registrations pertain to your area, contact any of the following:

- the local county agricultural commissioner's office
- a UC Cooperative Extension farm advisor
- a pest control dealer

Pesticide Labels

Regulations set the format for pesticide labels and prescribe the information they must contain. Some packages are too small, however, to have all this information printed on them. In these cases, EPA requires manufacturers to attach *supplemental labels* (Figure 4-1). On metal and plastic containers, manufacturers put supplemental labels in plastic pouches glued to the side of the containers. Paper packages usually have supplemental labels inserted under the bottom flaps.

When to Read the Pesticide Label

Read the pesticide label (Figure 4-2)

1. *Before buying the pesticide.* Make sure the pesticide is registered for your intended use. Confirm that there are no restrictions or other conditions that prohibit using this pesticide at the application site. Be certain its use is suitable under current weather conditions. Also, be sure it controls the life stage of your pest. Find out what protective equipment and special application equipment you need.

2. *Before mixing and applying the pesticide.* Learn how to mix and safely apply the material. Find out what precautions to take to prevent exposure to people and nontarget organisms. Learn what first aid and medical treatments are necessary should an accident occur.

3. *When storing pesticides.* Find out how to properly store the pesticide. Understand the special precautions to prevent fire hazards.

FIGURE 4-2.

The pesticide label is a complex legal document that you must read and understand before making a pesticide application. Make pesticide applications in strict accordance with the label instructions.

4. *Before disposing of unused pesticide and empty containers.* Learn how to prevent environmental contamination and hazards to people. (Before disposal, check with the agricultural commissioner in your area for local restrictions and requirements.)

What Pesticide Labels Contain

Refer to the corresponding numbers on the sample pesticide label (Figure 4-5) for examples of the following pesticide label sections:

Brand Name. A brand name is the
[1] name the manufacturer gives to the product. This is the name used for all advertising and promoting.

Chemical Name. Chemical names
[2] describe the chemical structure of a pesticide. Chemists follow international rules for naming chemicals.

Common Name. Chemical names of
[3] pesticide active ingredients are often complicated. Therefore, manufactures give most pesticides *common* or generic names. For example, 0,0-diethyl 0(2-isopropyl-6-methyl-4-pyrimidinyl) has the common name *diazinon*. Common names and brand names are not the same, and not all labels list common names for the pesticide.

Formulation. Labels usually list the
[4] formulation type, such as emulsifiable concentrate, wettable powder, or soluble powder. Manufacturers may include this information as a suffix in the brand name of the pesticide. For example, in the name Princep 80W, the "W" indicates a wettable powder formulation. Table 3-9 on page 84 lists definitions for many suffixes used with brand names.

Ingredients. Pesticide labels list the
[5] percentage of active and inert ingredients by weight. Inert ingredients are all components of the formulation that do not have pesticidal action. However, these may be toxic, flammable, or pose other safety or environmental problems. Some, however, are totally harmless, such as clay. If a pesticide contains more than one active ingredient, the label may state the percentage of each. Sometimes manufacturers group all inert ingredients together and their labels do not show the percentage of each one.

In the example given above, the name Princep 80W indicates that there is 80% by weight of the active ingredient 2-chloro-4,6-bis(ethylamino)-s-triazine. If this were a liquid formulation, the label would also indicate how many pounds of active ingredient there are in 1 gallon.

Contents. Labels list the net
[6] contents, by weight or liquid volume, contained in the package.

Manufacturer. Pesticide labels
[7] always contain the name and address of the manufacturer of the product. Use this address if you need to contact the manufacturer for any reason.

**Registration and Establishment
[8] Numbers.** The U.S. EPA assigns registration numbers to each pesticide. You need this EPA number if you are reporting the use of the pesticide. In addition, an *establishment number* identifies the site of manufacture or repackaging.

Signal Word. An important part of
[9] every label is the signal word (Figure 4-3). The words *Danger* and *Poison* (with a skull and crossbones) indicate that the pesticide is highly toxic. The word *Danger* used

FIGURE 4-3.

The signal word Warning *on this label indicates that the pesticide has a moderate toxicity and should be handled with care.*

KEEP OUT OF REACH OF CHILDREN
WARNING   AVISO

Si usted no entiende la etiqueta, busque a alguien para que se la explique a usted en detalle. (If you do not understand the label, find someone to explain it to you in detail.)

STATEMENT OF PRACTICAL TREATMENT
IF IN EYES: Flush eyes with a large amount of water for at least 15 minutes. Get prompt medical attention.
IF ON SKIN: Wash with plenty of soap and water. Get medical attention.
IF SWALLOWED: Do not induce vomiting. Dilute by giving 2 glasses of water to drink. Call a physician. Do not induce vomiting or give anything by mouth to an unconscious person.
IF INHALED: Move victim to fresh air. If not breathing, give artificial respiration, preferably mouth-to-mouth. Get medical attention.
NOTE TO PHYSICIAN: Contains petroleum distillates. Aspiration hazard may contraindicate the use of gastric lavage.

PRECAUTIONARY STATEMENTS
HAZARDS TO HUMANS AND DOMESTIC ANIMALS
WARNING
Causes eye irritation. Harmful if swallowed, inhaled or absorbed through the skin. Do not swallow, get in eyes, on skin or breathe spray mist.

PERSONAL PROTECTIVE EQUIPMENT (PPE)
Applicators and other handlers must wear:
• Long-sleeved shirt and long pants
• Waterproof gloves
• Shoes plus socks
• Protective eyewear
• Chemical-resistant headgear for overhead exposure

Discard clothing and other absorbent materials that have been drenched or heavily contaminated with this product's concentrate. Do not reuse them. Follow manufacturer's instructions for cleaning/maintaining PPE. If no such instructions for washables, use detergent and hot water. Keep and wash PPE separately from other laundry.

When handlers use closed systems, enclosed cabs, or aircraft in a manner that meets the requirements listed in the Worker Protection Standards (WPS) for agricultural pesticides [40 CFR 170.240(d) (4-6)], the handler PPE requirements may be reduced or modified as specified in the WPS.

FIGURE 4-4.

The "Precautionary Statements," "Statement of Practical Treatment," and "Statement of Use" on pesticide labels provide important information on hazards you must be aware of. Read these statements thoroughly before using the material.

alone indicates that the pesticide poses a dangerous health or environmental hazard. *Warning* indicates moderate toxicity, and *Caution* means low toxicity. (The section "Pesticide Toxicity Classification" in Chapter 3 explains these different toxicity categories.) Part of the registration process assigns each pesticide to a toxicity category. The level of hazard is a guide for the signal word manufacturers must use on their labels.

Precautionary Statements.

10   Precautionary statements describe the pesticide hazards (Figure 4-4). Read and follow the instructions given in a precautionary statement—this section includes as

many as three areas of hazard. Most important are the *hazards to people and domestic animals.* This part tells why the pesticide is hazardous. It lists adverse effects that may occur if people become exposed. It describes the type of protective equipment to wear while handling packages and while mixing and applying.

The second part of a precautionary statement describes environmental hazards. It tells you if the pesticide is toxic to nontarget organisms such as honey bees, fish, birds, and other wildlife. Here is where you learn how to avoid environmental contamination.

The third part of the precautionary statement explains special physical and chemical hazards. These include risks of fire or explosion and hazards from fumes.

Statement of Practical Treatment.

11   The statement of practical treatment provides emergency information. It tells what to do to decontaminate someone who becomes exposed to the pesticide. It describes the emergency first aid procedures for swallowing, skin and eye exposure, and inhalation of dust or vapors. This section tells you when to seek medical attention.

Statement of Use Classification.

12   As described above, the U.S. EPA classifies pesticides as either general-use or restricted-use. U.S. EPA *restricted-use pesticides* have a special statement printed on the label in a prominent place. Pesticides that do not

12

RESTRICTED USE PESTICIDE
Due to High Acute Toxicity to Humans

For retail sale and use only by Certified Applicators or persons under their direct supervision and only for those uses covered by the Certified Applicator's certification. Direct supervision for this product requires the certified applicator to review federal and supplemental label instructions with all personnel prior to application, mixing, loading, or repair or cleaning of application equipment.

1

Reckon® LV

5

insecticide   by **ToxCo®**

3
2

Active Ingredient:	By Weight
Methomyl	
(S-methyl-N-[(methylcarbamoyl) oxy]thioacetimidate)	29%
Inert Ingredients	71%
TOTAL	100%

4

Water Soluble Liquid

Contains 2.4 lbs active ingredient per gallon.

8

EPA Reg. No. 000-000
EPA EST. No. 0000-XX-0

6

Net 5 gallons

KEEP OUT OF REACH OF CHILDREN

9

DANGER   POISON

PELIGRO   VENENO

Si usted no entiende la etiqueta, busque a alguien para que se la explique a usted en detalle. (If you do not understand this label, find someone to explain it to you in detail.)

11

STATEMENT OF PRACTICAL TREATMENT

This Product is an N-Methyl Carbamate insecticide.
If swallowed: Call a physician or Poison Control Center. Drink 1 or 2 glasses of water and induce vomiting by touching the back of throat with finger. Do not induce vomiting or give anything by mouth to an unconscious or convulsing person.
If inhaled: Remove victim to fresh air. If not breathing, give artificial respiration, preferably mouth-to-mouth. Get medical attention.
If in eyes: Hold eyelids open and flush with a steady gentle stream of water for 15 minutes. Get medical attention.
If on skin: Wash with plenty of soap and water. Get medical attention.
ATROPINE IS AN ANTIDOTE—SEEK MEDICAL ATTENTION AT ONCE IN ALL CASES OF SUSPECTED POISONING.
If warning symptoms appear (see WARNING SYMPTOMS), get medical attention.
For medical emergencies involving this product, call toll free 1-000-000-0000.

10

PRECAUTIONARY STATEMENTS
HAZARDS TO HUMANS
AND DOMESTIC ANIMALS

DANGER! CONTAINS METHANOL. FATAL IF SWALLOWED. MAY CAUSE BLINDNESS IF SWALLOWED. MAY BE FATAL IF INHALED OR ABSORBED THROUGH EYES. CAUSES IRREVERSIBLE EYE DAMAGE.

(Precautionary Statements continued in next column.)

7

©1999 ToxCo, Inc., Villageton, Yourstate, 01234

FIGURE 4-5.

This example of a pesticide label illustrates the important sections.
These sections are described in the text.

Do not get in eyes, on skin, or on clothing. Do not breathe vapors or spray mist. Pilot should not assist in the mixing and loading operation.

WARNING SYMPTOMS—Methomyl poisoning produces effects associated with anticholinesterase activity which may include weakness, blurred vision, headache, nausea, abdominal cramps, discomfort in the chest, constriction of pupils, sweating, slow pulse, muscle tremors. If warning symptoms appear, refer to Statement of Practical Treatment on front panel of Reckon® LV label and seek medical attention at once.

PERSONAL PROTECTIVE EQUIPMENT

Some materials that are chemical-resistant to this product are listed below. If you want more options, follow the instructions for category B on an EPA chemical-resistance category selection chart.

Applicators and other handlers must wear:
Long-sleeved shirt and long pants.
Chemical-resistant gloves, such as barrier laminate or butyl rubber.
Shoes plus socks.
Protective eyewear.
For exposure in enclosed areas, a respirator with either an organic vapor-removing cartridge with a prefilter approved for pesticides (MSHA/NIOSH approval number prefix TC-23C or a NIOSH-approved respirator with any R, P, or HE filter [also N if product does not contain oil and bears no instructions that will allow application with an oil-containing material]), or a canister approved for pesticides (MSHA/NIOSH approval number prefix TC-14G).
For exposures outdoors, dust/mist filtering respirator (MSHA/NIOSH approval number prefix TC-21C or a NIOSH-approved respirator with any R, P, or HE filter [also N if product does not contain oil and bears no instructions that will allow application with an oil-containing material]).

Cleaners and repairers of application equipment must wear:
Long-sleeved shirt and long pants.
Chemical resistant gloves.
Chemical resistant footwear.
Protective eyewear.
Respirator as outlined above.
Chemical resistant apron.

Discard clothing or other absorbent materials that have been drenched or heavily contaminated with this product's concentrate. Do not reuse them. Follow manufacturer's instructions for cleaning/maintaining PPE. If no such instructions for washables, use detergent and hot water. Keep and wash PPE separately from other laundry.

ENGINEERING CONTROL STATEMENTS

Human flaggers must be in enclosed cabs.
When handlers use closed systems, enclosed cabs, or aircraft in a manner that meets the requirements listed in the Worker Protection Standard (WPS) for agricultural pesticides [40 CFR part 170.240 (d)(4–6)], the handler PPE requirements may be reduced or modified as specified in the WPS. The enclosed cabs must be used in a manner that meets the requirements listed in the WPS for agricultural pesticides. The handler PPE requirements may be reduced or modified as specified in the WPS.

ENVIRONMENTAL HAZARDS

This pesticide is toxic to fish and wildlife. Drift and runoff from treated areas may be hazardous to aquatic organisms in neighboring areas. Do not apply directly to water, or to areas where surface water is present, or to intertidal areas below the mean high water mark. Do not contaminate water when disposing of equipment washwaters.

This product is highly toxic to bees exposed to direct treatment on blooming crops or weeds. Do not apply this product or allow it to drift to blooming crops or weeds while bees are actively visiting the treatment area.

PHYSICAL AND CHEMICAL HAZARDS

Combustible. Do not use or store near heat or open flame. Keep container closed. Use with adequate ventilation.

DIRECTIONS FOR USE

It is a violation of federal law to use this product in a manner inconsistent with its labeling.

Do not apply this product in a way that will contact workers or other persons, either directly or through drift. Only protected handlers may be in the area during application. For any requirements specific to your State or Tribe, consult the agency responsible for pesticide regulation.

Do not apply this product through any type of irrigation system.

Do not formulate this product into other end-use products without written permission.

ToxCo RECKON® LV Insecticide should be used only in accordance with recommendations available through local dealers.

ToxCo will not be responsible for losses or damages resulting from use of this product in any manner not specifically recommended by ToxCo. User assumes all risks associated with such non-recommended use. RECKON® LV is a water soluble liquid to be diluted with water for application by mechanical ground or air equipment only. Use only in commercial and farm plantings. Not for use in home plantings nor on any commercial crop that is turned into a "U-Pick," "Pick Your own" or similar operation. Pilot should not assist in the mixing and loading operation.

AGRICULTURAL USE REQUIREMENTS

Use this product only in accordance with its labeling and with the Worker Protection Standard, 40 CFR part 170. This Standard contains requirements for the protection of agricultural workers on farms, forests, nurseries, and greenhouses, and handlers of agricultural pesticides. It contains requirements for training, decontamination, notification, and emergency assistance. It also contains specific instructions and exceptions pertaining to the statements on this label about personal protective equipment (PPE) and restricted-entry interval. The requirements in this box only apply to uses of this product that are covered by the Worker Protection Standard.

Do not enter or allow worker entry into treated areas during the restricted entry interval (REI).
PPE required for early entry to treated areas that is permitted under the Worker Protection Standard and that involves contact with anything that has been treated, such as plants, soil, or water, is:
Coveralls.
Chemical-resistant gloves, such as barrier laminate or butyl rubber.
Shoes plus socks.
Protective eyewear.

GENERAL INFORMATION

Scouting—Monitor insect populations to determine whether or not there is a need for application of RECKON® LV based on locally determined economic thresholds. More than one treatment of RECKON® LV may be required to control a population of pests.

Insect Predators—RECKON® LV at rates of ⅝ to ¾ pt. per acre helps conserve certain beneficials, including big-eyed bugs, damsel bugs, flower bugs and spiders in cotton and soybeans. While these beneficials cannot be relied upon to control pests, they are of potential value and should be monitored along with pests in pest management programs on these crops.

Resistance—Some insects are known to develop resistance to products used repeatedly for control. When this occurs, the recommended dosages fail to suppress the pest population below the economic threshold. Because the development of resistance cannot be predicted, the use of this product should conform to resistance management strategies established for the use area. These strategies may include incorporation of cultural and biological control practices, alteration of active classes of insecticides on succeeding generations and targeting the most susceptible life stage. Consult your local agricultural authorities for details.

Compatibility—Since formulations may be changed and new ones introduced, it is recommended that users pre-mix a small quantity of desired tank mix and observe for possible adverse changes (settling out, flocculation, etc.). Avoid mixtures of several materials and very concentrated spray mixtures.

Do not use RECKON® LV with Bordeaux mixture, "Du Ter" (triphenyltin hydroxide), lime sulfur, "Rayplex" iron nor in highly alkaline solutions. Use mildly alkaline mixtures immediately after mixing to prevent loss of insecticidal activity.

SPRAY PREPARATION

Spray equipment must be clean and free of previous pesticide deposits before applying RECKON® LV.

Fill spray tank ¼ to ½ full of water. Add RECKON® LV directly to spray tank. Mix thoroughly. Use mechanical or hydraulic means; do not use air agitation. Spray mix should not be stored overnight in spray tank.

(Directions for Use continued on supplemental labeling.)

STORAGE AND DISPOSAL

STORAGE: Do not subject to temperatures below 32° F. Store product in original container only. Do not contaminate water, other pesticides, fertilizer, food or feed in storage. Not for use or storage in or around the home.

PRODUCT DISPOSAL: Do not contaminate water, food, or feed by disposal. Pesticide wastes are acutely hazardous. Improper disposal of excess pesticide, spray mixture, or rinsate is a violation of Federal Law. If these wastes cannot be disposed of by use according to label instructions, contact your State Pesticide or Environmental Control Agency, or the Hazardous Waste representative at the nearest EPA Regional Office for guidance.

CONTAINER DISPOSAL: Triple rinse (or equivalent), then offer for recycling or reconditioning if container reuse is permitted, or puncture and dispose of in a sanitary landfill, or by incineration, or, if allowed by state and local authorities, by burning. If burned, stay out of smoke. Return empty stainless steel containers for refilling and reuse.

LIMITATION OF WARRANTY AND LIABILITY

NOTICE: Read This Limitation of Warranty and Liability Before Buying or Using This Product. If the Terms Are Not Acceptable, Return the Product at Once, Unopened, and the Purchase Price Will Be Refunded.

It is impossible to eliminate all risks associated with the use of this product. Such risks arise from weather conditions, soil factors, off target movement, unconventional farming techniques, presence of other materials, the manner of use or application, or other unknown factors, all of which are beyond the control of ToxCo. These risks can cause: ineffectiveness of the product; crop injury; or injury to nontarget crops or plants.

ToxCo does not agree to be an insurer of these risks. WHEN YOU BUY OR USE THIS PRODUCT, YOU AGREE TO ACCEPT THESE RISKS.

(Warranty information continued on supplemental labeling.)

Crops	Insects	Rate Reckon® LV Pts. Per Acre	Last Application—Days To Harvest	To Livestock Grazing/ Feeding	REI
Anise	Cabbage Looper	3	7		48 hrs
(fennel)	Beet Armyworm	1½ to 3			
	Do not apply more than 4.5 lbs a.i./acre/crop.				
	Do not make more than 10 applications/crop.				

(Restricted-entry information continued on supplemental labeling.)

13
16
17
14
18
13
15

contain this statement are *general-use pesticides*, except where special state restrictions apply. For information, check the DPR list, *State Restricted-Use Pesticides*, available from county agricultural commissioners. Some labels have *restrictive* statements indicating that they are for agricultural or commercial use only. A restrictive statement is different from a statement of use classification.

Directions for Use. The directions for use are an important part of the pesticide label. It is a violation of the law if you do not follow these instructions. The only exceptions are cases where federal or state laws specify acceptable deviations from label instructions (see the following section).

The directions for use list all the target pests that manufacturers claim their pesticides control. It also includes the crops, plant species, animals, or other sites where you can use the pesticides (Figure 4-6). Here is where you find special restrictions that you must observe. These include crops that you may or may not plant in the treated area (*plantback restrictions*). They also include restrictions on feeding crop residues to livestock or grazing livestock on treated plants.

These instructions tell you how to apply the pesticide. They specify how much to use, where to use the material, and when to apply it. The directions also include the *harvest intervals* (or *preharvest intervals*) for all crops whenever appropriate. A harvest interval is the time, in days, required after application before you may harvest an agricultural crop.

Agricultural Use Requirements. This special statement appears in the *Directions for Use* section on labels of pesticides approved for use in production agriculture, commercial greenhouses and nurseries, and forests. It refers to the Worker Protection Standard (40 CFR part 170). You must use the pesticide according to this standard as well as the requirements on the pesticide label. It provides information on the personal protective equipment (PPE) required for *early-entry workers*. It also gives the *restricted-entry interval* (REI) for workers (see below).

Restricted-Entry Statement. Usually a period of time must elapse before anyone can enter a treated area unless they are wearing personal protective equipment. This period is the *restricted-entry interval*. Restricted-entry intervals may vary according to the toxicity and special hazards associated with the pesticide. The crop or site being treated and its geographic location also influence the length of this interval. Some pesticide uses in California require longer restricted-entry intervals than those listed on the pesticide label. Check with the local agricultural commissioner for this information.

Misuse Statement. The misuse statement reminds users to apply pesticides according to label directions.

Storage and Disposal Directions. Directions for properly storing and disposing of the pesticide and empty pesticide containers are another important part of the label. Proper disposal of unused pesticides and pesticide containers reduces human and environmental hazards. Some pesticides have special storage requirements because improper storage causes them to lose their effectiveness. Improper storage may even cause explosions or fires.

Warranty. Manufacturers usually include a warranty and disclaimer on their pesticide labels. This information informs you of your rights as a purchaser and limits the liability of the manufacturer.

FIGURE 4-6.

Pesticides must be applied only in the manner described in the "Directions for Use" section.

DIRECTIONS FOR USE

It is a violation of Federal law to use this product in a manner inconsistent with its labeling. This label must be in the possession of the user at the time of pesticide application.

Observe all cautions and limitations in this label and the labels of products used in combination with PROWL 3.3 EC. The use of PROWL 3.3 EC not consistent with this label can result in injury to crops, animals, or persons. Keep containers closed to avoid spills and contamination.

DO NOT apply this product in a way that will contact workers or other persons, either directly or through drift. Only protected handlers may be in the area during application. For any requirements specific to your State or Tribe, consult the agency responsible for pesticide protection.

FIGURE 4-6.

Pesticides must be applied only in the manner described in the "Directions for Use" section.

DEVIATIONS FROM LABEL DIRECTIONS

Sometimes regulations allow you to use pesticides in a manner that varies from label directions. These methods generally involve safer or less disruptive uses of the pesticide. For instance, University of California *Pest Management Guidelines* sometimes recommend pesticide rates that are lower than label instructions. Researchers recommend these rates to protect beneficial organisms.

Following are the only label deviations allowed by California law. These exceptions may change at any time or may not apply in certain instances. Always check with DPR or your local agricultural commissioner before using a pesticide in any manner that varies from label directions.

Decrease in rate per unit treated. Some guidelines call for less pesticide than the amount listed on the label. This is usually because a lower rate is less disruptive to natural enemies. Consider, for example, the guidelines for controlling spider mites in almonds. If there are adequate levels of beneficials, they recommend as little as 1/10 of the label rate of specific acaricides. The lower rate reduces pest numbers to a level where predators can maintain control.

However, be cautious about using lower rates. Sometimes using lower rates speeds up the development of pesticide resistance in the target organism. To avoid possible problems when using lower rates, check first with the local farm advisor.

Under no circumstances can you legally increase the amount of pesticide you apply beyond the maximum label rates.

Decrease in the concentration of the mixture applied. Label instructions usually state the volume of water to use when preparing a spray mixture. It is always possible to use more water than this, however too much water may cause excessive dilution and runoff. This results in not enough of the pesticide getting to the target pest. In most cases, use only as much water as necessary to obtain thorough coverage. Be sure this is not less than what the label states.

Increase in concentration as long as it corresponds with published recommendations of the University of California. There are times when it would be convenient to use a more concentrated mixture than the dilution rate specified on the label. Although you would apply no more than the labeled rate of pesticide, you would prefer using less carrier (water or oil). If there are current, published UC guidelines for doing this, you can increase the concentration. However, these guidelines are pesticide-specific. Comply with all other label instructions. Remember, verbal recommendations of any type are not acceptable.

Application at a frequency less than specified. Label instructions often prescribe how often to apply a pesticide. Manufacturers recommend this frequency to maintain adequate control of the pest being treated. It is permissible under the law to make applications less frequently than the label recommends. If your monitoring confirms that less frequent applications adequately control pests, there is no need to make additional treatments. Additional applications sometimes increase other pest problems by disrupting beneficials. Besides, it is expensive to use unneeded pesticides.

However, reducing the frequency of a pesticide application below label recommendations may result in inadequate control. Before reducing application frequency, carefully monitor the pest population.

It is never permissible to apply a pesticide more frequently than the interval listed on the label. You may apply the pesticide repeatedly if the label does not limit the number of applications or it states "apply as needed." Monitor the pest to be sure that repeated applications are necessary.

Use to control a target pest not on the label when the commodity or site is on the label and use against an unnamed pest is not expressly prohibited. You may wish to use a pesticide on a commodity or site listed on the label, but the label does not list the target pest. As long as the label does not *forbid* use of this pesticide against the pest on the commodity or site, you may use it. Be certain the label lists the commodity or target site (for other pests). Follow all other label instructions.

Use of any method of application not prohibited, provided other label directions are followed. Most label recommendations do not specify exactly how to apply the pesticide. Should this be the case, it is possible to use any practical method. However, be sure the method you choose allows you to follow all other label directions.

Applying a pesticide by ground or by air is an example. If there is no prohibition against aerial application on the label, you may use either method. However, you must comply with all label directions. (It may not be possible to apply a pesticide by air when the label prohibits the lower dilution rate required for aerial application.)

Mixing with another pesticide or fertilizer, unless prohibited. You may want to combine one pesticide with one or several others or with fertilizers. This type of application saves time and reduces application costs. Unless specifically prohibited by directions on any of the labels, it is permissible to apply pesticides in combination.

Even though the label does not prohibit mixtures, you may experience incompatibility problems with certain combinations of pesticides or pesticides and fertilizers. Check for incompatibility before mixing large volumes. Refer to Chapter 3 for ways to determine incompatibility and resolve incompatibility problems.

Never mix a pesticide with another pesticide or fertilizer if the label prohibits such a mixture. Label restrictions may specify general classes of chemicals such as sulfur-containing materials, alkaline chemicals, or oils.

Exceptions to or substitutions for personal protective equipment (PPE) requirements. State regulations provide for the following exceptions to some pesticide label PPE requirements:

- If you are using a closed system to handle pesticide products with the signal word *Danger* or *Warning,* you may substitute coveralls, chemical resistant gloves, and a chemical resistant apron for personal protective equipment required by the pesticide label.* Properly mixing pesticides packaged in water-soluble packets is considered to be using a closed system.

- If you use a closed system to handle pesticide products with the signal word *Caution*, you may substitute *work clothing* for the personal protective equipment required by the pesticide label.* Properly mixing pesticides packaged in water-soluble packets is considered to be using a closed system.

- If you are applying pesticides from an enclosed cab (including the cockpit of an aircraft), you may substitute *work clothing* for personal protective equipment required by the pesticide product labeling. If respiratory protection is required, you must wear this while applying pesticides from ground application equipment unless the cab is approved for respiratory protection.**

- You may substitute a chemical-resistant suit for coveralls and/or a chemical resistant apron.

- If you are applying pesticides from an aircraft, you are not required to wear gloves during operation of the aircraft. However, wear gloves when entering or exiting if the aircraft is contaminated with pesticide residues. While in the cockpit, keep your gloves in a chemical-resistant container, such as a plastic bag.

PESTICIDE USE RECORDS

If you apply pesticides for hire or meet any of the following criteria you must maintain records of pesticide use. You must keep these records for 2 years. Make them available to the director of the DPR or the local agricultural commissioner upon request. Keep pesticide use records if you use any pesticide

- designated for *agricultural use*, as defined in the Food and Agricultural Code Section 11408 (pesticides designated for use only on livestock are exempted)
- designated by the DPR as *restricted* (listed in Section 6400 of the California Code of Regulations)
- designated for industrial use as a postharvest commodity treatment
- listed on the *Groundwater Protection List* found in Section 6800(b) of the California Code of Regulations and used for any outdoor institutional or outdoor industrial use

Include the following information in your pesticide use records:

- date of application
- name of the operator of the property treated
- location of property treated
- crop commodity or site treated
- total acreage or units treated at the site
- pesticide, including the U.S. EPA or state registration number on the pesticide label
- amount used

Besides the information required above, if you are the operator of property that produces an agricultural commodity

---

* If the closed system you use operates under positive pressure, you must use protective eyewear. Also, have all personal protective equipment required by pesticide product labeling immediately available for use in an emergency.

** If you are working in an enclosed cab, other than an aircraft, you must have with you all personal protective equipment required by pesticide product labeling. Keep this PPE immediately available and store it in a chemical-resistant container, such as a plastic bag. Wear this label-required personal protective equipment if it is necessary to work outside the cab and contact pesticide treated surfaces. Remove and store this PPE in a plastic bag before reentering the cab.

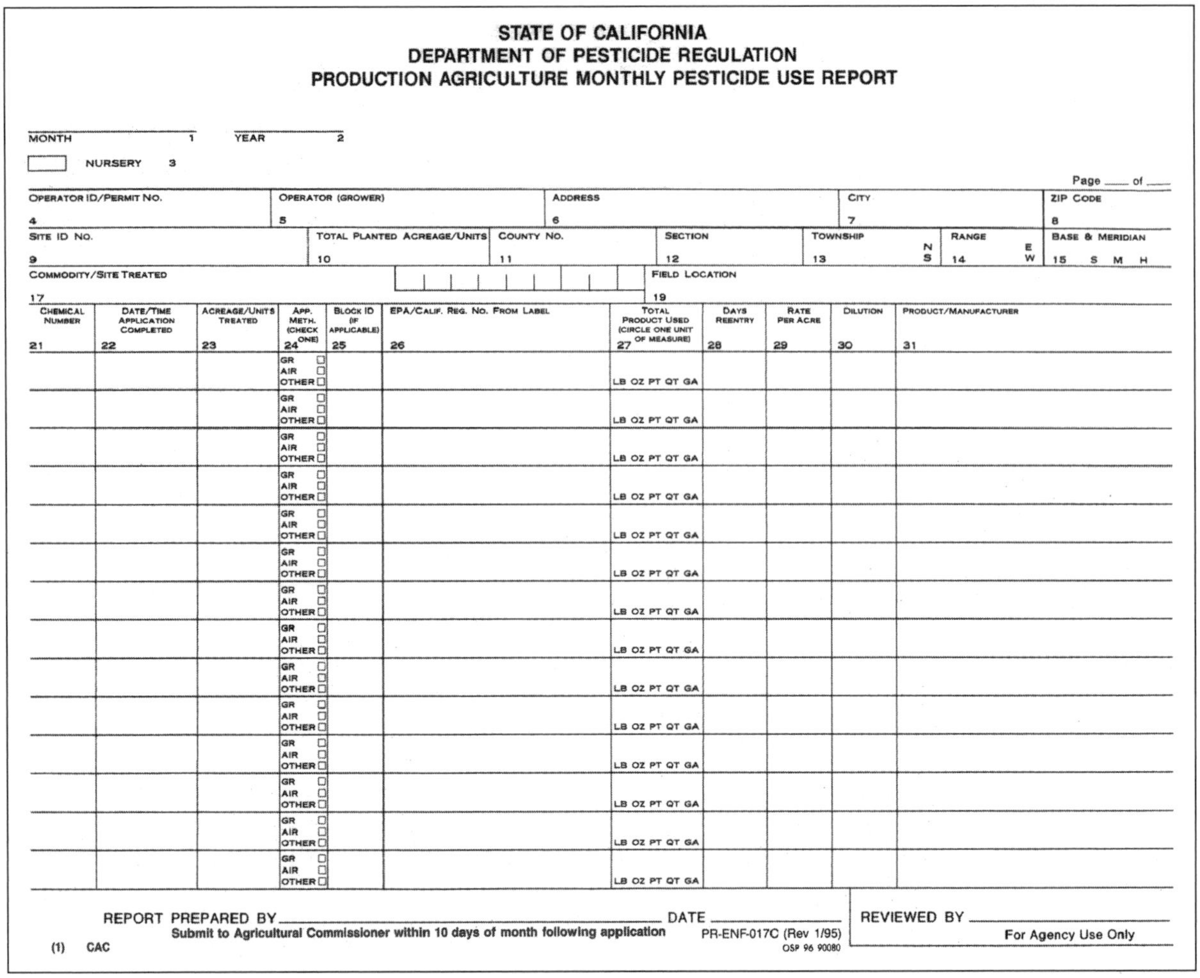

STATE OF CALIFORNIA
DEPARTMENT OF PESTICIDE REGULATION
PRODUCTION AGRICULTURE MONTHLY PESTICIDE USE REPORT

FIGURE 4-7.

You must report the use of all pesticides applied to agricultural commodities to the local agricultural commissioner by the 10th of the month following the month of application. Pesticides used in other locations may also need to be reported, as described in the text.

or are a pest control business applying pesticides to such property, you must include in the records the following information for each pesticide applied:

- location of the property treated, by county, section, township, range, base and meridian
- hour the treatment was completed
- the operator identification number issued to the operator of the property treated
- the site identification number issued to the operator of the property treated
- total acreage (planted) or units at the site
- names of people who made and supervised the application, if the

pesticide application was made by a pest control business

If you are the operator of property that produces an agricultural commodity, you must maintain records of pesticides applied by the pest control business to this property. These records must specify the sites where pesticides were applied by the pest control business.

PESTICIDE USE REPORTING REQUIREMENTS

If you are involved in the production of agricultural commodities or apply pesticides in certain other areas, follow the procedures described below before buying or using pesticides. However, if you perform pest control for hire, you are exempt from these requirements. (In this context, performing pest control "for hire" means that you are a self-employed pest control operator or an employee of a firm that contracts to apply pesticides for others, and you or your employer do not own, manage, or operate the site where you apply the pesticides.)

Operator and Site Identification Numbers

Production Agriculture. If you are the operator of agricultural property, you must obtain an *operator identification number* before buying or using *any* pesticides in the production of agricultural commodities. Obtain operator identification numbers from agricultural commissioners in each county where you perform pest control work. If pesticides are applied by a commercial applicator (pest control business), provide the company making the application with this operator identification number.

Before using pesticides for the production of an agricultural commodity, the operator of the property must obtain *site identification numbers* from the local agricultural commissioner for each site where pest control work will be performed. These site identification numbers are valid for the same concurrent period as the operator identification number.

Nonagricultural Sites. You must obtain an *operator identification number* if you apply any of the pesticides listed below to cemeteries, golf courses, parks, rights-of-way, postharvest agricultural commodities, and certain other nonagricultural sites. Obtain operator identification numbers from the agricultural commissioners of each county in which you perform pest control. As the operator of the property, you are not required to obtain an operator identification number when a person perform-

ing pest control for hire purchases and applies these pesticides.

Following are the pesticides for which you must have an operator identification number if they are applied on nonagricultural sites:

- any pesticide designated for *agricultural use*, as defined in the Food and Agricultural Code Section 11408 (pesticides designated for use only on livestock are exempted)
- any pesticide designated by the DPR as *restricted* (listed in Section 6400 of the California Code of Regulations)
- any pesticide designated for industrial use as a postharvest commodity treatment
- any pesticide listed on the *Groundwater Protection List* found in Section 6800(b) of the California Code of Regulations and used for any outdoor institutional or outdoor industrial use

Pesticide Use Reports for Production Agriculture

Agricultural Property Operator. The operator of property that is producing an agricultural commodity must report the use of all pesticides applied to the crop, commodity, or site (Figure 4-7). Send or deliver these reports to the commissioner of the county in which the pest control was performed. These reports are due by the 10th day of the month following the month in which the pesticide was applied. Reports are not required from the operator of the property if a pest control business reports the pesticide use to the commissioner.

Pest Control Business. Pest control businesses must report the use of pesticides applied by them for the production of agricultural commodities. Deliver these by hand or mail to the commissioner of the county in which the pest control was performed within 7 days of completion of the pesticide application. Also, within 30 days of completion of the pesticide application, send a copy of this report to the operator of the property where the pesticide was applied.

Monthly Summary Pesticide Use Reports (Nonagricultural Sites)

Anyone meeting the criteria listed below and who applies pesticides to nonagricultural sites must report a summary of the monthly use of pesticides to the commissioner of the county in which the work was performed. Mail or hand-deliver the report to the commissioner by the 10th day of the month following the month in which the work was performed. Include the following information on this report:

- name and address of the person (or business) who applied the pesticides
- county where the pest control was performed
- month and year of pesticide use
- crop, commodity, or site treated, except when using a designated use code as specified on the Monthly Summary Pesticide Use Report form
- pesticide names, including the U.S. EPA or state registration numbers on the pesticide labels
- amount of each pesticide used
- number of applications made with each pesticide and the total number of applications made during the month
- total acres or units treated with each pesticide, except when using a designated use code, as specified on the Monthly Summary Pesticide Use Report form

Monthly summary pesticide use reports are required if you

- apply any pesticide designated for *agricultural use*, as defined in the Food and Agricultural Code Section 11408 (pesticides designated for use only on livestock are exempted)
- apply pesticides for hire
- use a pesticide for industrial postharvest commodity treatment
- use any pesticide listed on the *Groundwater Protection List* found in Section 6800(b) of the California Code of Regulations, for any outdoor institutional or outdoor industrial purpose

Negative Pesticide Use Reports

During any month, if a licensed agricultural pest control business performs no pest control work in a county where the business is registered with the commissioner, it must submit a report stating this fact. File this report with the county agricultural commissioner by the 10th day of the following month.

RESTRICTED-USE PESTICIDES

State and federal laws restrict *Danger* materials so that only certified commercial or private pesticide applicators can buy or use them. These laws similarly restrict other pesticides that meet specific hazard criteria. Counties may also place local restrictions on particular pesticides. Criteria for restricting the use of certain pesticides in California include

- danger to public health
- hazard to applicators and farmworkers
- hazard to domestic animals, honey bees, and crops from direct application or drift
- hazard to the environment from drift onto streams, lakes, or wildlife estuaries
- hazards related to persistent residues in the soil resulting in contamination of the air, waterways, estuaries, or lakes, causing damage to fish, wild birds, and other wildlife

- hazards to subsequent crops due to persistent soil residues
- use of a federal restricted-use pesticide

Get information on federal, state, and county use restrictions from the county agricultural commissioners' offices in counties where you make applications.

Applicator Certification

You must be a *certified pesticide applicator* before you can be issued a restricted-use permit. Obtain your certification by one of the following means:

Certified Private Applicator

This category applies to operators of agricultural and other properties or their designees. You must successfully pass the *private applicator certification* examination administered by the county agricultural commissioner in the county where the property is located. Certification must be renewed every 3 years by reexamination or by attending the required 6 hours of approved continuing education.

Certified Commercial Applicator

This classification applies to people performing pest control for hire and others who apply or supervise the application of restricted-use pesticides as part of their employment in nonagricultural and/or agricultural areas. Growers who use or supervise the use of *minimal exposure pesticides* in agricultural areas must also be qualified commercial applicators. You must successfully pass one of the following examinations, depending on the nature of your work:

- Maintenance Gardener Pest Control Business
- Qualified Applicator Certificate (QAC)
- Qualified Applicator License (QAL)
- Pest Control Operator Business
- Pest Control Aircraft Pilot Certificate

These examinations are administered by the Department of Pesticide Regulation throughout California on a regular basis. Obtain application materials for these examinations from the local agricultural commissioner's office or from DPR. The qualified applicator certificate and license classifications contain the following 11 categories in which individuals can be tested and certified. You must hold a current certification in the appropriate category or categories in order to apply or supervise the application of restricted-use pesticides in those areas. The categories include

(a) Residential, Industrial, and Institutional Pest Control
(b) Landscape Maintenance Pest Control
(c) Right-of-Way Pest Control
(d) Agricultural Pest Control (plant)
(e) Forest Pest Control
(f) Aquatic Pest Control
(g) Regulatory Pest Control
(h) Seed Treatment
(i) Agricultural Pest Control (animal)
(j) Demonstration and Research
(k) Health-Related Pest Control

Continuing Education. All commercial applicators, as defined above, must renew their certification every 2 years by attending approved continuing education courses. Maintenance Gardener Pest Control Business license holders who possess only the landscape maintenance category must attend 8 hours of approved continuing education, including 2 hours of laws and regulations. QAC and QAL holders possessing only the Seed Treatment category must attend 4 hours of approved continuing education, including 2 hours of laws and regulations. QAC and QAL holders in all other categories must have 20 hours of approved continuing education, including 4 hours of laws and regulations, to renew their certification. Pest Control Aircraft Pilots must have 4 hours of aerial application and 4 hours of laws and regulations as part of their 20 hours of continuing education every 2 years.

Restricted-Use Permits

Agricultural commissioners issue *restricted-use permits* (Figure 4-8) for specific agricultural sites and crops. California law does not require permits to use federally restricted pesticides in *nonagricultural* areas. However, in nonagricultural applications only certified applicators can buy and use these pesticides. For some materials, the state imposes additional restrictions. For instance, materials classified as restricted in California require a permit for *any* use other than use by structural pest control operators. For nonagricultural uses, these permits are not site-specific.

You must present a valid pesticide applicator license, certificate, or private applicator certificate to the agricultural commissioner when you apply for a restricted-use permit. Before issuing site-specific permits, commissioners consider local conditions. These include the proximity of the application to dwellings, schools, hospitals, recreational areas, and animals. They also evaluate the potential for injury to adjacent crops or plantings. The commissioners consider how weather might affect the pesticide application. They evaluate how you plan to protect honey

---

YOLO COUNTY DEPARTMENT OF AGRICULTURE
70 COTTONWOOD STREET, WOODLAND, CA 95695

Office: (530) 666-8140
Recorder: (NOI) (530) 662-1487
FAX: (530) 662-6094

RESTRICTED MATERIALS PERMIT

Operation Name and Address:			PERMIT #:		
			County HQ District #:		
			Expiration Date:		
			Effective Date:		
Grower Name and Address:			Home Phone:		
			Shop Phone:		
			FAX:		
			Mobile Phone:		

Permittee Type		Permit Type	Possession	NOI Method of Submission	
Private App ☐	Ag PCO ☐	Seasonal ☐	Poss & Use ☐	Phone ☐	Fax ☐
QA Cert ☐	Non-Ag ☐	Job ☐	Poss Only ☐	Box ☐	Modem ☐
				In Person ☐	
				NOI required 24 hours prior to application	

Chemical Number	Pesticide/Manufacturer	Pest(s)	Formulation	Method(s) of Application	Applicator(s)

Non-Ag Use:
Conditions:

I understand that this permit does not relieve me from liability for any damage to persons or property caused by the use of these pesticides. I waive any claim of liability for damages against the County Department of Agriculture based on the issuance of this permit. I further understand that this permit may be revoked when pesticides are used in conflict with the manufacturer's labeling or in violation of applicable laws, regulations and specific conditions of this permit. I authorize inspection at all reasonable times and whenever an emergency exists, by the Department of Pesticide Regulation or the County Department of Agriculture of all areas treated or to be treated, storage facilities for pesticides or emptied containers and equipment used or to be used in the treatment. [Form PR-ENF-125 (Rev. 07/92) Pesticide Enforcement Branch]

Permit Applicant:	Sign:
Title:	Issue Date:
Issuing Officer:	Issue Date:

Employees handle pesticides (Y or N)

Contact People	Phone	PCO	PCA	PCD	Other
		☐	☐	☐	☐
		☐	☐	☐	☐
		☐	☐	☐	☐

Site#	Location/Site Narrative	District	Sector	Township	Range	Meridian
	Crop		Quantity	Unit		Condition

FIGURE 4-8.

The county agricultural commissioner must issue a restricted-use permit before many federal restricted and all California restricted pesticides can be applied to agricultural areas. Permit holders must comply with all conditions of the permit, including notifying the commissioner at least 24 hours before beginning an application.

bees, if these are present. They also assess your storage and container disposal procedures.

Sidebar 9 describes how to obtain a restricted-use permit. Commissioners usually issue permits each year for an entire season. However, for certain perennial crops and nonagricultural uses, they have the discretion to issue permits for longer than one year. Growers may designate authorized representatives, such as employees or licensed pest control advisers, to become certified private applicators for their operations. To become certified applicators, growers or their representatives must pass the Private Applicator Certification examination. Local agricultural commissioners' offices administer these examinations.

Regulations require that before you apply a restricted material on an agricultural crop, you must notify the agricultural commissioner who issued the permit. You must give this notice at least 24 hours in advance by filing a *Notice of Intent.*

Licensed pest control businesses and certified private applicators may buy and apply some federal restricted-use pesticides without a permit if there are no additional state restrictions. However, if a permit is required, a pest control business must have a written recommendation from a licensed pest control adviser. They also need a copy of the restricted-use permit issued to the grower or person responsible for the crop.

Exceptions. Usually, you do not need permits for the agricultural use of pesticides that are not designated as federal or state restricted. However, if local agricultural commissioners determine that a certain pesticide presents an undue hazard under local conditions, they can restrict its use. Structural pest control operators, licensed pest control dealers, and commercial warehouses do not need permits to possess restricted pesticides.

Exempt Pesticides. DPR exempts some restricted-use pesticides from permit requirements. These are pesticides that DPR determines require no further restrictions beyond those imposed by federal regulations and the label. DPR maintains a list of exempt materials.

SIDEBAR 9

How to Obtain a Restricted-Use Permit

■ TO OBTAIN A RESTRICTED-USE PERMIT

Once you have become qualified as a *certified applicator,* follow the steps below to obtain a restricted-use permit:

1. Telephone the agricultural commissioner's office in the county where the restricted material will be used. Make an appointment for issuance of a restricted-use pesticide permit.

2. Prepare a list of the restricted materials that will be used during the calendar year.

3. Prepare a list of pests to be controlled by the restricted materials.

4. (For agricultural use only.) Prepare a map of each location where restricted-use pesticides will be used. Include the following information:

   ☐ Legal location of property (section, township, range).

   ☐ Physical location of property (nearest crossroads) and nature of surrounding properties.

   ☐ Number of acres to be treated.

   ☐ Location and types of adjoining crops.

   ☐ Location of residences, roads, schools, hospitals, recreation areas, farm labor housing, feed lots, bee colonies, game preserves, and waterways within ½ mile.

5. If applicable, the name, address, and telephone number of pest control operators who will be applying these pesticides.

6. Take all this information to the agricultural commissioner's office when applying for a restricted-use pesticide permit.

WHAT WILL HAPPEN

1. You will be asked to fill out an application and to verify that you hold a valid pesticide applicator's license or certificate (certified *private* applicator or certified *commercial* applicator).

2. The commissioner or a biologist will review the following information with you:

   ☐ Pesticide use requirements.
   ☐ Methods of transporting, storing, and disposing of pesticides.
   ☐ Bee protection, if applicable.
   ☐ Environmental precautions.
   ☐ Equipment care and calibration.
   ☐ Posting requirements, if needed.
   ☐ Mixing and loading.
   ☐ Employee training and supervision.
   ☐ Protective clothing and equipment.
   ☐ Emergency medical requirements.
   ☐ Record keeping and reports.
   ☐ County policies and requirements.

AFTER THE PERMIT IS ISSUED

1. File a *Notice of Intent* with the commissioner's office at least 24 hours before making a restricted-use pesticide application. (This may be done in writing, in person, or by telephone. Some offices have 24-hour telephones with an answering device to receive messages.) Provide the following information:

   ☐ Your name, date, and time.
   ☐ Name on permit if different from your name.
   ☐ Your telephone number.

   ☐ Permit number.
   ☐ Location of application, including field number if applicable.
   ☐ The pesticide to be used, its formulation, amount to be applied, and dilution.
   ☐ Method of application (ground sprayer, air, etc.).
   ☐ Legal location of application, if applicable.
   ☐ Pests to be controlled.
   ☐ Commodity and acreage (if agricultural application) or what pesticide will be used on.
   ☐ Name of applicator of pesticide.
   ☐ Beginning date and time of application.
   ☐ Location of any hazards that were not listed on the permit (livestock, poultry, crops, residences, etc., adjacent to treatment area).

2. When applicable, notify beekeepers at least 48 hours before applying the pesticide.

3. If necessary, notify all people living near the treatment area. In agricultural situations, notify workers within ¼ mile of the area to be treated if they are working on property under your control. Make sure they are informed of symptoms of pesticide poisoning and understand not to enter treated areas until the end of the restricted-entry interval.

4. Post treated area if necessary.

AFTER PESTICIDE IS APPLIED

1. Dispose of pesticide containers according to instructions from county agricultural commissioner's office.

2. File *Pesticide Use Report* by the 10th of the month following the month of application (Pest Control Businesses must file a use report within 7 days of application).

3. Record pertinent information about the application (see text, pages 123–124), and keep this information on file for two years.

4. Remove posted signs, if used, at the appropriate time.

REVIEW QUESTIONS

1. The *federal* laws regulating the manufacture, sale, transporting, and use of pesticides are administered by:
   - ☐ a. USDA
   - ☐ b. NIOSH
   - ☐ c. DPR
   - ☐ d. U.S. EPA

2. Regulations pertaining to pest control and pesticide use in California are part of:
   - ☐ a. The Federal Insecticide, Fungicide, and Rodenticide Act (FIFRA)
   - ☐ b. EPA Worker Protection Standard
   - ☐ c. The California Code of Regulations
   - ☐ d. Fish and Wildlife Service Regulations

3. The laws and regulations controlling pesticide use in *California:*
   - ☐ a. Are optional as long as federal regulations are followed
   - ☐ b. Allow some pesticide handling practices prohibited at the federal level
   - ☐ c. May be more restrictive than federal laws
   - ☐ d. Are exactly the same as the federal laws and regulations

4. The Worker Protection Standard (WPS) provides additional protection to agricultural workers by:
   - ☐ a. Replacing FIFRA with a stricter worker safety law
   - ☐ b. Requiring that pesticide manufacturers perform additional testing prior to product registration
   - ☐ c. Strengthening FIFRA requirements for protection of workers
   - ☐ d. Eliminating the requirement for use of restrictive protective equipment

5. A general-use pesticide is a product that can be purchased and used by:
   - ☐ a. Anyone
   - ☐ b. Certified applicators only
   - ☐ c. Licensed applicators only
   - ☐ d. General-use pesticide permit holders

6. You can only use a *nonregistered* pesticide if you have obtained:
   - ☐ a. A Special Local Need (SLN) registration
   - ☐ b. Permission from the county agricultural commissioner
   - ☐ c. Approval from the DPR
   - ☐ d. An emergency exemption from registration

7. Section 18 exemptions are issued by the:
   - ☐ a. DPR
   - ☐ b. U.S. EPA
   - ☐ c. Cal-EPA
   - ☐ d. USDA

8. Which of the following pieces of information is not always included on the pesticide product label?
   - ☐ a. Signal word
   - ☐ b. Common name
   - ☐ c. Chemical name
   - ☐ d. Precautionary statements

9. What does the "Statement of Practical Treatment" on the pesticide label tell you?
   - ☐ a. First aid instructions
   - ☐ b. PPE requirements
   - ☐ c. Application instructions
   - ☐ d. Mixing and loading instructions

10. Which of the following deviations from label directions is legal in California?
    - ☐ a. Applying less than the label rate
    - ☐ b. Applying more than the label rate
    - ☐ c. Treating a crop or site not on the label
    - ☐ d. Making more frequent applications than the label allows

11. Why must you seek expert advice before using an application rate or pesticide concentration lower than what is specified on the product label?
    - ☐ a. Using less than label rates is usually illegal
    - ☐ b. Reduced application rates can cause illegal residues on treated crops
    - ☐ c. Lowering the application rate increases exposure risk to workers
    - ☐ d. Using less than label rates may promote pesticide resistance

12. How long must you keep pesticide use records?
    - ☐ a. 6 months
    - ☐ b. 1 year
    - ☐ c. 2 years
    - ☐ d. 5 years

13. When making a nonagricultural application, which of the following pesticides could be used legally without an operator identification number?
    - ☐ a. A pesticide that is restricted in California but not federally
    - ☐ b. A general-use pesticide approved for agricultural use
    - ☐ c. A pesticide approved for use only on nonagricultural sites
    - ☐ d. An industrial use pesticide for postharvest commodity treatment

14. A *restricted-entry interval* **(REI) refers to the amount of time that must pass after a pesticide application before:**

- ☐ a. Workers may enter the treated area without wearing protective clothing
- ☐ b. A crop may be harvested
- ☐ c. A crop may be irrigated
- ☐ d. Another pesticide can be applied

15. Growers must have valid Grower Identification Numbers before they can purchase:

- ☐ a. Federal restricted-use pesticides only
- ☐ b. Pesticides having Special Local Need (SLN) registrations only
- ☐ c. Pesticides used only on nonagricultural sites
- ☐ d. All pesticides used in the production of agricultural commodities

5

Hazards Associated with Pesticide Use

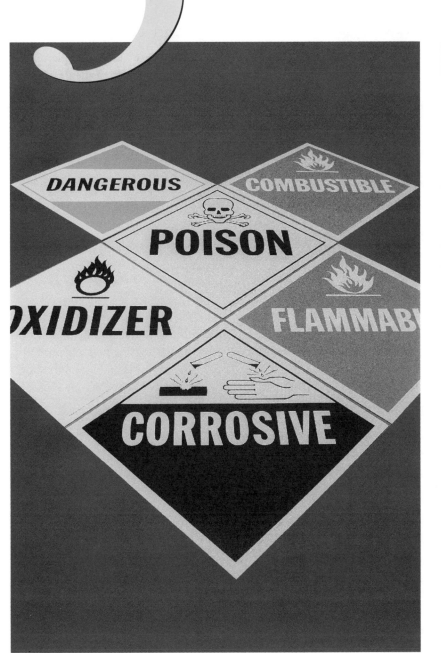

Many pesticides are hazardous materials that may harm people or the environment if improperly used.

MANY PESTICIDES are hazardous chemicals that have the potential to injure people or upset the environment. Residues of specific pesticides have led to water quality loss in various locations. Occasionally, the improper use of pesticides has injured nontarget vegetation, honey bees, birds, or other wildlife.

If you apply pesticides carelessly, some may damage treated surfaces or, through drift, surfaces near the treatment area. In addition, indiscriminate use of pesticides may result in pesticide resistance. Many pesticides, if not used wisely, also have the potential to disrupt biological control by destroying natural enemies.

POTENTIAL FOR HUMAN INJURY

Pesticides, like other poisonous chemicals, injure people by interfering with biological functions. The nature and extent of injury depends on the pesticide's toxicity and the amount entering the tissues. Some pesticides are very toxic and produce injury at low doses. A few drops of these might cause severe illness or death. Other pesticides are so mildly toxic that a person would have to consume several pounds before experiencing any effect.

However, because potential hazards exist with most pesticides, anyone working with these chemicals must avoid exposure. Treat all pesticides with respect. It is impossible to accurately predict what effects can result from long-term repeated exposures to even the least toxic pesticides.

How People Get Exposed to Pesticides

There are several ways people can come in contact with pesticides. However, the most serious exposure potential occurs during mixing and application. To greatly reduce exposure risks, wear proper work clothing and use other protective equipment during mixing and application. In addition, following label guidelines for restricted-entry and harvest intervals protects workers and consumers.

Poisoning symptoms or injuries can result from a single exposure to a large quantity of pesticide. In other cases, illness might occur after exposure to repeated small doses over time. It is common for different individuals to vary in their sensitivity to the level of pesticide exposure. Some people show no reaction to a dose that might cause severe illness in others. A person's age and body size often influence his or her response to a given dose. Thus, smaller doses might have more impact on infants and young children than they do on adults. Also, adult females can be more sensitive to lower doses than adult males.

Accidents

The most harmful pesticide exposure risks occur during accidents that involve spills, splashes, or equipment failure. Usually these accidents happen

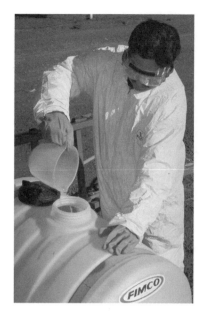

FIGURE 5-1.

The agricultural industry has the highest number of pesticide-related accidents. Accidents that result in pesticide injury or poisoning occur mainly during mixing and application. These accidents are often the result of carelessness or improper techniques. This person is wearing special equipment that protects against injury or poisoning in case of an accident.

while mixing or making an application (Figure 5-1). Carelessness is sometimes the cause. Although accidents can happen anywhere pesticides are used, each year the agricultural industry has the highest number of pesticide-related incidents.

Spills, explosions, or similar accidents during manufacturing and packaging of pesticides are also major concerns. These incidents have the potential to seriously injure plant employees or people living or working near the plants. In addition, spills, fires, or explosions in pesticide warehouses may jeopardize employees, emergency workers, and others. Even people involved in transporting pesticides risk possible injury should pesticide containers rupture, spill, or catch fire. Accidents during pesticide transport seriously endanger the public.

Work-Related Exposure

Pesticide applicators and handlers are most at risk from pesticide exposure because they work closely and frequently with these materials. However, laborers, tractor drivers, irrigators, and other employees risk exposure if they work in recently treated areas. Restricted-entry intervals are important pesticide use restrictions designed to protect agricultural workers from exposure (Figure 5-2). Techniques such as reducing drift and making spray applications when workers or the public are not present nearby also help. Another important step involves training employees on how to avoid contact with pesticide residues.

People who maintain or repair application equipment may contact pesticide residues on that equipment. Oil-soluble pesticides are a major concern. These accumulate in grease deposits and on oily surfaces and may be difficult to remove. Frequent cleaning of the application equipment lowers risks to maintenance workers and operators because cleaning removes grease and pesticide residue. If equipment cleaning is impossible before repairs or maintenance, mechanics must wear label-prescribed personal protective equipment to avoid unnecessary exposure. People who clean or repair pesticide contaminated equipment are also considered pesticide handlers and must receive pesticide handler training.

Workers in packing sheds and food processing plants may also contact pesticide residues. These residues may be on produce if growers used persistent

FIGURE 5-2.

Restricted-entry intervals following agricultural pesticide applications have helped to reduce farmworker injury. Growers often post treated fields, like the one shown here, to warn workers not to enter during the restricted-entry interval.

FIGURE 5-3.

Children are the major group of nonagricultural pesticide poisoning victims. Improper storage of pesticides in the home is the prime reason why children find and ingest pesticides.

pesticide materials. Regulations establish harvest intervals for treated produce to protect consumers from pesticide residues. These intervals also help reduce exposure to field, packing shed, and processing plant workers because the intervals provide more time for pesticide breakdown.

It is difficult for greenhouse and nursery workers to avoid close contact with treated foliage. This is due to the density of plants and narrow aisles found in greenhouses. Also, most greenhouses have limited ventilation, which can increase the potential for breathing spray mists or vapors. It also increases the risk of getting dusts or mists onto the skin or into the eyes during applications. Similar conditions exist for pest control operators working in enclosed areas of dwellings, warehouses, factories, and offices.

Potential for Exposure in Residences

Excessive or improper use or storage of pesticides in and around residences subjects inhabitants to possible exposure. *Accidental ingestion of pesticide products by children accounts for the major portion of nonagricultural pesticide poisoning cases (Figure 5-3).*

Possible Food Contamination

Illegal pesticide residues found on food are a rare but possible source of pesticide exposure. Incidents in which people have become poisoned by residues on food are few and have always been the result of pesticide misuse. Labels of pesticides registered for use in food production, storage, and handling areas specify how to avoid contaminating food products. To allow agencies to monitor for illegal pesticide residues on foodstuffs, health codes and other regulations provide for product testing. Regulations also allow inspections of processing, storage, and retail food establishments.

Traces of some types of pesticides used during crop production can remain on produce for varying periods of time. Also, it is possible for plants to pick up soil residues of some pesticides—even some pesticides used on previous crops. Hence, government agencies establish residue tolerance standards. These regulations limit the amounts and types of pesticides allowable on human and animal food. They sometimes require preharvest intervals to allow time for breakdown between pesticide application and harvest.

Traces of pesticides may also get onto food products after harvest. Warehouse operators use certain pesticides to prevent damage to foodstuffs during storage. Food processors often must use some types of pesticides to protect produce and prevent pest problems in and around processing plants. Retail food store managers occasionally have pesticides applied to control pests that infest these facilities. Restaurants may need to control rodent or insect pests with pesticides to comply with health codes.

Pesticides used in residences provide another possible source of food contamination. However, regulations strictly prohibit pesticide applications to foods or to food preparation surfaces, dishes, or utensils.

Drinking water contamination offers another potential way for people to ingest pesticides. Improper use or disposal of pesticides has resulted in cases of groundwater contamination. Refer to the "Groundwater Contamination" section of this chapter for ways you can protect groundwater from pesticide contamination.

Pesticide Exposure Through Other Sources

Contact with nonfood items may also expose people to pesticide residues. Entering treated residences or work areas too soon after application could result in exposure. Some manufacturers treat clothing, furniture, carpeting, and even some children's toys with certain pesticides. The pesticides protect these items from insect damage or reduce the buildup of fungi or bacteria. Another low-level source of exposure occurs if people come in close contact with pets that have been treated for fleas or ticks. Lawns, shrubs, and other areas of residential, industrial, and public landscape can also be sources of pesticide exposure.

How Pesticides Enter the Body

The tissues of an exposed person can absorb certain types of pesticides. These pesticides enter the body through the skin, eyes, lungs, or mouth (Figure 5-4).

Skin Exposure

Skin (or *dermal*) contact is the most frequent route of pesticide exposure. If certain pesticides contact the skin they may cause a skin rash or mild skin irritation (known as dermatitis). Other types of pesticides cause more severe skin injury, such as burns. Internal poisoning may also result if a pesticide absorbs through the skin: the blood

FIGURE 5-4.

The most common ways for pesticide exposure to occur are through the skin (dermal), through the mouth (oral), through the lungs (respiratory), and through the eyes (ocular).

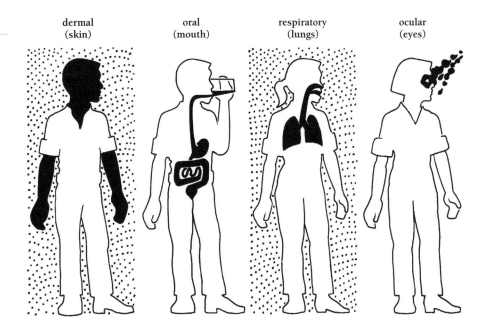

dermal (skin)   oral (mouth)   respiratory (lungs)   ocular (eyes)

carries these pesticides to other organs within the body.

The ability of a pesticide to penetrate the skin depends on chemical characteristics of the pesticide and its formulation. Oil-soluble pesticides pass through skin more easily than those that are soluble in water. To prevent skin exposure, always wear work clothing and the label-prescribed personal protective equipment when working with pesticides. Also, avoid contact with recently treated plants, animals, and commodities. Wash thoroughly if you accidentally get a pesticide on your skin. However, *washing is not an alternative to preventing exposure.*

Eye Exposure

The active or inert ingredients of some pesticide formulations are caustic to the eyes. Besides their vulnerability to injury, the eyes provide another route for entry of certain pesticides into your body. Protect your eyes by wearing a faceshield, goggles, or safety glasses. California law *requires* that protective eyewear be worn

- during all mixing and loading activities
- while adjusting, cleaning, or repairing contaminated mixing, loading, or application equipment
- during most types of ground application

If pesticides get into your eyes, flush them with a gentle stream of clean water for 15 minutes. Hold the eyelids open during flushing. Seek immediate medical attention if any irritation develops.

Respiratory Exposure

The lungs quickly absorb certain pesticides, and the blood transports these pesticides to other parts of the body. Some pesticides cause serious lung injury. Breathing dusts or vapors during mixing or application is difficult to avoid unless one uses appropriate respiratory equipment. *Always* wear label-recommended respirators during mix-

ing and application. Make sure any respirator you use fits properly and is in good condition.

Exposure Through the Mouth (Oral)

It is extremely rare for someone to accidentally drink a pesticide. The exceptions are when pesticides are improperly stored or negligently put into food containers and these are found by children.

Exposure through the mouth occurs more commonly if spray materials or pesticide dusts splash or blow into your mouth during mixing or application. Ingestion occasionally happens by eating or drinking contaminated foods or drinks. Smoking while handling pesticides increases your risk of ingesting pesticides.

Linings of your mouth, stomach, and intestines readily absorb some pesticides. If you swallow sufficient quantities, sometimes even small amounts, you may get sick. Protective equipment, such as a respirator or faceshield, minimizes this risk of pesticides getting into your mouth.

Before eating, drinking, or smoking, be sure to wash your hands thoroughly. Keep food and drinks away from areas where pesticides are being applied or mixed. *Never put pesticides into food or drink containers.* Keep all pesticides in their original packages. Do not mix or measure pesticides with utensils that someone could use later for food preparation or serving.

Effects of Exposure

The type and severity of injury or poisoning from pesticide exposure depends on the toxicity and mode of action of the pesticide. Also, the amount absorbed and the speed of absorption influences the severity of the injury. In many cases, your body's speed in breaking down and excreting the pesticide affects the extent of injury.

Prompt first aid and medical treatment may reduce potential injury.

Very small doses of most pesticides usually cause no injury or poisoning symptoms. Depending on the toxicity of the pesticide, larger doses may cause severe illnesses. Effects of exposure may be localized, such as irritation of the eyes, skin, or throat. Some effects may also be generalized if the pesticide absorbs through the skin. Once exposure occurs, certain pesticides may affect several different internal systems at the same time. The type and characteristics of the pesticide and the amount of exposure determine the extent of involvement and damage.

Many things produce symptoms that are similar to those of pesticide poisoning. Certain plants cause skin irritation, for example. Heat stress or excessive alcohol consumption can give you a headache or make you nauseous. Nevertheless, seek medical attention if you have been in a situation where pesticide exposure *could* have occurred and you are not feeling well. If your symptoms are caused by pesticide exposure, make every effort to locate the source of exposure and take steps necessary to prevent it from happening again.

Symptoms

Symptoms are any abnormal conditions that a person sees or feels. They also are conditions detected by examination or laboratory tests that indicate the presence of an injury, disease, or disorder. When the dose is large enough to produce injury, there may be either immediate or delayed appearance of symptoms (Table 5-1). Immediate symptoms are those observed soon after exposure. However, symptoms from pesticide exposure may not show up for weeks, months, or even years. These delayed symptoms may either come on gradually or appear suddenly. They may be difficult to associate with their cause because of the lapse of time between exposure and observable effect.

Poisoning symptoms vary among classes of pesticides and pesticides within a class. The presence and severity of symptoms are usually proportional to the amount of pesticide (dosage) entering the tissues. Common symptoms for many pesticides include skin rashes, headaches, or irritation of the eyes, nose, and throat. These types of symptoms may go away quickly and are sometimes difficult to distinguish from symptoms of allergies, colds, or flu.

TABLE 5-1.

Common Pesticide Poisoning Symptoms Related to Contact with Pesticide Dust, Liquid, or Vapors. *

TYPE OF CONTACT	SYMPTOMS
skin	staining of the skin reddening of skin in area of contact mild burning or itching sensation painful burning sensation blistering of the skin cracking and damage to nails
eye	discomfort, including watering and slight burning severe, painful burning (permanent eye damage may occur)
inhaling or swallowing	sneezing irritation of nose and throat nasal stuffiness swelling of mouth or throat coughing breathing difficulties shortness of breath chest pains

*Note: Many of the symptoms listed in this table may also be caused by other factors such as irritating plants, allergies, colds, or flu. Usually, a medical examination is needed to determine the actual cause of such symptoms.

Other symptoms indicate exposure to more toxic pesticides. These include blurred vision, dizziness, heavy sweating, weakness, nausea, stomach pain, vomiting, diarrhea, extreme thirst, and blistered skin.

Exposure to some materials may also result in apprehension, restlessness, anxiety, unusual behavior, shaking, convulsions, or unconsciousness. Although some types of pesticide poisoning produce these symptoms, they may indicate other physical disorders or diseases, including heat stress. Usually diagnosis requires careful medical examination, laboratory tests, and observation.

Heat Stress. Heat-related illness may mimic certain types of pesticide poisoning. Symptoms of heat illness include tiredness, weakness, headache, sweating, nausea, dizziness, and fainting. Severe heat illness can cause a person to act confused, get angry easily, or behave strangely. California regulations require that pesticide handlers receive training on recognizing, avoiding, and treating heat stress along with training on recognizing pesticide illness.

Types of Injuries

A single massive dose absorbed during one pesticide exposure incident may cause an injury. An injury may also result from smaller doses absorbed during repeated exposures over time. The illness or damage may have a sudden onset and last a short while. It also may continue for a long time. Injuries caused by pesticides usually are *reversible*. Either the body repairs itself or medical treatment cures the condition. Accidental exposure to a few types of pesticides, however, may cause *irreversible* or permanent damage. Sometimes this leads to chronic illness, disability, or death.

OTHER EFFECTS ON PEOPLE

Allergies

Certain individuals occasionally exhibit allergic reactions when exposed to some types of pesticides. The material causing the reaction may be the pesticide or one of the components of the pesticide formulation. Allergic symptoms often include breathing difficulties, sneezing, eye watering and itching, skin rashes, apprehension, and general discomfort. Sensitive people should avoid exposure to pesticides that produce allergic reactions. Try different types of pesticides or formulations or switch to nonchemical control methods.

Anxieties

Some people have serious concerns about the possible dangers of pesticides to their health. Symptoms of illness appear if they suspect or know they were exposed. The illness is real, although there may be no actual pesticide injury. Sometimes odors trigger this reaction. People often mistakenly associate pesticide odors with toxicity, believing that the stronger or more offensive the odor, the more toxic the pesticide. (Obviously this is not true. For example, methyl bromide is extremely toxic but usually has no detectable odor. Other pesticides that have strong, objectionable odors may be far less hazardous.)

Insufficient or inaccurate information regarding hazards of pesticides contributes to people's anxieties over pesticide exposure. Accidents, poisonings, and pesticide residues in food usually receive much media attention. However, the public rarely hears about the regulations and restrictions designed to protect them from harmful exposure.

GROUNDWATER CONTAMINATION

Potential contamination of groundwater with pesticides is a serious concern. About 97% of the total water in the world is salt water in the oceans. This water is unsuitable for most uses. Less than 1% of all the water on the planet is fresh water in an available form. People use this water for drinking, irrigation, and household and manufacturing purposes. Two-thirds of the fresh water (or about 2 million cubic miles) is groundwater trapped beneath the soil. The rest is surface water in lakes, ponds, streams, and rivers. Frozen water in polar ice caps and glaciers is also fresh water but is unavailable for use. Groundwater provides 40% of California's water needs. Cities obtain almost half of their water, including drinking water, from these groundwater sources. Most of the water used in rural areas is groundwater. Groundwater, therefore, is our most important fresh water source.

Researchers and regulators recognize that the potential for groundwater contamination from pesticides is very great. Originally people thought pesticides did not threaten groundwater. However, this was only because available testing techniques were unable to detect contamination. At the time, studies suggested that microorganisms, environmental factors, and soil degraded or adsorbed most pesticides before they reached groundwater. Researchers suspected that the pesticides that did enter groundwater decomposed rapidly. More recently, however, newer detection methods have proved earlier assumptions to be inaccurate. The new equipment shows that small amounts of chemicals, including certain pesticides, exist in some groundwater locations. Now, regulators fear that hazardous levels of toxic chemicals in groundwater could affect much of the state's population. This concern has prompted lawmakers to develop stringent laws to protect this resource. These laws regulate pesticide use and disposal.

How Groundwater Accumulates

Water applied to the soil surface slowly filters through soil particles until it reaches groundwater basins. This is a process known as *percolation*. Common water sources are rainfall, surface irrigation, and melting of ice, snow, and glaciers. Some lake, pond, river, and stream water also percolates into groundwater basins, although much also flows out to the oceans. The amount and rate of percolation depend on the size of soil particles. Fine particles, such as clay and loam, retain more water than coarse, sandy soil. Therefore percolation is slower as soil texture becomes finer.

Groundwater becomes trapped in large underground masses known as *aquifers*. Aquifers are usually areas of water-saturated sand and gravel having one or more impermeable layers. These rock or clay and silt layers confine the water. Aquifers may be hundreds of miles in length and width. They may range in depth to as much as several thousand feet (Figure 5-5). In California, nearly half of the landmass overlies groundwater basins. It is common to find several layers of aquifers in the same area. Impermeable barriers separate an aquifer from ones above or below it. Interruptions in the barriers allow some aquifers to interconnect.

Water trapped in aquifers flows toward the sea, but it flows much more slowly than surface water. Water in a stream or river has a flow rate measured in feet per second. However, underground water may only flow a few feet per year.

Groundwater in California is especially vulnerable to contamination. This is because this groundwater is directly below so much of the cultivated, industrial, and residential land area.

FIGURE 5-5.

Water is present in underground reservoirs called aquifers, diagrammed here. Sand and gravel formations contain this water. Impermeable layers of clay and silt or solid rock prevent water from leaving the aquifer.

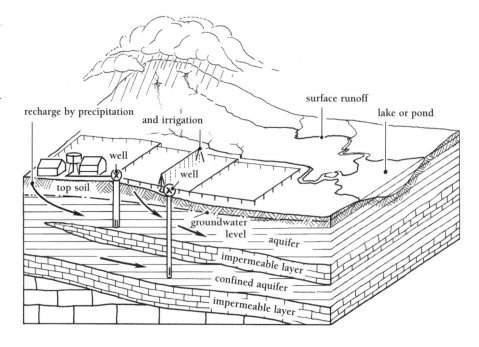

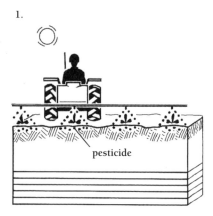

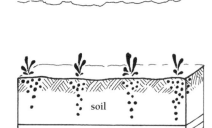

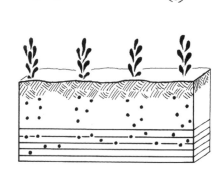

1.

2.

3.

FIGURE 5-6.

Water enters aquifers by percolation through the soil. As water passes down through the soil it may dissolve some pesticides and carry them into the aquifer. This process is called leaching.

Contamination, when it occurs, may be difficult or impossible to contain. Because the water flows so slowly, it takes hundreds of years to remove contaminants from the system.

Ways Pesticides Enter Groundwater

Pesticides enter groundwater in two ways. One is by leaching out of the soil. The other is by direct entry through wells or other structures that are in contact with aquifers. Leaching occurs as rainwater or irrigation water percolates through the soil, dissolving water-soluble chemicals including some pesticides (Figure 5-6).

Several types of pesticides can leach and percolate into groundwater. These usually require incorporation into the soil by mechanical means or by irrigation or rainfall. Pesticides applied to crop surfaces are subject to being washed off by water or *abraded* by wind. When this happens, they may enter the soil and leach into groundwater.

Nonpoint Pollution. Pesticides entering groundwater from normal application practices are *nonpoint pollution sources*. In these cases, application practices distribute the pesticide over large areas. Only extremely small

FIGURE 5-7.

Point pollution sources are areas where large quantities of pesticide or other pollutants are discharged into the environment. Nonpoint pollution sources are those arising from normal application where the pesticide or other material is applied over a large area.

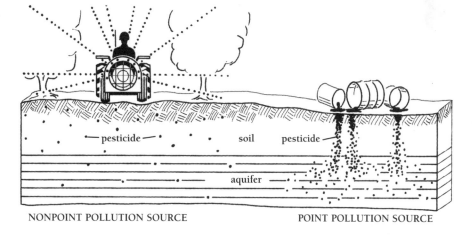

NONPOINT POLLUTION SOURCE   POINT POLLUTION SOURCE

FIGURE 5-8.

Water wells are direct channels into an aquifer and may provide connections between several aquifers. Pesticides and other contaminants can enter groundwater directly through wells.

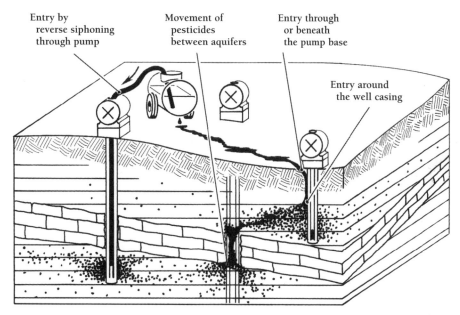

amounts, if any at all, enter the groundwater from any one location.

Point Pollution. Larger quantities of contaminants that enter groundwater at small, defined locations are *point pollution sources* (Figure 5-7). These sources usually result from manufacturing accidents, storage and handling, transportation, or improperly constructed disposal sites or holding facilities.

Direct Channels. Wells are direct channels into an aquifer and may provide a connection between several aquifers (Figure 5-8). Careless or improper pesticide handling near wells has a high risk of contaminating groundwater.

Examples include

- spilling pesticides near a well while filling a spray tank
- filling pesticide application equipment from a well without using an air gap
- injecting pesticides into an irrigation system without any backflow protection
- disposing of surplus pesticides or washing contaminated equipment near a well

Improperly sealed, abandoned wells provide possible routes for pesticides and other contaminants into the underground system. Occasionally pesticide waste or runoff may enter groundwater through direct channels such as sinkholes or exposed shallow aquifers.

Factors Influencing Groundwater Contamination

Many factors influence the potential for groundwater contamination. An important factor is the nature of the pesticide itself. For instance, pesticides used in years past included many chlorinated hydrocarbon compounds. These are often highly persistent in the environment but immobile—the chemical structure of these compounds causes them to bind tightly to soil particles. Such pesticides do not move down through the soil profile but remain concentrated near the soil surface. Therefore, they usually do not pollute groundwater.

Recently, however, pesticide use trends have been toward less persistent chemicals, but many of these are highly mobile in the soil. These include some of the phenoxy, urea, and carbamate compounds that do not bind tightly with soil particles. Some are soluble in water, so they leach more easily. Table 5-2 compares the soil mobility of several different pesticides.

Soil type affects the potential to contaminate groundwater. In addition, geological formations beneath the application site affect percolation. Liquids percolate faster through sand or gravel soils than they do through denser silt, loam, and clay. The amount of organic material in the soil controls pesticide retention and may speed up its breakdown. The following soil factors alter the stability of pesticides and affect their ability to reach groundwater:

- temperature
- pH
- moisture content
- dissolved salts
- quantity and type of soil organisms

There is less risk if no aquifer lies beneath the treatment area or if the aquifer is very deep. Shallow water tables beneath treated areas are more susceptible to contamination. This is because pesticides pass through less soil and are therefore not subject to as much breakdown. Some locations have layers of impermeable subsoil that prevent pesticides from leaching into the groundwater. The slope of the treated land often determines whether contaminated water runs off or leaches. Table 5-3 summarizes factors that influence groundwater contamination by pesticides.

Pesticides that decompose quickly are less apt to cause groundwater contamination. Recent research, however, suggests that groundwater environments may slow the breakdown of some pesticides. Groundwater is not exposed to air or ultraviolet light. Also, it is cooler than soil surfaces and lacks much of the biological activity found in soil.

How to Keep Pesticides from Contaminating Groundwater

The following techniques will help you to prevent pesticides from contaminating groundwater.

Storage. Store pesticides in enclosed areas, on an impermeable (concrete) surface, and protected from rain. In case of fire or rupture of storage containers, be sure to contain runoff and remove contaminated soil.

Mixing and Loading. Avoid spilling pesticides. If a spill occurs, clean up and dispose of wastes as described in Chapter 7. Remove contaminated soil. Triple rinse liquid containers and pour rinse water into the spray tank for application to the target site. Take rinsed containers to a designated disposal site or a pesticide container recycling center. Do not overfill spray tanks. Use an air gap on filling pipes to prevent backflow of contaminated water into water supplies.

Application. Whenever possible, select pesticides with low soil mobility and use materials that degrade rapidly

TABLE 5-2.

Mobility of Different Pesticides, Illustrating Ability to Leach through the Soil. *

MOBILITY CLASS	PESTICIDE
Class 1 very unlikely to leach through soil	aldrin benomyl (Benlate) chlordane dacthal (DCPA) DDT dieldrin diquat disulfoton (Disyston) endrin ethion heptachlor lindane morestan paraquat (Gramoxone) parathion phorate (Thimet) trifluralin (Treflan)
Class 2 slightly able to leach through soil	azinphos-methyl (Guthion) bensulide (Betasan) carbaryl (Sevin) chlorpropham diazinon diuron linuron molinate (Ordram) prometryn (Caparol) propanil pyrazon (Pyramin)
Class 3 moderately able to leach through soil	alachlor atrazine diphenamid endothall fenuron prometone propham (IPC) simazine terbacil 2,4,5-T
Class 4 leaches readily through soil	amitrole bromacil 2,4-D fenac MCPA picloram (Tordon)
Class 5 very mobile in the soil	chloramben dalapon dicamba TCA

*Some chemicals listed here are no longer used as pesticides.

in the soil. Avoid pesticide drift off the target site through application techniques and by making applications during optimal weather. In areas where high risks to groundwater exist

- reduce pesticide use by integrating chemical control with other methods of control
- use pesticides only when necessary
- apply only the amounts that will adequately control pests
- reduce the frequency of application whenever possible

Disposal. Never dump excess pesticide or pesticide mixtures onto the soil

TABLE 5-3.

Factors Influencing Pesticide Leaching.

CATEGORY	FACTORS

cultural practices	amount and type of pesticide used
	method of pesticide application
	irrigation practices at treatment site:
	   frequency of irrigation
	   timing of irrigation in relation to pesticide application

geologic conditions
   of treatment area
	slope
	underlying formations
	proximity of surface water channels such as ponds,
	   lakes, rivers

interaction of pesticides
   in soils
	properties of pesticides:
	   water solubility
	   volatility
	   soil adsorption
	   decomposition
	soil influence on pesticides:
	   soil texture
	   soil organic matter content
	   soil water content

or into sewers, drains, or septic systems. Send unused pesticide waste to a Class I disposal site.

Cultural Practices. Avoid excessive irrigation after a pesticide application and prevent irrigation water runoff.

Records. Maintain records of the quantity and type of pesticides applied to an area. Use the records when planning future pest control measures to prevent pesticide accumulation.

IMPACT ON NONTARGET ORGANISMS

Some types of pesticide you use may be harmful to nontarget organisms at the application site and in the surrounding environment. Before making a pesticide application, become familiar with the treatment area and its surroundings. Avoid using pesticides that disrupt natural enemies and other beneficial organisms or harm wildlife or nontarget plants.

Natural Enemies and Other Beneficials

Some beneficials feed on or parasitize pest insects and mites and help keep their populations low. These are *natural enemies* and include well-known and many lesser known species. In addition, honey bees, wild bees, certain wasps, and other insects are important pollenizers for crops. Beneficials such as beetles, flies, and soil insects and mites help decompose dead plant and animal material. Beneficial fungi and nematodes play an important part in this decomposition. They also contribute to the long-term natural control of pests. Fumigation and other pesticide applications destroy these beneficial soil organisms.

Disrupting the natural control of pests often promotes an increased dependency on the use of pesticides and may cause pest resurgence or secondary pest outbreaks. To reduce damage to beneficials

- choose pesticides that are less toxic to beneficial species
- apply pesticides at times when natural enemies are least likely to be harmed, such as during dormant periods
- lower dosages (when possible)
- use spot treatments when possible to minimize harmful effects

Pest Resurgence and Secondary Pest Outbreaks. A complex of natural enemies usually lives among insect and mite pest populations. These natural enemies help control the size of the pest population. This natural control is a type of biological control.

Unless a pesticide is highly selective, it will kill not only the pest but many of the pest's natural enemies. If pesticides do not destroy natural enemies, they die off anyway because the pesticides destroy their food supply—the pest. Since natural enemies depend on pest species for food, they require more time than pests to increase their population size. Therefore, after a pesticide application, pests can move back into the treated area where there will be fewer natural enemies. This enables the pest population to grow rapidly and sometimes become bigger than it was before the pesticide treatment. This phenomenon is known as *pest resurgence*.

Another problem associated with pesticide use is that of *secondary pest outbreak*. Secondary pests are those that natural enemies normally control. Also, competition for food from the primary pest keeps their numbers low. Eliminating natural enemies or primary pests often results in an increase in secondary pest populations. Secondary pests may then grow and cause economic damage.

Honey Bees. Some insecticides and fungicides are harmful to honey bees and can cause severe economic hardship to beekeepers and loss of certain crops due to poor pollination. Pesticides harmful to bees cause more damage if applied while bees are foraging for nectar and pollen (Figure 5-9). Therefore, avoid using materials toxic to bees when crops or weeds are in bloom. Sprays applied early in the morning, late in the afternoon, or during the night cause less harm, because bees do not forage at these times.

There are legal restrictions controlling the application of certain pesticides while bees are foraging. Check with county agricultural commissioners for pesticide application cutoff dates. Notify beekeepers 48 hours before making a spray application. This gives them time to remove hives from the area if necessary.

Wildlife

Many pesticides can kill wildlife through poisoning or cause indirect harm by altering the animals' food sources or habitats. Vertebrates, including birds, often feed or nest in areas where people apply pesticides. Sometimes these animals are the unintended victims of baits used to control target pests. In addition, pesticides present in flooded fields or irrigation water may poison waterfowl. Although a pesticide dose may not directly cause death, the effect might weaken a nontarget animal, leading to illness or death, because it may be unable to get food and water or protect itself from natural enemies. Some pesticides may have an impact on the ability of wildlife to reproduce.

Fish are susceptible to many pesticides that get into waterways, even at low concentrations. Drift and direct spraying are obvious ways pesticides get into water. They also move from the soil through irrigation and rainwater runoff. Soil erosion creates potential for pesticides to get into waterways. Also, accidents and illegal dumping can cause serious waterway contamination. Some persistent pesticides concentrate rapidly in aquatic environments through normal food chains. This is a process called *bioaccumulation* (Figure 5-10).

Endangered Species. Federal and state governments create laws to protect and prevent the extinction of certain rare or very vulnerable animals and plants. Enforcement agencies can impose severe fines and imprisonment on people who break these laws.

Enforcement agencies restrict the use of certain pesticides in areas where endangered species exist. Before using any pesticide, check the pesticide label for precautions to protect endangered

FIGURE 5-9.

Certain pesticides may poison honey bees if applied while the bees are foraging for nectar or pollen. Avoid using materials toxic to bees when crops or weeds are in bloom. Apply sprays early in the morning, late in the afternoon, or at night to reduce chances of killing foraging bees. Also, use pesticides that have a low toxicity to bees.

FIGURE 5-10.

Some pesticides accumulate through the biological food chain. Small invertebrates and hatchling fish eat microorganisms and algae containing pesticides. These animals are in turn eaten by larger fish and birds. Each passes greater amounts of pesticide to the larger animal.

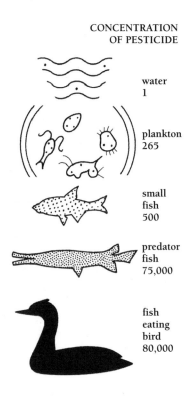

CONCENTRATION
OF PESTICIDE

water
1

plankton
265

small
fish
500

predator
fish
75,000

fish
eating
bird
80,000

species and for the location of restricted areas. For further information, consult your local University of California Cooperative Extension office. Farm advisors in these offices may also provide you with information on nonchemical pest control methods. Try using these methods in areas where endangered species exist.

For information on endangered species laws and ways to protect these plants or animals, check with the nearest Endangered Species Office of the U.S. Fish and Wildlife Service or the local or regional office of the California Department of Fish and Game.

Nontarget Plants

Pest managers use herbicides to control weeds and undesirable plants in forests, along roadsides, and on rangelands. However, some of these herbicides may have detrimental effects on nontarget plants. Many plant species are important in natural and undeveloped areas. They protect the watershed, reduce erosion, provide food and shelter for wildlife, and are part of the native flora. Plants in natural areas are usually part of an ecological balance. Disrupting this balance by any means favors the increase of undesirable plants or plants having minimal benefit.

Phytotoxicity. Phytotoxicity may be a problem with a given pesticide on certain crops or ornamental and landscape plants. The pesticide active ingredient is not always what causes phytotoxicity. It may result from solvents in the formulation or impurities (such as salts) in the water mixed with the pesticide. Excessive application rates, inadequate mixing, or improper pesticide dilution may also cause plant damage. Environmental conditions, such as temperature and humidity at the time of application, can often influence phytotoxicity. Plants stressed for water or nutrients may be more susceptible to injury.

PESTICIDE RESISTANCE

Resistance is a condition in which pests become tolerant to a pesticide that once controlled them. At first, higher rates or more applications of a certain pesticide are needed to achieve the same amount of control. Finally this pesticide has little effect, no matter how much you use. Switching to a different pesticide may help. However, sometimes when pests develop resistance to one chemical they also become resistant to others. This happens even with chemicals from different chemical classes. This phenomenon is called *cross resistance*.

Resistance involves a change in the genetic characteristics of pest populations. One generation inherits the characteristic from a previous generation. Initially, a pest population may possess a few individuals that are able to break down or chemically modify a pesticide.

FIGURE 5-11.

Resistance to pesticides involves changes in the genetic characteristics of pest populations that are inherited from one generation to the next. Increased or frequent use of certain pesticides often hastens resistance.

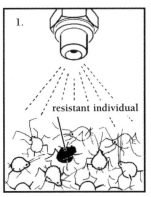

1.

Some individuals in a pest population have genetic traits that allow them to survive a pesticide application.

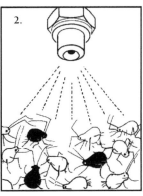

2.

A proportion of the survivors' offspring inherits the resistance traits. At the next spraying these resistant individuals will survive.

3.

susceptible individual

If pesticides are applied frequently, the pest population will soon consist mostly of resistant individuals.

If you apply that pesticide, these individuals survive. When the resistant individuals reproduce, most of their offspring have this trait (Figure 5-11).

Insect resistance to lime-sulfur was first reported in 1914. Resistance to arsenicals (arsenic-containing pesticides) began causing problems in the 1920s. Pest resistance to DDT, the first synthetic pesticide to be manufactured, developed in the 1950s. Increased uses of pesticides during the past 50 years have magnified the problem of pesticide resistance. Today, every major class of pesticide has some pest that is resistant to it. Pesticide resistance has developed in insect, mite, plant pathogen, weed, and rodent pests.

Pesticide resistance is a manageable problem in many cases. How manageable it is depends in part on *genetic* and *biological* factors that we cannot control. But resistance management also depends on *operational* factors that we can control.

Genetic Factors

Genetic factors that influence the development of resistance are how the organism inherits resistance and how many of the individuals in the population have the genes for resistance. If resistance genes are common, the population inherits them easily. Resistance

will spread quickly and may be difficult to manage.

Biological Factors

Biological factors that influence the development of resistance are the unique characteristics of the pest and its habits. Biological factors include

- lifespan of the pest
- the number of offspring a pest produces over time
- the pest's ability to move large distances
- food requirements of the pest

A population of short-lived, rapidly developing, immobile pests with many offspring will develop resistance rapidly. In this type of population, the pesticide quickly eliminates individuals susceptible to it. This leaves only resistant individuals to breed with each other and rapidly build up in numbers. In addition, if these pests do not move around much, very few susceptible individuals migrate in to breed with the resistant group. Rapidly reproducing mites, aphids, fungi, cockroaches, and rodents are pests of this type. All of these exhibit pesticide resistance.

Operational Factors

Operational factors are the unique characteristics of the pesticide and the way it is used that either favor or reduce resistance. You can often use these factors to manage resistance. They include

- the type of pesticide used
- the persistence of pesticide residues
- the pesticide application rate
- which life stage of the pest you treat
- whether you combine the pesticide with other pesticides

Manufacturers are working to develop new pesticides and new formulations to replace chemicals with resistance problems. Chemicals with new modes of action are becoming harder to develop, however. In addition, there are very high development and registration costs associated with producing new pesticides.

To prolong the usefulness of existing pesticides, place more emphasis on limiting opportunities for resistance to develop. Do this by reducing pest population exposure to pesticides. Incorporate other control methods, such as biological controls, crop rotation, and use of resistant plant varieties, into your pest management program.

Resistance Management

Pests develop resistance to pesticides fastest when pest managers base control entirely on the use of closely related pesticides. On the other hand, resistance management uses as many different control options as possible. Successful pest managers use pesticides to eliminate the susceptible individuals and one or more of the nonchemical factors to destroy the resistant individuals.

The first step in resistance management is to choose a chemical that selectively kills the pest but does not kill its natural enemies. This enables the natural enemies to continue to exert their control. Second, choose a nonpersistent pesticide that allows the next stage or next generation of pest, including some susceptible individuals, to survive. Third, alternate selective pesticides with ones having different modes of action, or use pesticides or pesticide combinations that have more than one mode of action. It is difficult for the pest to develop resistance in two different ways at the same time. Fourth, apply the pesticide when the pest is in the life stage that is causing economic damage, such as larvae feeding on leaves. In this way, the pest cannot use the genetic and physiological defenses of other life stages to combat the pesticide. Apply the chemicals over a limited area. Use spot treatments or strip treatments so that some susceptible, untreated pests survive. Consider treating only alternating generations. Finally, if resistance develops to the point at which the pesticide is no longer effective, stop using it.

RESIDUES

Whenever you apply a pesticide, it remains as a residue on treated surfaces for a time. The nature of the pesticide or the type of formulation (persistence) affects the amount of residue. The frequency and amount of pesticide used (accumulation) also determines the amount of residue present. Finally, residues are subject to interaction with the environment (breakdown or recombination).

Residues are important and necessary in some types of pest control. This is because they provide continuous exposure to the pest, improving chances of control. However, residues are undesirable when they expose people, domestic animals, or wildlife to unsafe levels of pesticides. Pesticide materials that miss the treatment surface can remain as residues in soil, water, or on surfaces in nontarget areas. Also, empty pesticide containers hold small amounts of residues that require proper disposal to prevent environmental contamination (Figure 5-12).

FIGURE 5-12.

Pesticide wastes include partially full containers of pesticide that are not used, leftover mixtures in spray tanks, rinse water from pesticide containers, rinse water from inside and outside of spray equipment, and, as shown here, empty pesticide containers.

Government agencies establish acceptable pesticide residue tolerances. These are the maximum amounts of pesticide chemicals that may remain on or in raw agricultural commodities. Researchers use laboratory and animal testing to establish *tolerances,* amounts of pesticide considered harmless to consumers. The U.S. EPA always includes a generous margin of safety in the tolerance level. During registration, the EPA establishes tolerances for each pesticide. Levels vary depending on the mode of action, toxicity, and all other uses of the pesticide. When establishing tolerance levels, regulators consider the total diet of the consumer, plus their nonfood exposure, over a lifetime of 70 years. State and federal agencies monitor produce to ensure that growers do not exceed pesticide residue tolerances, and they usually seize any produce found having greater than maximum allowable pesticide residues. They may require growers to destroy this produce if there is no way to reduce residues to tolerance levels.

In the United States, pesticide misuse occasionally causes hazardous pesticide residues on produce. Residues exceeding tolerances can occur in the following ways during crop production:

- The crop can *accumulate* pesticides from the soil.
- A grower may apply a pesticide to an unregistered crop.
- The applicator may apply too much of a pesticide to the crop.
- The grower may apply the pesticide too close to harvest.
- Drift from another area may contaminate the crop.

Postharvest use of pesticides also may leave residues on produce. Not following pesticide label directions or using improper fumigation techniques may exceed residue tolerances. Improper use of pesticides in warehouses, markets, or restaurants may also cause illegal residues on food.

Although hazardous pesticide residues on produce grown in the United States are rare, they are still an important public concern. For instance, a 1994 consumer survey conducted by the Food Marketing Institute reported that 72% of the respondents felt pesticide residues on foods represented a very serious health hazard. Although food spoilage was a bigger concern than pesticides, other lesser concerns listed in this survey were antibiotics and hormones, nitrites, irradiated foods, and food additives.

Pesticide Persistence

The amount of time from application until a pesticide breaks down is known as its persistence. Chlorinated hydrocarbon insecticides and certain classes of herbicides do not break down rapidly in the environment. These are highly persistent. Toxic effects against insects or weeds remain for as long as several years while the pesticide is present in the soil.

Pesticide persistence is a benefit in situations in which long-term pest control is desirable. This includes treating building foundations to prevent termite entry. It also includes treating soil for season-long weed control. A material that has a lengthy persistence has some drawbacks, however:

- chances of poisoning are greater
- labels usually require longer restricted-entry intervals

- persistence increases chances of the chemical leaving the treatment site through water movement, soil leaching, and wind and rain erosion

Plantback Restrictions. Persistence may, for a specified time, restrict the crops that a grower may plant in the treated area. Regulations establish plantback restrictions to prevent injury or residues in subsequent crops. When plantback restrictions apply, the pesticide label specifies which crops a grower can plant or those that cannot be planted. It also states how long after application a grower must wait before planting other types of crops. Plantback restrictions are another important reason for keeping accurate pesticide application records.

Accumulation

Accumulation is the buildup of a persistent pesticide resulting from repeated applications or exposures. Accumulation may occur in the soil, in groundwater, in plant and animal tissues (bioaccumulation), or in ponds and lakes. An example of pesticide accumulation is illustrated by copper compounds used as fungicides. These pesticides have been used for over 100 years in deciduous fruit and nut orchards. Because copper degrades very slowly, constant use causes it to accumulate in the soil over a period of years. In some areas the concentration of copper in the soil has become toxic to organisms living or growing there.

Breakdown and Recombination

Special hazards may exist when pesticides break down in the environment. Some break down into different toxic compounds before breaking down further. Others fail to break down properly due to unusual environmental conditions. Occasionally some pesticides recombine with other chemicals in the environment and produce unforeseen compounds. Each location in the environment has unique characteristics that may influence the way chemicals break down. These factors also influence how they react with target and nontarget organisms.

Several variables influence chemical efficacy, breakdown, and recombination. These include

- soil type and moisture
- soil organic matter content
- air flow, temperature, rainfall
- the presence of plants and animals

For example, soil texture and organic matter content influence the activity and breakdown of some herbicides. Application rates, therefore, must be adjusted to correspond to each type of soil where these herbicides are applied.

Avoiding Hazardous Residues

Reduce chances of creating hazardous pesticide residues by taking the following steps:

- Comply with label instructions for timing, placement, and rate of application.
- Avoid incompatible mixtures that cause pesticide waste.
- Whenever possible, apply pesticides during dormant or fallow periods to prevent spraying edible produce.
- Avoid pesticide spills.
- Fill application equipment in ways that prevent pesticide mixtures from siphoning back into wells.
- Calibrate application equipment properly and make an accurate measurement of the area you plan to spray—this will prevent you from mixing too much material.
- Select pesticides that break down rapidly, and use formulations that reduce problems of drift.

For outdoor applications, use cultural practices such as managing soil and water movement to reduce pesticide residues in the environment. Control the amount and timing of irrigation water to eliminate runoff and slow the rate of percolation. In agriculture, use practices such as reduced tillage, contour farming, terracing, grass-lined waterways, and subsurface drainage to reduce soil erosion. Collect and reuse tailwater (the water that runs off the low end of a field) from irrigated fields to keep residues within the treatment site.

DAMAGE TO TREATED SURFACES

Pesticides may sometimes spot or damage treated surfaces or surfaces exposed to pesticide drift. The pesticide, solvents, or salts in the water used with the spray mixture may be responsible for this damage. Application rates and the concentration of the spray mixture can influence spotting, pitting, or staining. Follow label instructions for mixing and application. When in doubt, apply a small amount to a test area to be sure no damage occurs.

REVIEW QUESTIONS

1. **Which of the following types of worker is considered a pesticide handler?**
   - ☐ a. People who clean application equipment
   - ☐ b. Packing shed workers
   - ☐ c. Tractor drivers
   - ☐ d. Irrigators

2. **When is it legally allowable for a pesticide handler to *not* wear protective eyewear?**
   - ☐ a. During mixing or loading of the pesticide
   - ☐ b. While adjusting, cleaning, or repairing contaminated equipment
   - ☐ c. While repairing cleaned application equipment
   - ☐ d. While operating an airblast sprayer from an open tractor

3. **Pesticide residues on food are:**
   - ☐ a. A frequent cause of poisoning
   - ☐ b. Rarely the cause of poisoning
   - ☐ c. Not monitored on the federal level
   - ☐ d. Illegal at any level

4. **Which of the following is the most frequent route of pesticide exposure among agricultural workers?**
   - ☐ a. Oral (through the mouth)
   - ☐ b. Dermal (through the skin)
   - ☐ c. Inhalation
   - ☐ d. Eye

5. **Which formulation offers the greatest possibility of dermal absorption?**
   - ☐ a. Water-soluble liquids
   - ☐ b. Powder formulations
   - ☐ c. Oil-soluble formulations
   - ☐ d. Granulars

6. **The symptoms of pesticide exposure and heat stress:**
   - ☐ a. Are not at all similar
   - ☐ b. Require the same treatment
   - ☐ c. May be very similar
   - ☐ d. Are impossible to tell apart

7. **Pesticide poisoning symptoms:**
   - ☐ a. Always occur within 15 minutes after exposure
   - ☐ b. Always continue for several months or even years
   - ☐ c. Rarely require medical attention
   - ☐ d. May be delayed in their appearance

8. **Normal pesticide application practices may produce what kind of pollution of groundwater sources?**
   - ☐ a. Nonpoint
   - ☐ b. Point
   - ☐ c. Direct
   - ☐ d. Channel

9. **Pesticide contamination of wells can cause pesticides to enter groundwater through:**
   - ☐ a. Direct channels
   - ☐ b. Percolation
   - ☐ c. Leaching
   - ☐ d. Nonpoint pollution

10. **Which of the following *is not* a factor in the soil-leaching ability of a pesticide?**
    - ☐ a. Time of application
    - ☐ b. The chemical nature of the pesticide
    - ☐ c. Soil type
    - ☐ d. The pesticide's persistence

11. **Which of the following *is not* a significant factor in breaking down a pesticide in the soil?**
    - ☐ a. Soil temperature
    - ☐ b. Moisture content of the soil
    - ☐ c. Quantity and type of soil organisms
    - ☐ d. Growth stage of plants in the treated area

12. **Which of the following practices will reduce environmental contamination by pesticides?**
    - ☐ a. Make frequent applications of various pesticides
    - ☐ b. Avoid nonchemical control methods whenever possible
    - ☐ c. Reduce the frequency of applications whenever possible
    - ☐ d. Use maximum allowable rates of pesticides at all times

13. **Failure to use a backflow device when loading spray tanks or applying pesticide through irrigation systems:**
    - ☐ a. Has no significant effect on water quality
    - ☐ b. Is only allowed in arid parts of the state
    - ☐ c. May result in serious contamination of groundwater
    - ☐ d. Facilitates quick and effective application of pesticides

14. **Insect predators and parasites and honey bees are all considered:**
    - ☐ a. Secondary pests
    - ☐ b. Natural enemies
    - ☐ c. Beneficials
    - ☐ d. Pollenizers

15. **A secondary pest is one that:**
    - ☐ a. Becomes a problem when a pesticide application kills its natural enemies and eliminates competition from primary pest species
    - ☐ b. Holds serious pests in check by parasitizing their young and competing for food
    - ☐ c. Quickly replaces more serious pests because of its ability to resist attack by natural enemies
    - ☐ d. Is usually eliminated when pesticides are used to control primary pest species

16. **To reduce the possibility of building up a pest's resistance to a pesticide, you can:**
    - ☐ a. Choose a broad-spectrum pesticide that kills the pest and its natural enemies
    - ☐ b. Use only pesticides that have very long persistence
    - ☐ c. Use a pesticide that is selective only to the pest
    - ☐ d. Never use spot or strip treatments

17. **Which of the following may produce a pesticide residue on a crop that exceeds legal tolerances?**
    - ☐ a. Avoiding making applications close to harvest times
    - ☐ b. Allowing pesticide residue to drift onto the crop from a nearby area
    - ☐ c. Using the lowest effective rate of pesticide active ingredient
    - ☐ d. Avoiding use of highly persistent pesticides

6 Protecting People and the Environment

Specially designed equipment can protect applicators from excessive exposure to pesticides.

THIS CHAPTER DESCRIBES how to prevent accidental exposure to pesticides. Quite simply, you avoid pesticide-related problems by

- reading and following the pesticide label
- developing safe work habits
- wearing the required personal protective equipment
- protecting people from pesticide exposure
- avoiding practices that may injure plants and animals in the environment
- preventing pesticides from drifting onto waterways and other nontarget areas
- obeying all laws that apply to pesticide handling, storage, and application in your work situation

PESTICIDE APPLICATOR SAFETY

You are the key to preventing pesticide accidents. By following the pesticide label and obeying the laws and regulations dealing with pesticides, you can avoid most problems. In addition, when mixing pesticides together or with other materials, confirm that these combinations are safe. Also, check your equipment to be sure it is functioning properly—remember, faulty, broken, or worn equipment causes accidents. Finally, never take alcohol or drugs before, during, or immediately after applying pesticides.

Blood Tests for Exposure Monitoring

California's pesticide worker safety regulations require a special blood test for employees who handle *organophosphate* or *N-methyl carbamate* insecticides. This test is mandatory if employees handle these materials for more than 6 calendar days in any 30 consecutive day period. (Handling begins the moment you open a pesticide container for mixing or application. It continues until you have bathed and changed clothing after completing handling the pesticide. In case of a spill or other emergency, exposure begins at the onset of the incident. Exposure continues until you have bathed and changed clothing.)

The blood test is a *red cell and plasma cholinesterase determination*. The test establishes a baseline for measuring exposure to organophosphate and N-methyl carbamate insecticides. These insecticides interfere with your body's nervous system by blocking the production of *cholinesterase*. This is the enzyme that helps to regulate nerve impulses and muscle activity. It counteracts the effects of another chemical, *acetylcholine*, that normally transmits nerve signals (Figure 6-1).

These insecticides have the potential to impair your nervous system if you should receive a sufficient exposure. Each person has a unique baseline level of cholinesterase in their blood and in their blood plasma. The lowering of a person's cholinesterase may indicate that exposure to one of these insecti-

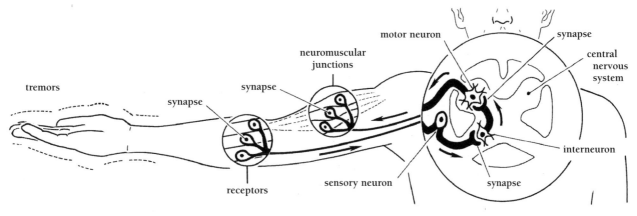

FIGURE 6-1.

Organophosphate and N-methyl carbamate insecticides interfere with the transmission of nerve signals across a synapse.

cides has occurred. (There are also other factors besides insecticides that could lower your cholinesterase.) If your cholinesterase level drops, your physician may advise you to stop handling this group of insecticides for a while. Your physician may then prescribe additional tests to determine when your cholinesterase level returns to normal.

Training

California and federal pesticide laws establish minimum standards of training for all employees handling pesticides as part of their work. This mandatory training includes the following:

Using Pesticides Safely

- the importance of wearing clean work clothing daily
- how to handle, open, and lift containers; how to pour; and how to operate mixing and application equipment
- procedures for triple-rinsing containers; disposing of containers
- how to confine spray to the target area; how to avoid contamination of people, animals, waterways, and sensitive areas
- how and where to store containers; procedures to follow when containers cannot be locked up

- the importance of washing hands thoroughly before eating, smoking, drinking, or using the bathroom; need to shower thoroughly when finished working for the day
- information on reading and understanding pesticide labels and Material Safety Data Sheets, including the signal words, precautionary statements, first aid instructions, application rate, and mixing and application instructions
- recognizing pesticide poisoning symptoms
- the types of protective equipment you should use and how to fit and properly wear this equipment and inspect it for wear and damage
- fitting, use, and maintenance of respiratory equipment
- when and how to use enclosed cabs, closed mixing systems, and other equipment and engineering controls

Emergencies and Health

- first aid and decontamination procedures
- procedures for handling nonroutine tasks or emergency situations such as spills, leaks, or fires
- location of the name, address, and telephone number of the clinic, physician, or hospital emergency

room for treatment; company policy for reporting injury or illness and obtaining medical treatment
- information about the symptoms and long-term health effects resulting from overexposure
- when medical supervision is required and general provisions of medical supervision
- how to recognize and avoid heat stress and what to do should it occur

General Information
- the applicable laws and regulations and the importance of complying with them
- the rights of the employee to receive information regarding pesticides to which they may be exposed; protection against discharge or other discrimination due to exercising these rights
- location of and access to documents pertaining to the company's Hazard Communication Program, the pesticide labels, Pesticide Safety Information Series sheets, Material Safety Data Sheets, pesticide use records, medical records, and other documents

Your employer is responsible for providing the personal protective equipment and necessary training you need. Your employer is also responsible for cleaning and maintaining the personal protective equipment. If you are self-employed and require training information, contact your local agricultural commissioner's office.

In addition, all agricultural fieldworkers entering treated areas within 30 days of the expiration of any restricted-entry interval must receive pesticide-related training. Sidebar 10 lists the information that fieldworker training must cover. *Qualified trainers* must train fieldworkers and pesticide handlers in agricultural areas. Qualified trainers include
- pest control advisers (PCAs)
- certified private or commercial applicators
- registered foresters
- University of California farm advisors
- agricultural commissioners and biologists
- people who have attended an approved train-the-trainer program

Continuing Education. Being employed as a pesticide handler obligates you to keep current on new information. This includes issues of pesticide use, pesticide safety, and pest management. Keeping current is necessary because
- lawmakers change or revise pesticide laws and regulations from time to time
- pesticide chemicals are constantly being improved, with several new chemicals introduced each year
- pesticide use changes with increased knowledge of pests and their habits
- techniques of pesticide application often reflect new technologies in application equipment and formulation types
- researchers modify pest management techniques as they discover new information about pests
- pest managers discover new pests every year, and certain pests show resistance to pesticides used previously for their control

Without continuing education, a pesticide applicator can quickly lose touch with modern pest control practices and pesticide application techniques.

A good way to keep yourself current is to attend meetings of professional organizations affiliated with your work. Most occupational areas involved in pesticide use have one or more professional organizations. Several of these associations publish newsletters that contain new pest management and pesticide use information. In addition, the UC Cooperative Extension Service (county farm advisors' offices) sponsors workshops and seminars. These programs focus on aspects of pest control, pest management, and pesticide use.

SIDEBAR 10

Criteria for Fieldworker Training

Worker Protection Standard (WPS) training for fieldworkers must include at least the following information. This training must be provided to any workers who enter pesticide-treated areas for the 30 days following expiration of a restricted-entry interval. Training must be provided to workers when an area has been treated with any type of pesticide, such as herbicides, fungicides, and insecticides. Training is not required if workers or employers can verify such training has been provided within the past five years.

■ INFORMATION THAT MUST BE COVERED

- ☐ Where and how workers may come in contact with pesticides or pesticide residues during work, including hazards from chemigation and drift.
- ☐ The routes by which pesticides can enter the body (skin, mouth, inhalation, and eyes).
- ☐ Symptoms of acute pesticide poisoning or injury; long-term and delayed health effects from pesticide exposure, including sensitization.
- ☐ First aid for pesticide injury and poisoning; emergency decontamination.
- ☐ How workers can protect themselves from exposure (work clothing; avoiding skin, eye, and mouth contact; personal hygiene).
- ☐ Obtaining medical help.

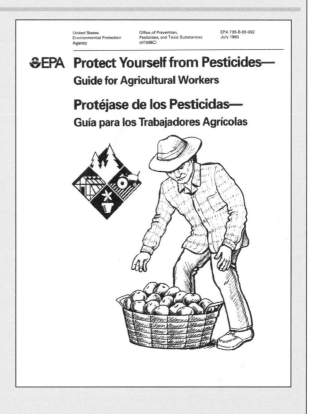

United States Environmental Protection Agency

Office of Prevention, Pesticides, and Toxic Substances (H7506C)

EPA 735-B-93-002 July 1993

♦EPA Protect Yourself from Pesticides—
Guide for Agricultural Workers

Protéjase de los Pesticidas—
Guía para los Trabajadores Agrícolas

- ☐ After-work care of contaminated work clothes.
- ☐ Warnings about taking home pesticides or pesticide containers.
- ☐ An explanation of the WPS entry restrictions, application limitations, posting, oral warnings, access to pesticide use information, and protection from employer retaliation.

Also, county agricultural commissioners' offices regularly conduct meetings to update people on pesticide laws and regulations. Special courses are also available through local community colleges, state colleges and universities, and the University of California.

Planning

Planning for pesticide safety helps to prevent accidents. Find out about the pesticides you use by studying Material Safety Data Sheets and pesticide labels. From these you will learn about the dangers and what precautions you need to take. Inspect areas where you will be working to locate potential hazards that

may affect your safety. Finally, plan what you need to do if an accident happens. Sidebar 11 is a checklist for planning a pesticide application.

Material Safety Data Sheet. Material Safety Data Sheets (MSDSs) provide detailed information about pesticide hazards (Figure 6-2). You will find the following information on MSDSs:

- the chemical characteristics of active and other hazardous ingredients
- fire and explosion hazards
- health hazards
- reactivity and incompatibility characteristics

FIGURE 6-2.

Material Safety Data Sheets provide valuable information about pesticide hazards.

MONSANTO MATERIAL SAFETY DATA   ROUNDUP® ULTRA herbicide   Page 1 of 6

MONSANTO PRODUCT NAME
ROUNDUP® ULTRA Herbicide

1. CHEMICAL PRODUCT AND COMPANY IDENTIFICATION

Product Name: ROUNDUP® ULTRA herbicide
Synonyms: MON 65005
EPA Reg. No.: 524-475
Company ID: Monsanto Company
800 North Lindbergh
St. Louis, MO 63167, U.S.A.
Phone #s: Emergency Phone Number (call collect): (314) 694-4000
Non-Emergency Information: 1-800-332-3111
Revisions: Sections containing a revision or new information are marked with a ♣

MSDS Number: S00012770   Date: November, 1995   Supersedes: None

SIDEBAR 11
Checklist for Planning a Pesticide Application

PERSONAL

☐ Medical checkup and necessary blood tests?
☐ Properly trained for this type of application?

PESTICIDE

☐ Read and thoroughly understood label?
☐ Checked to be sure use consistent with target pest and application area?
☐ Read Material Safety Data Sheet for information on hazards?
☐ Obtained necessary permits?
☐ Know proper rate of pesticide to be applied?

EQUIPMENT

☐ Proper personal protective equipment (boots, gloves, respiratory equipment, protective clothing, eye protection, headwear)?
☐ Necessary measuring and mixing equipment?
☐ Suitable application equipment for this job (tank capacity, pressure range, volume of output, nozzle size, pump compatible with formulation type)?
☐ Application equipment properly calibrated?
☐ Emergency water and first aid supplies?
☐ Necessary supplies to contain spills or leaks (absorbent materials, cleaning supplies, holding containers)?

TRANSPORTING

☐ Can transport pesticides safely to application site?
☐ Pesticides and containers secured from theft or unauthorized access?

☐ Vehicles properly marked and permits obtained, if necessary, for transporting hazardous materials and hazardous wastes?

MIXING AND LOADING

☐ Safe mixing and loading site located?
☐ Obtained clean water for mixing?
☐ Water pH tested?
☐ Proper adjuvants obtained for correcting pH, preventing foaming, and improving deposition?
☐ Checked compatibility of pesticide tank mixes or fertilizer-pesticide combinations?
☐ Liquid containers triple rinsed and rinsate put into spray tank?

TREATMENT SITE

☐ Boundaries of treatment site inspected?
☐ Environmentally sensitive areas within and around treatment area identified?
☐ Notified people working or living in or near treatment area, including fieldworkers and their supervisors in agricultural applications?
☐ Treatment site properly posted with required signs?
☐ Soil types determined and noted, if these are factor in pesticide efficacy?
☐ Livestock, pets, honey bees, other animals properly protected?
☐ Aspects of groundwater determined, if applicable?
☐ Hazards within treatment site identified, including electrical wires and outlets, ignition

sources, obstacles, steep slopes, and other dangerous conditions?

☐ Plants in treatment area in proper condition for pesticide application (correct growth stage, not under moisture stress, other requirements as specified on pesticide label)?

WEATHER CONDITIONS

☐ Weather is suitable for application (low wind, proper temperature, lack of fog or rainfall)?

APPLICATION

☐ Application pattern established suitable for treatment area, hazards, and prevailing weather conditions?

☐ Application rate selected that will give most uniform coverage?

☐ Equipment frequently checked during application to assure that everything worked properly and provided a uniform application?

CLEANUP

☐ Application equipment properly cleaned and decontaminated after application?

☐ Personal protective equipment safely stored and then cleaned or laundered according to approved methods?

☐ Disposable materials burned or disposed of in approved way?

DISPOSAL

☐ Paper pesticide containers burned or disposed of according to local regulation?

☐ Plastic and metal containers triple rinsed?

☐ Plastic and metal containers properly stored until disposed of in suitable disposal area?

STORAGE

☐ Unused pesticides returned to supplier or stored in locked facility for later use?

☐ Storage facility is suitable for pesticides?

REPORTS

☐ Necessary reports filed with requesting agency?

FOLLOW-UP

☐ Treatment areas inspected after application to assure that pesticide controlled the target pests without causing undue damage to nontarget organisms or surfaces of items in treatment area?

DAMAGE

☐ Damage, if it occurred, promptly reported?

- storage information
- emergency spill or leak cleanup procedures
- LD_{50} and LC_{50} ratings for various test animals
- emergency telephone numbers of the manufacturer

Manufacturers prepare these sheets and make them available to every person selling, storing, or handling pesticides. Ask your employer for them, or, if self-employed, obtain them from the chemical manufacturer or pesticide supplier. You can obtain MSDSs for every labeled pesticide.

Pesticide Label. Thoroughly read and understand the entire pesticide label. The label gives specific information for each type of application. It is also the legal document that you must follow for any pesticide use. Look for signal words (*Danger, Warning, Caution*). Check the label for required personal protective equipment. Make sure that you have and use this equipment and that it is in good condition. Review the label for any special environmental precautions. Always be sure the label lists the intended application site or commodity. Finally, consult the label for information on how to dispose of unwanted pesticide and empty containers.

Hazards. To increase your awareness of hazards, read the MSDS and the pesticide label. These include important information about the dangers to you, to people and animals, and to the environment. Carefully inspect the treat-

SIDEBAR 12

Emergency Numbers for Pesticide Accidents and Spills

WHEN PEOPLE HAVE BEEN EXPOSED TO PESTICIDES

Dial 9-1-1 for emergency medical assistance. Notify the operator that the problem is a pesticide exposure. Provide an accurate location and information on the type of pesticide involved.

After obtaining medical treatment for exposed persons, determine if a spill has taken place. Follow instructions below for a spill.

Contact the nearest agricultural commissioner's office to report the incident. Find the telephone number in the white pages of the local telephone book under the county where the accident occurred.

FOR PESTICIDE SPILL ON STATE OR FEDERAL HIGHWAYS

Notify local office of the California Highway Patrol and the local fire department (dial 9-1-1). Inform the emergency operator that a pesticide

spill has occurred; provide accurate location and type of pesticide.

Contact CHEMTREC at 800-424-9300 for assistance in cleaning up a pesticide spill.

Contact State of California Office of Emergency Services. Usually a written report will need to be filed. Check white pages of telephone directory under "State Government Offices" section or contact the main office in Sacramento: Governor's Office of Emergency Services, 2800 Meadowview Road, Sacramento, CA 95832, (916) 262–1843.

Contact local agricultural commissioner's office. Find the telephone number in the white pages of the local telephone book under the county where the accident occurred.

FOR PESTICIDE SPILL ON LOCAL CITY OR RURAL ROADS OR PRIVATE LAND

Contact local police or sheriff and local fire department (dial 9-1-1). Inform the emergency operator that a pesticide spill has occurred. Provide accurate location and type of pesticide.

Contact CHEMTREC at 800-424-9300 for assistance in cleaning up a pesticide spill.

Report spill to Office of Emergency Services. Contact local agricultural commissioner's office. Find the telephone number in the white pages of the local telephone book under the county where the accident occurred.

ment area to look for conditions or objects that may affect the safety of the application:

- Evaluate the weather and make sure it is suitable for an application. If appropriate, choose a time of day when the pesticide application will be least disruptive.
- Become familiar with the boundaries of the treatment site. When

applicable, determine soil type and variations in soil types. Soil type might influence the efficacy of herbicides or other soil-applied pesticides. It may also influence percolation into groundwater. Look for environmentally sensitive areas such as streams, irrigation ditches, ponds, lakes, homes, schools, or parks.

• Arrange to protect or remove pets, livestock, honey bees, or other animals in the area.

Special hazards may exist if you apply pesticides inside and around homes, businesses, offices, and other buildings. Be careful around food, food preparation areas and utensils, bedding, pets, and surfaces contacted by people. Find out if infants or toddlers live or play in the treatment area.

Planning for Accidents. Plan for the possibility of an accident. This includes locating an appropriate medical facility before you need emergency care. Also, find out where to get assistance with spill cleanup. Post in your vehicle the telephone number of a medical facility close to where you are working. Also, write down the telephone numbers of the local fire department, sheriff, and highway patrol (see Sidebar 12). The emergency number "9-1-1" usually gives you immediate access to medical help, local fire services, and law enforcement agencies.

Plan what to do if there is a pesticide spill and be prepared to protect the public from danger. Know the proper first aid to administer to victims of pesticide exposure or heat stress. Understand the steps you must take to reduce injury to yourself and others in case of an accident. Be sure you have emergency water for washing your eyes and skin.

Pesticide Combinations

Often, the toxicity, mode of action, or efficacy of a pesticide changes when you combine it with another material. Combinations can alter the toxicity of pesticides to people as well as to target pests. For instance, some combinations change the amount and speed that certain pesticides enter your body. This could affect your body's ability to quickly deactivate the toxic material. Adjuvants that enhance penetration or toxic action sometimes increase hazards to people. Read the pesticide label for important information and restrictions on pesticide combinations.

Avoiding Medications, Alcohol, and Drugs

Alcohol, drugs, and certain medications cause drowsiness, impair judgment, and often influence your ability to apply pesticides safely. These substances may also alter the toxicity of pesticides in case of exposure. For example, a severe illness may result if a person consumes alcohol shortly after exposure to the fungicide *thiram*. If you are taking any medication, consult a physician before handling, mixing, or applying pesticides. Do not take alcohol or drugs before, during, or immediately after a pesticide application.

SAFETY EQUIPMENT

Safety equipment helps protect your body and clothing from pesticide exposure. Some of this equipment also protects your eyes and prevents you from inhaling pesticide vapors. However, safety equipment is effective only if it fits correctly and you use it properly. Always keep it cleaned and maintained according to manufacturers' instructions.

The greatest risk of pesticide poisoning comes from pesticides contacting your skin. Oil-soluble pesticides pass through skin faster than water-soluble pesticides. In addition, some parts of your body absorb pesticide more quickly than other areas. In a test using the organophosphate insecticide *parathion* (Figure 6-3), for example, researchers found the forearm to be the least susceptible area for pesticide absorption. The palms of the hands and soles of the feet absorb parathion slightly faster than the forearm. The top of the hand is almost 2½ times more susceptible to absorption than the forearm. The scalp, face, and forehead are 4 times more susceptible. The ear canal absorbs at a rate almost 5½ times faster than the forearm. Absorption in the armpit is nearly

FIGURE 6-3.

Different areas of the body may absorb pesticides through the skin at different rates. This illustration shows the results of an early study where researchers placed minute amounts of methyl parathion on body areas of various volunteers. They determined absorption rates by measuring the chemical in the volunteers' urine after a known period of time. (Testing pesticides on human subjects is not allowed in the United States.)

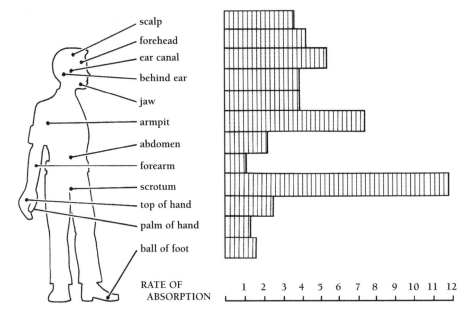

scalp
forehead
ear canal
behind ear
jaw
armpit
abdomen
forearm
scrotum
top of hand
palm of hand
ball of foot

RATE OF
ABSORPTION

1 2 3 4 5 6 7 8 9 10 11 12

FIGURE 6-4.

Pesticide labels tell you what personal protective equipment to wear during pesticide applications. Some applications, such as spraying orchards (left), expose handlers to higher levels of pesticide than do low-volume applications (right).

7½ times greater. In this study, the scrotum was the most susceptible area of the body to parathion absorption. This area was nearly 12 times more absorptive than the forearm.

The way you apply pesticides also influences the exposure you receive. For instance, your exposure risk is greater with an air blast sprayer than with a low-volume boom sprayer (Figure 6-4). Applying chemicals in enclosed areas is usually more risky than applying pesticides outdoors.

Follow the pesticide label for the protective clothing and equipment you must use. In most instances, using safer equipment than the label-required equipment increases your protection. The only exception is with the use of certain fumigants. Protective clothing

and gloves sometimes trap some fumigants close to your skin. This actually increases your exposure rather than protecting you. Follow label instructions explicitly for the proper protective clothing and equipment when applying fumigants.

Personal Protective Equipment

The following personal protective equipment protects you during normal pesticide handling activities as well as when accidents occur. For example, a ruptured hose might soak you with pesticide before you can shut off the sprayer. Wearing personal protective equipment reduces your chances of injury if this happens.

FIGURE 6-5.

Minimal work clothing for low-hazard pesticides includes one- or two-piece garments of closely woven fabric that cover the entire body except the head, hands, and feet.

FIGURE 6-6.

Coveralls are suitable for many types of pesticide applications. They have the advantage of being able to be easily removed if contaminated or when work is finished.

Bodywear

You have many choices of protective clothing. Your personal preference and the type of work you perform may influence the styles or materials of the bodywear you select. However, this bodywear must conform to pesticide label requirements. Common styles provided by employers include coveralls and aprons. Manufacturers produce protective clothing from several types of materials. Some materials offer more chemical resistance than others or are more suitable for specific types of pesticides. Usually you have choices in weight and strength of the fabric and fabric resistance to ripping and puncturing. Different materials also provide options in comfort and durability. No single material provides everything, so select bodywear for your most important need— *protection from pesticide exposure.*

If the label requires waterproof or chemical resistant bodywear, you must observe certain temperature restrictions. You cannot apply these pesticides if the daytime temperature exceeds 80°F or the nighttime temperature exceeds 85°F. You can ignore these requirements if you make the application from an air-conditioned cab. You can also wear a body cooling device, such as an ice vest, underneath your protective clothing.

Minimal Protective Clothing. Never handle, mix, or apply pesticides without wearing at least some minimal work clothing to prevent chemicals from contacting your skin. Minimal protection required under low-hazard circumstances includes a one or two-piece garment of closely woven fabric (or equivalent) that covers the entire body except the head, hands, and feet (Figure 6-5). If you wear coveralls over your regular clothing you have additional protection from pesticides. Coveralls have the advantage of being easily removed if they become contaminated or when you finish working (Figure 6-6).

Cotton fabric is popular for its comfort and coolness. However, never use it without additional protective clothing if there are chances of contacting wet spray or concentrated liquids. Tightly woven fabrics act as wicks and efficiently carry liquids to the inside of the garments. This increases your potential for skin exposure (Figure 6-7).

Disposable Protective Clothing. Manufacturers produce disposable protective clothing from several types of materials suitable for pesticide application. Disposable fabrics made from nonwoven, bonded fiber materials are superior to woven fabrics. This is

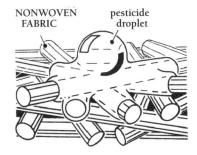

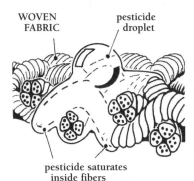

FIGURE 6-7.

Woven fabrics promote wicking, as shown in the lower figure. It takes longer for pesticide droplets to pass through nonwoven fabrics, as shown in the top drawing.

FIGURE 6-8.

Disposable protective clothing is inexpensive and lightweight, and it resists puncturing and tearing. Throw it away after use. Unless the fabric is specially coated, it is unsuitable for use when the label calls for a waterproof or chemical-resistant garment.

FIGURE 6-9.

Chemical-resistant garments provide the maximum amount of protection from pesticide exposure.

because they do not promote wicking and are more resistant to liquid penetration. *Uncoated* disposable clothing is not suitable if the pesticide label states that the clothing be "waterproof" or "chemical resistant." However, manufacturers laminate or bond some nonwoven fabrics to other materials to make them waterproof. Disposables are usually lightweight but remarkably strong and resistant to tearing or puncturing (Figure 6-8). Disposables have the major advantage of not requiring cleaning or decontamination after use. Throw them away when soiled.

Reuseable Protective Clothing. Most reuseable protective clothing consists of woven or nonwoven fabrics coated with or laminated to waterproof materials. The amount of protection offered against pesticide exposure depends on the type of waterproofing material. Neoprene, latex rubber, and polyvinyl chloride (PVC) all are very effective (Figure 6-9).

Do not use protective clothing that has a woven fabric lining. Although woven linings are more comfortable and give the garment strength, they can become contaminated with pesticides. This increases the risk of exposure. Linings made of nonwoven, nonabsorbent materials, such as dacron, are safer (Figure 6-10).

Some waterproofing materials react with pesticides and oils to become stiff and cracked. This greatly reduces the protection they offer. Discard reuseable clothing once it loses its ability to repel water or if it becomes torn, cracked, or punctured.

Manufacturers produce protective clothing for many different purposes, often only for protection against rain. Select fabrics that are resistant to the chemicals you work with, such as petroleum oils, organic solvents, and abrasive dusts. The clothing must also resist tearing, snagging, and abrasion and have a nonabsorbent lining. Look

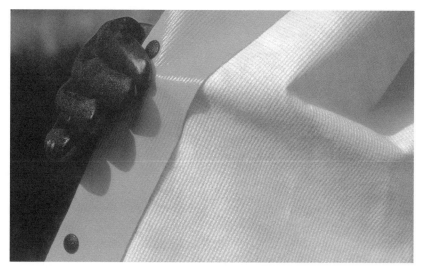

FIGURE 6-10.

Be sure linings of protective clothing are made of nonabsorbent materials to prevent pesticide contamination.

FIGURE 6-11.

Follow label instructions for use of waterproof aprons. Select a style with a wide bib to provide added protection.

for strong and noncorrosive fasteners. One-piece coveralls offer the best protection. If you select two-piece suits, pants should be the bib overall style to provide sufficient overlap with the jacket. Select coveralls or jackets with attached hoods for greater protection of the neck and head. Garments should allow movement without binding.

Aprons. Aprons protect the front of your body during pesticide mixing and while handling opened pesticide containers (Figure 6-11). However, do not use aprons instead of other protective clothing during pesticide application unless the label permits their use. Read the pesticide label to determine when to wear a protective apron. Select aprons made of waterproof materials. Be sure they are long enough to protect your clothing. Wide bib styles provide splash protection to the upper chest. Disposable aprons made for one-time use are generally not suitable for pesticide handling. The thin plastic materials tear or puncture easily. Reuseable aprons are more durable but require regular cleaning and decontamination. Discard them if they develop tears or holes.

Head Protection

Hats made from fabric absorb liquids and can become seriously contaminated. In addition, the fabric and mesh of baseball-style caps do not protect you from spray droplets. If you wear a hat, be sure it is water resistant and wide-brimmed. Headbands and sweatbands must also be waterproof. An alternative to a wide-brimmed hat is a hooded, waterproof jacket.

Gloves

Chemical-resistant gloves are an essential part of your safety equipment, and you must wear them when handling most pesticides. Never use leather or fabric gloves (unless specified on the pesticide label) because they absorb water and pesticides. Choose gloves made from natural rubber, latex, butyl, nitrile, or neoprene (Figure 6-12). Select a material that offers the best resistance to the types of pesticide you are using. Some materials are suitable for total immersion in a liquid toxicant for extended periods. Other materials provide protection only against accidental splashes or occasional immersion. The thickness of

FIGURE 6-12.

Use only unlined chemical-resistant gloves made of natural rubber, latex, butyl, neoprene, or nitrile.

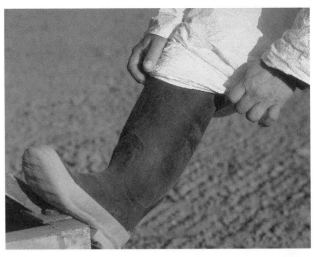

FIGURE 6-13.

Chemical-resistant footwear protects your feet from pesticide exposure.

the glove material also determines the amount of protection—thicker materials are better. Choose materials that resist puncturing and abrasion.

Wear unlined gloves since fabrics used for linings may absorb pesticides. This makes them dangerous to use and difficult to clean. If necessary, use woven, removable glove liners to insulate your hands from the cold or to absorb perspiration. Discard or launder glove liners after each use.

Make sure the cuffs of gloves are long enough to extend to the mid-forearm. Usually, wear the sleeves of your protective clothing on the outside of your gloves to keep out pesticides. Some special application situations, however, require holding one or both hands overhead while spraying liquids. In these cases, tuck the sleeve of the elevated arm inside the gloves. Be careful when lowering your arm to prevent pesticides from entering the glove.

Check pesticide labels for special glove recommendations. For instance, labels prohibit using waterproof gloves with some fumigants, since they increase the chances of skin contact.

Footwear

Labels of some pesticides require the use of waterproof boots or boot cover-ings (Figure 6-13). Select protective footwear made from rubber or synthetic materials such as PVC, nitrile, neoprene, or butyl. Choose the material based on its ability to protect you from the pesticides with which you work (Table 6-1). Some pesticides, 1,3-dichloropropene (Telone II) for example, penetrate most protective waterproof materials.

Waterproof rubber and synthetic materials are poor conductors of electrical current. They therefore offer good protection against electrocution when working in wet areas where there are electrical hazards.

Waterproof footwear is available in conventional boot and overshoe styles (Figure 6-14). Some boots have internal steel toe caps to protect your toes against falling objects. Select footwear that fits well and is comfortable to wear. Protective footwear should be calf-high. Wear the legs of your protective pants on the outside of the footwear to keep out any spray or spills. For increased protection, use rubber bands to seal pant legs tightly around the outside of the boots. Choose a sole design that is slip-proof on wet surfaces and easy to clean (Figure 6-15).

Waterproof boots do not "breathe" like leather or fabric shoes, so wear clean cotton or wool socks to absorb perspiration.

TABLE 6-1.

Guide to Selecting Suitable Chemical-Resistant Materials for Personal Protective Equipment.

CHEMICAL EXPOSURE	RESISTANT MATERIALS						
	PVC	Nitrile	Neoprene	Butyl rubber	Standard rubber	Leather	Fabric
hydrocarbon materials, oils, and solvents (most pesticides)	●	●●	●	●	✛	✛	✛
ketones and aldehydes	○	✛	●	●●	●	✛	✛
alcohols	●●	●●	●●	●●	●	✛	✛
organic esters	○	✛	●	●●	●	✛	✛
inorganic metals	●●	●●	●●	●●	●●	✛	✛

●● highly satisfactory
● often acceptable
○ occasionally acceptable
✛ do not use

FIGURE 6-14.

Protective footwear is also available in overshoe styles to wear over regular shoes or boots.

FIGURE 6-15.

When choosing chemical-resistant boots, select a sole pattern that cleans easily and does not collect mud.

Eye Protection

Always wear eye protection while handling pesticides. It is essential during mixing and loading and while adjusting, cleaning, or repairing contaminated equipment. In California, regulations require protective eyewear during most types of pesticide application even if the requirement is not on the pesticide label. The only situations in which eye protection is usually *not* necessary are if

- Pesticides are being injected or incorporated into the soil.

- Pesticides are being applied through vehicle-mounted spray nozzles that are located below and behind the operator with the nozzles directed downward.
- The operator is working in an enclosed cab.
- The pesticides being applied are rodenticides, predacides, or avicides that are not in a liquid or gaseous form.

Eye protection is available as goggles, face shields, and face shields combined with respirators. Unless the pesticide

FIGURE 6-16.

Unless the label specifies the type of eyewear, you may use safety glasses that have a brow piece and side shields when handling pesticides.

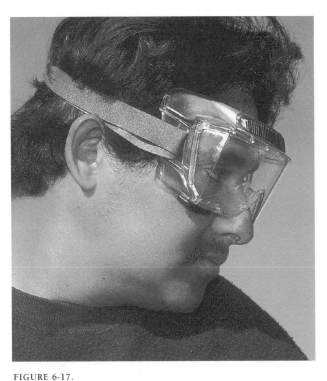

FIGURE 6-17.

Protective goggles protect the eyes during mixing and applying pesticides. Some styles allow the user to wear prescription glasses.

label specifies the type of eye protection, you may wear safety glasses if they include a brow piece and side shields (Figure 6-16).

Goggles. Goggles are the most common form of eye protection. Wear goggles whenever the pesticide label specifically mentions their use. To protect the eyes adequately, there must be full side shields (Figure 6-17). Nonfogging lenses are available for most styles, and you can buy solutions to reduce or eliminate fogging of ordinary lenses. You can wear some goggle styles over eyeglasses.

Elastic or synthetic rubber straps hold goggles in place when you wear them. Because elastic straps contain fabric, they easily absorb pesticide and possibly increase exposure to the back of the head. Avoid this problem by using a hood or protective headwear over the strap. Replace or thoroughly wash the elastic band if it becomes contaminated. Straps made of neoprene or other syn-

thetic materials are safer because they are nonabsorbent and easy to clean.

Goggle lenses may become coated with spray droplets during some pesticide applications. If this happens, carry cleaning supplies or an extra pair of goggles. Check and clean your goggles each time you stop to refill the spray tank. Use caution, however, to prevent scratching plastic lenses. Never wipe lenses to remove dirt—clean them with soap and water. Scratched lenses make the goggles useless, although some styles of goggles are available with replaceable lenses.

Faceshields. Faceshields (Figure 6-18) protect your eyes and prevent liquids from splashing onto your face while mixing pesticides. However, do not use them without additional eye protection during application. This is because they do not prevent airborne sprays or dust from floating in around the edges of the faceshield. Faceshields

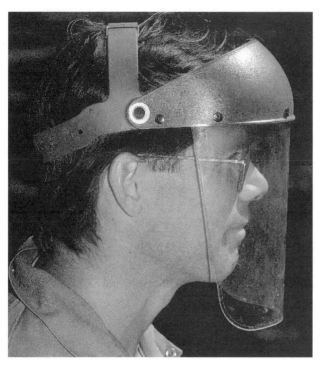

FIGURE 6-18.

Faceshields provide some eye protection and keep pesticides from splashing onto your face. Wear these with safety glasses or goggles for added eye protection.

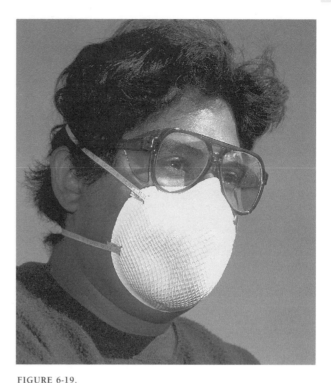

FIGURE 6-19.

Some pesticide labels require the use of NIOSH-approved dust/mist filtering respirators.

are comfortable to wear, allow better air circulation, and provide a greater range of vision than goggles.

Plastic faceshields require the same care as goggles to protect them from scratching. When not in use, faceshields and goggles should be stored in plastic bags to keep them clean and prevent scratching.

Respiratory Equipment

Respirators protect the lungs and respiratory tract from airborne pesticides. You can choose from several types and styles suitable for mixing and applying pesticides. Select respiratory equipment based on the requirements listed on the pesticide label.

Disposable Masks. The simplest form of respiratory protection is a disposable dust and mist mask (Figure 6-19). Disposable dust and mist masks are lightweight, soft, and fairly comfortable to wear. Two elastic straps hold them in

place. Most have soft metal bands at the top edge. Shape this around the bridge of your nose for a better seal. A few styles include a small activated-charcoal cartridge to remove some organic vapor. All disposable masks used for pesticide handling must bear the NIOSH Approval Number "TC-21C" or indicate that it has been approved in accordance with part 84 of the Code of Federal Regulations (42 CFR part 84). NIOSH-approved respirators with any "R," "P," or "HE" type filters are suitable for products containing oil or products that have instructions that would allow application with an oil-containing material. For products that do not contain oil and whose labels bear no instructions that allow application with oil-containing materials, NIOSH-approved respirators with any "N," "R," "P," or "HE" filters are suitable. The pesticide label refers to these approval numbers when it requires you to use this type of respiratory protection.

FIGURE 6-20.

For certain pesticides, labels require that you wear an organic vapor-removing cartridge respirator with a prefilter approved for pesticides. These must be NIOSH approved.

FIGURE 6-21.

Many cartridge respirators have removable filtering cartridges. Be sure the cartridges you use are approved for pesticides.

Cartridge Respirators. Some pesticide labels require the use of cartridge respirators with the NIOSH Approval Number "TC-23C" or indications that it has been approved in accordance with part 84 of the Code of Federal Regulations (42 CFR part 84)(Figure 6-20). NIOSH-approved organic vapor (OV) cartridge respirators with any "R," "P," or "HE" type prefilters are suitable for products containing oil or products that have instructions that would allow application with an oil-containing material. For products that do not contain oil and whose labels bear no instructions that allow application with oil-containing materials, NIOSH-approved organic vapor (OV) cartridge respirators with any "N," "R," "P," or "HE" prefilters are suitable. The pesticide label refers to these approval numbers when it requires you to use this type of respiratory protection.

Cartridge respirators remove low levels of pesticide vapors, dusts, and mists from the air you breathe. Do not use these for protection against fumigants (gases). Never use cartridge respirators in atmospheres that pose an immediate threat to life or health. This includes situations such as atmospheres containing carbon monoxide or having an oxygen level below 19.5%.

Cartridge respirators have fitted rubber facepieces and two-stage cartridge filters (Figure 6-21). In some models the filter cartridges are replaceable, while others require replacing the entire respirator. Cartridge respirators have a one-way exhalation valve. Inhaled air must pass through the cartridge filters, but the valve permits exhaled air to bypass the filters. At least two adjustable elastic headbands hold the facepieces in place. Cartridges made for pesticides include a particulate prefilter to trap airborne particles mechanically. They also have an activated carbon organic vapor cartridge to adsorb gases (Figure 6-22).

Cartridge respirators need to fit properly to be effective and safe. They should be in good working condition and be cleaned after each use. Beards and long sideburns affect the way cartridge respirators seal around the face. This prevents them from giving adequate protection (Figure 6-23). Regula-

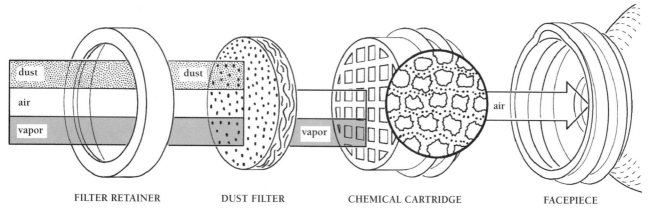

FILTER RETAINER   DUST FILTER   CHEMICAL CARTRIDGE   FACEPIECE

FIGURE 6-22.

Respirator cartridges include a mechanical dust filter that removes dust and droplet particles and an activated charcoal chemical cartridge to remove vapors.

FIGURE 6-23.

Cartridge respirators must seal around the face to be effective and to prevent unfiltered air from entering. Beards or long sideburns prevent proper sealing. It is illegal for people with beards or long sideburns to use cartridge respirators.

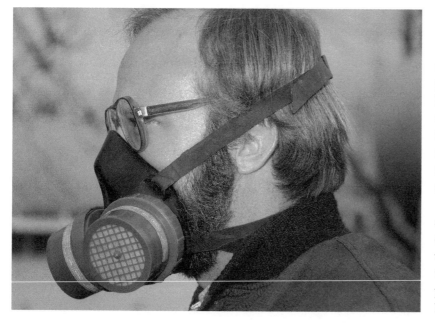

tions prohibit pesticide applicators with beards or long sideburns from wearing cartridge respirators.

California's pesticide regulations require that all cartridge respirators be *fit tested* before use (see Sidebar 13). Isoamyl acetate is one of the materials used to test for proper fit. This chemical has a strong banana-like odor. Another test uses an irritant smoke. If the wearer can detect one of these indicators, the facepiece is admitting unfiltered air. Adjust the facepiece until the odor is absent or try another size, brand, or

style. You should also perform a *fit check* each time you use a cartridge respirator. This involves holding your hands or small plastic bags over the cartridges while wearing the respirator. Inhale to check for leaks around the facepiece or exhalation valve. Then, cover the exhalation valve and exhale to check for leaks around the inhalation valves. Repair or replace the respirator if you find any leaks.

The cartridges on respirators have a limited effective life. Replace the organic vapor cartridges if you

- have difficulty breathing
- begin to smell a pesticide odor
- detect any taste
- experience any irritation

These signs may indicate that the organic vapor unit cannot absorb more pesticide and has lost its effectiveness. Besides the above guidelines, change cartridges following pesticide label instructions, equipment manufacturer's recommendations, or, lacking information to the contrary, *at the end of each daily work period.*

You need eye protection when using any respirator. Therefore, be sure you can wear the respirator comfortably with goggles or a faceshield. Some cartridge respirators include a full facepiece with built-in eye protection (see Figure 6-24).

SIDEBAR 13

Isoamyl Acetate (Banana Oil) Test for Properly Fitting Cartridge Respirators

The chemical isoamyl acetate, commonly referred to as "banana oil," is available from major chemical suppliers and is widely used to check respirator fit. Its odor is easy to detect and the chemical can be used with any pesticide respirator equipped with organic vapor cartridges or canister.

When conducting a fit test, it is important to know that some brands of respirators are available in small, medium, and large sizes. If possible, have several different sizes available during the test to ensure proper fit. Try respirators from different manufacturers since one brand may fit better than others.

If a respirator does not fit properly, the applicator will not be adequately protected. Therefore, be sure to follow the test procedures outlined below.

1. Be sure there is no banana oil odor in the test area that may influence the wearer's ability to detect its presence. Once a respirator is selected, have the wearer adjust it until there is a good face-to-mask seal.

2. Saturate a piece of cotton or cloth with banana oil. The person performing the test should wear rubber gloves and avoid skin contact with the respirator wearer.

3. Pass the saturated material close to the respirator in a clockwise and counterclockwise motion. Have the wearer stand still and breathe normally and then deeply. If the wearer smells banana oil, readjust the respirator or select a different size or style before starting again.

4. If the odor cannot be detected while the wearer is standing still, have the person perform side-to-side and up-and-down head movements. Also have the wearer talk loudly enough to be heard by someone standing nearby. Then have the person make other movements, such as bending over, that may occur during spray application.

5. If the banana oil odor cannot be detected during the above movements, it indicates a satisfactory fit. Seal the respirator in a plastic bag marked with the wearer's name. Keep a record of when the fit test was conducted, along with the size and brand of respirator selected for each user.

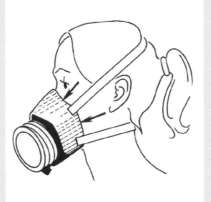

FIGURE 6-24.

Some cartridge respirators have built-in eye protection.

FIGURE 6-25.

A battery-powered fan forces filtered air through a flexible hose into a helmet or hood in this type of powered-air cartridge respirator. This design allows you to wear eyeglasses. People with beards and long sideburns can use this style of respirator. The filters, motor, and battery pack are worn on a waist belt.

FIGURE 6-26.

This self-contained supplied-air respirator provides the wearer with uncontaminated air from a compressed air tank.

Powered-Air Cartridge Respirator. The powered-air cartridge respirator forces filtered air through a tube to a hood, helmet, or face mask (Figure 6-25). You usually wear the motor, pump, batteries, and filters on a waist belt. These devices have large, efficient filters, and provide comfortable protection for lengthy application jobs. Like other cartridge respirators, use these only when the atmosphere poses no immediate threat to life or health. Use them only when the oxygen level is 19.5% or greater.

These respirators often incorporate faceshields for eye protection. They are comfortable to wear because the user does not actively force air through filters or valves. The constant supply of forced air around the user's face eliminates the need for a mask-to-face seal. Therefore, a person with a beard or long sideburns can wear this type of respirator.

Supplied-Air Respirators. You can get maximum respiratory protection from a supplied-air respirator. Use this type of equipment when working in areas being fumigated. These also protect you when working with concentrated amounts of highly toxic pesticides. Wear this type of respirator if the atmosphere contains less than 19.5% oxygen. Emergency workers wear these when responding to toxic spills or fires or when rescuing injured people. Several styles and types are available. Supplied-air respirators do not require filters or cartridges to remove toxic materials. This is because they provide an outside source of clean, uncontaminated air.

Self-contained supplied-air respirators (often called a *self-contained breathing apparatus*—SCBA) provide clean air from pressurized tanks that the user wears, similar to a scuba diver (Figure 6-26). External air models connect the wearer to a distant air pump or stationary tank by means of a hose. If you are using an external air model, locate the air pump where safe, fresh air is available.

Self-contained units provide a limited quantity of air. Once you exhaust the air supply, the system cannot provide any protection. Therefore manufacturers equip these units with warning devices to alert users when the air supply is getting low. Air tanks may be heavy and bulky, but they give unlimited mobility.

Hose-connected supplied-air respirators provide a large or unlimited quantity of fresh air. However, the range of available hose restricts the wearer's mobility. The maximum hose length is usually 300 feet. Long hoses are cumbersome and awkward to handle—users must take precautions to avoid kinking, snagging, or hose damage.

Supplied-air respirators use either half or full facepieces; full facepiece models provide eye protection. Other models attach to a hood (or helmet) that encloses the entire head and have a clear plastic faceshield.

Facepieces use a pressure demand regulator that admits fresh air into the mask as the wearer begins to inhale. Air flow diminishes when the user exhales. Self-contained units use this method because of the limited air supply. Hoods provide a continuous flow of fresh air around the entire head, whether inhaling or exhaling. Hoods do not require critical sealing around the face and can be worn with beards, long sideburns, and eyeglasses. Use a hood when the air supply comes from an external source through a hose.

Cleaning and maintenance of supplied-air respirators are critical to their safe operation. Masks must fit properly and exhalation valves have to be in good working order. This prevents any outside air from entering. Keep hoods free of holes or tears. Regularly inspect air hoses, both from self-contained tanks or from air pumps, and replace them if cracked or worn. Keep air pressure regulators clean, dry, and protected from damage.

Cleaning and Maintaining Personal Protective Equipment

Always keep protective safety equipment in good working condition. Protective equipment is effective only as long as it is free from pesticide contamination and works properly. Therefore, you must frequently clean and inspect this equipment. Replace or repair equipment when you spot a problem.

Respirators

Extend the life of cartridge or supplied-air respirators through regular cleaning and safe storage. The ability of a respirator to protect you from harmful pesticides depends in part on how well you maintain it.

Inspection. Before cleaning your respirator at the end of each day, inspect it for wear and damage. Check the headbands for fraying, tears, or loss of elasticity and replace them if necessary. Remove filters and replace the gaskets if they are defective (brittle, broken, or warped). Never use these types of cartridge respirators without gaskets since gaskets prevent contaminated air from bypassing the filter cartridge. Valve assemblies are essential parts of a cartridge respirator and must be in good working order. Disassemble and inspect valve flaps for wear, deformities, or punctures. Replace parts if you suspect they might leak. Check the threads of all valves and cartridge parts to make sure they are in good condition. Look for cracks and scratches.

Examine the facepiece for cracks, cuts, scratches, and any signs of aging. If you find damage, replace the defective parts.

When replacing items on a respirator, use only approved replacement parts for that specific brand and model. If you use unapproved parts, the respirator is not in compliance with the law and may be ineffective.

FIGURE 6-27.

After use, remove cartridges and wash respirators in warm, soapy water. Use a soft brush or cloth to remove pesticide residue.

FIGURE 6-28.

Wash boots before removing them. Use a brush and soapy water, then rinse with clean water. Do not get the boots wet inside. Let boots air out after washing; store them in a clean plastic bag once they dry.

Cleaning. After removing filters from reuseable cartridge respirators, soak the facepiece, gaskets, and valve parts in a solution of warm water and mild liquid detergent. Do not use abrasives or cleaning compounds containing alcohol or other organic solvents. You must use anti-germicidal cleaners if more than one worker wears the same respirator. Use a soft brush or cloth to remove any pesticide residue (Figure 6-27). Rinse the respirator and valve parts in clean water. Air dry rather than using applied heat.

After it is completely dry, reassemble the respirator and store it in a clean plastic bag. This protects it from dirt and environmental deterioration. Keep the cartridges in a separate sealed bag if they are still good.

Boots and Gloves

Wash rubber boots and gloves under running water *before you take them off* to remove pesticide residues. Use a detergent solution and soft brush, then rinse with clean water (Figure 6-28). Do not get the insides of the boots wet. At the end of each day, wash rubber gloves with soap and warm water. Inspect them for holes while washing and discard the gloves if you find any. You may wash gloves in a washing machine by placing them into a cloth net bag. Use warm water and wash according to the instructions given below for protective clothing. Turn gloves inside out for drying. Store dry boots and gloves in plastic bags to keep them clean and prevent deterioration.

FIGURE 6-29.

Wash safety glasses, goggles, and faceshields in warm, soapy water. Use a soft brush or cloth to remove pesticide residue. Blot dry and store in a clean plastic bag.

Faceshields and Goggles

Use care when washing faceshields and goggles to avoid scratching the plastic. Submerge them in warm, soapy water. If necessary, remove pesticide residue with a soft, wet cloth or soft brush (Figure 6-29). Do not rub anti-fogging lenses, since this reduces their effectiveness. Rinse well with clear water and air dry or blot with a soft cotton cloth; rubbing increases chances of scratching. Inspect goggles and faceshields for excessive scratches and for cracks and loss of headband elasticity. You can replace scratched lenses on many styles without replacing the entire goggle. Store goggles and faceshields in paper bags to keep them clean.

Protective Clothing

Do not rewear contaminated protective clothing until you have washed it. Wash contaminated garments at the end of each work day if possible. Immediate washing reduces the chances of you or others being exposed to any residues. Throw away clothing that has had large quantities of pesticides spilled on it. Send this to a site approved for pesticide residues. Local agencies allow burning in some locations, but first check with the agricultural commissioner's office. Clean moderately or lightly contaminated clothing by washing.

Change out of contaminated clothing at your work site if possible. Empty pockets and cuffs of garments to remove excess pesticide residue. Until you launder them, place contaminated garments into a clean plastic bag. Never reuse plastic bags since these may acquire a buildup of pesticide residues. Do not combine contaminated clothing with any other laundry before, during, or after washing.

Minimal Protective Clothing. Soak minimal protective clothing in hot, soapy water for at least ½ hour. This includes long-sleeved shirts, full-length pants, coveralls, socks, and underwear. To improve pesticide removal, apply a prewash product, such as a solvent soak, prewash spray, or liquid laundry detergent. Add extra amounts to heavily soiled spots. Launder in a washing machine using hot water and liquid laundry detergent. Liquid detergent removes oil-based pesticides better than powdered detergent. Use the maximum amount recommended in the detergent instructions. Set the washing machine to its longest cycle (at least 12 minutes) and use the highest water level. Use household bleach if necessary but be aware that bleach does not contribute to the decontamination process. See Sidebar 14.

Wash pesticide-contaminated clothing separately from all other laundry to prevent transferring residues. Separate clothing contaminated with different types of pesticide. Do not combine these into one wash load. When putting clothing into the washing machine, protect your hands from exposure by wearing gloves (Figure 6-30). Check for garments that have a pesticide odor or visible pesticide spots or stains. Rewash these 1 or 2 more times in the same manner.

After washing is completed, run the washer through another complete cycle using hot water and detergent but with-

SIDEBAR 14

Techniques for Washing Pesticide-Contaminated Clothing

1. Keep pesticide-contaminated clothing separate from all other laundry.

2. Do not handle contaminated clothing with bare hands; wear rubber gloves or shake clothing from plastic bag into washer.

3. Wash only small amounts of clothing at a time. Do not combine clothing contaminated with different pesticides—wash these in separate loads.

4. Before washing, presoak clothing:

   ☐ Soak in tub, automatic washer, or spray garments outdoors with a garden hose.

   ☐ Use a commercial solvent to soak product, or apply prewash spray or liquid laundry detergent to soiled spots.

5. Wash garments in washing machine, using hottest water temperature, full water level, and normal (12-minute) wash cycle. Use maximum recommended amount of *liquid* laundry detergent. Neither bleach nor ammonia seem to affect the removal of most pesticides. Never use both.

6. If garments have pesticide odor, visible spots, or stains before washing, rewash one or two more times as in step 5.

7. Clean washing machine before using for other laundry by repeating step 5, using full amount of hot water, normal wash cycle, laundry detergent, but no clothing.

8. Hang laundry outdoors on clothesline to avoid contaminating automatic dryer.

Do not attempt to wash heavily contaminated clothing; destroy it by burning or by transporting to an approved disposal site. Follow these suggestions for reducing chances of contaminating the family laundry and endangering family members:

1. Whenever possible, wear disposable protective clothing that can be destroyed after use.

2. Always wear all required protective clothing when working with pesticides.

3. Wear clean protective clothing daily when working with pesticides. Wash contaminated clothing *daily*.

4. Remove contaminated clothing at work site and empty pockets and cuffs. Place clothing in clean plastic bag until it can be laundered. Keep contaminated clothing separated from all other laundry.

5. Remove clothing immediately if it has had a pesticide concentrate spilled on it.

FIGURE 6-30.

Avoid touching pesticide-contaminated work clothing with your bare hands. Wear rubber gloves or dump the clothing into the washer from the plastic bag. Do not combine this clothing with any other household clothing.

out any laundry. This step helps to remove pesticide residues left in the washer and prevents contaminating other loads of laundry.

Whenever possible, hang washed clothing outdoors for drying. The ultraviolet light in sunlight breaks down many pesticides, and air drying avoids contaminating the clothes dryer. If you use a clothes dryer, never combine the washed work clothing with other laundry.

Waterproof Protective Clothing. Remove as much pesticide residue as possible from waterproof clothing before laundering. Wash these items with a hose and scrub brush outdoors. Wash them in an area where the runoff will not cause contamination and before removing these garments, if possible. After taking it off, store the protective clothing in a clean plastic bag until you can launder it. To decontaminate the protective clothing, begin by soaking the garments in warm, soapy water for ½ hour. Next, wash the items in a washing machine, using warm (not hot) water and liquid laundry detergent. Keep these garments separate from all other clothing to prevent contamination. Hang waterproof clothing up to dry. Do not put it in a clothes dryer because the heat of the dryer may damage the waterproofing material. If you hang the clothing in direct sunlight, turn it inside out. This prevents deterioration of the waterproofing material and helps to deactivate any pesticide material remaining on the inside lining.

Storing Personal Protective Equipment

Never use personal protective equipment for any other purpose. When not in use, keep it stored in a clean, dry place, and protected from temperature extremes and bright light. If possible, store these items in sealable plastic bags. Light, heat, dirt, and air pollu-

tants all contribute to the deterioration of rubber, plastic, and synthetic rubber products. Never store any PPE in areas where you keep pesticides.

Problems Associated with Personal Protective Equipment

You may experience problems or occasional frustrations with personal protective equipment. Sometimes these problems cause applicators to become careless and stop wearing the required protective equipment. Fortunately you can overcome most problems. First, select the right type of equipment for the job. Make sure equipment fits properly and is in good working order. Finally, if possible, avoid applications when the temperature is too warm.

Fitting

Accurate sizing helps to improve comfort by eliminating binding or slipping. Properly fitted respiratory equipment prevents unsafe air leaks. When selecting waterproof pants and jackets for the correct size, try them on with the same weight of regular clothing you would wear during an actual pesticide application.

If weather is cold, wear a long-sleeved shirt and sweater or coat under the waterproof jacket. Be sure you are comfortable and can move freely, without binding. During hot weather, wear lightweight cotton clothing under the protective equipment. This provides an absorbent layer and assists in cooling your body.

Discomfort and Inconvenience

Discomfort and inconvenience are probably the main reasons that some applicators dislike wearing protective equipment. Eye protectors fog up, become covered with spray, and restrict the wearer's range of vision. Protective clothing can be cold during cold weather and very hot in warm or hot weather. Heavy, stiff materials can restrict movement. Gloves impair feeling in the hands, promote sweating, and are cold or hot, depending on the weather. Respirators are uncomfortable to wear if they restrict breathing.

Despite these problems, you must always wear required protective equipment during mixing and application. If you become uncomfortable, stop and make adjustments or replace the equipment with another style. Whenever possible, plan pesticide applications during times of day when the temperature is moderate. Take short breaks and get out of the protective equipment for a few minutes. If conditions are too extreme, trade off jobs with a coworker.

Limits to Protection

Personal protective equipment has limitations to the amount of protection provided—it never completely protects you. You still must prevent pesticides from being spilled, splashed, or sprayed onto your body. The equipment helps to reduce exposure, but you must do everything possible to prevent the exposure from happening. Some pesticides can penetrate protective materials—pesticide solvents and adjuvants may enhance penetration.

Pesticides confined next to your skin cannot dissipate through air movement or volatilization. Therefore, if you get pesticides on your skin or clothing *before* putting on protective equipment, the equipment may increase the amount of pesticide absorbed. You will also contaminate the inside of the protective garment. Always wear *clean* protective equipment over *clean* clothing.

Other Protective Devices

Enclosed Cabs. Enclosed cabs installed on tractors protect operators from exposure to pesticides (Figure 6-31). Some types provide protection from spray droplets and mists while providing the operator with a comfortable air-conditioned environment. These cabs, however, do not replace the label respirator requirements. Respirators, if required, must be worn while making an application from inside this type of cab. Using this type of cab eliminates the temperature restrictions on applications when applying pesticides that require the use of chemical resistant body wear (above 80°F during the day and 85°F at night).

Other types of enclosed cabs are acceptable for respiratory protection. Properly designed and maintained cabs provide a high degree of protection.

FIGURE 6-31.

Enclosed cabs protect operators against pesticide exposure. This model includes a pesticide air filtering system that eliminates the need for the operator to wear a respirator while inside the cab.

These work well in orchards and vineyards or other areas where pesticide exposure potential is high. Most models offer options of heating and cooling of the air forced into the cab for added operator comfort. Cab insulation reduces noise from the tractor and spraying equipment. Many have front and rear window washers and wipers.

Cabs acceptable for respiratory protection protect you only if you regularly clean and service them. Clean or replace pesticide filters whenever they exceed their filtering capacity. If you mix pesticides or get out of the cab during a pesticide application, put on protective equipment. However, be sure to remove contaminated protective clothing before getting back inside the cab. For maximum convenience and protection, assign another person the duties of mixing pesticides and refilling the sprayer.

Select a respiratory-enclosed cab based on your needs and expectations. For example, consider the power source for the blower. Units that connect to the tractor hydraulic system move large volumes of air but may be noisy. Electric motor drives are quieter but may not have as much power because of lim-

itations of the tractor electrical system. The volume of air that the unit supplies influences the amount of protection provided.

Factors that contribute to the filtering ability of these cabs include
- size of the unit
- volume of air being moved
- number of filter stages
- type of filtering material used
- appropriateness of the filter media to the pesticides being used

Multiple-stage filters that include a pre-filter, a high efficiency particulate air filter (HEPA), and an activated carbon filter are the safest for reducing pesticide exposure. Blowers that move large volumes of air must have large-capacity filters.

Other features of enclosed cabs that might influence their function include
- the visibility afforded the operator
- how the height of the cab relates to application sites where it will be used
- the strength of the cab for protecting the operator from tree limbs or in case of tractor rollover
- the availability of heating and air conditioning

Closed Mixing Systems. Your employees must use a closed mixing system when mixing, loading, diluting, or transferring liquid formulations of pesticides with the signal word *Danger* (Figure 6-32) if these pesticides are being used for the production of an agricultural commodity. They must also use closed systems when loading or transferring dry formulations of pesticides with the signal word *Danger* after mixing these with water or other diluent.

Closed mixing systems enable accurate and safe measuring of pesticides being put into the spray tank. The closed-system requirement does not apply if employees handle 1 gallon or less of liquid formulations with the signal word *Danger* per day and the liquid pesticide is in an original container of 1

FIGURE 6-32.

Closed mixing systems are required when mixing more than 1 gallon per day of liquid Danger *pesticides for the production of an agricultural commodity. They allow you to accurately measure the liquid pesticides. Most systems rinse the empty containers.*

FIGURE 6-33.

When working with fumigants, use an atmosphere monitoring device before entering treated areas. Color changes in the glass tubes indicate the concentration of a toxicant in the atmosphere. Specific types of tubes are used for different fumigants.

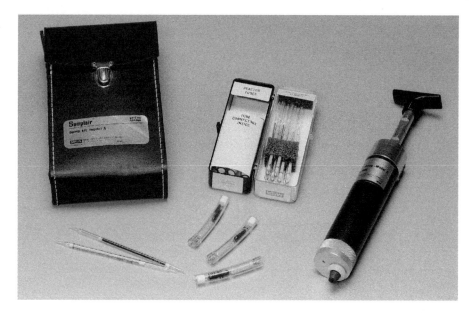

gallon or smaller. See the DPR Pesticide Safety Information Series A-3 for legal requirements of closed mixing systems.

Packaging. Special pesticide packaging helps to reduce exposure to concentrated pesticide active ingredients. This packaging includes preweighed water-soluble bags for powdered formulations. These dissolve in the spray tank, reducing your exposure to the powder and dust.

Atmosphere-Monitoring Equipment. Never enter an enclosed fumigated area, even after venting, without measuring for toxic levels of pesticide vapors (Figure 6-33). Several different atmosphere-monitoring devices detect and measure vapors. When taking measurements, wear required respirators and protective clothing or use remote sensing equipment. Take measurements in several locations within the confined space, since fumigant vapors sometimes become trapped in localized pockets.

Choose atmosphere-monitoring equipment that is suitable to the type of fumigation work you perform. Be certain that the equipment provides accurate readings at the concentration levels you encounter. Learn about the shortcomings of these devices, since other contaminants in the atmosphere can produce erroneous readings. Get proper training on this equipment so you can reliably detect dangerous levels of pesticides.

FIELDWORKER SAFETY

In agriculture, fieldworkers may be working near where you are making a pesticide application. You must protect these fieldworkers from any type of pesticide exposure. Do not allow workers into an area that is being treated with a pesticide. Whenever possible, make spray applications at times when workers are not present in surrounding areas. These times may include very early morning, late afternoon, or during the night. Preventing drift also lessens exposure risks to fieldworkers in adjacent areas.

Notification

In an agricultural situation, before applying any pesticide you must notify all employees of the farming operation who are working within ¼ mile of the treatment area. Do this *orally* or by *posting* unless the pesticide label specifies the method you must use. Inform workers when you plan to make the application so they will not enter the treated area. Tell them what pesticides you will apply and describe the hazards if they should become exposed. Inform them when they can reenter the area.

Restricted-Entry Interval

A restricted-entry interval is the time that must elapse after a pesticide application before anyone can go back into the treated area. Pesticide labels list restricted-entry intervals. For example, almost all pesticides with the signal word *Danger* have a minimum restricted-entry interval of 48 hours. Most pesticides with the signal word *Warning* have a minimum restricted-entry interval of 24 hours. Most pesticides with the signal word *Caution* have a minimum restricted-entry interval of 12 hours. However, California regulations are sometimes more restrictive than the label. Pesticide use recommendations written by licensed pest control advisers must indicate the required restricted-entry interval. The local agricultural commissioner is also able to provide this information. In all situations where the restricted-entry interval on the label differs from California requirements, the longest restricted-entry interval applies. Check with the county agricultural commissioner's office for special restricted-entry intervals when you apply mixtures of certain pesticides.

Posting

Sometimes you *must* post treated areas with warning signs (Figure 6-34). Posting is a way to notify employees about a treated area as an alternative to oral notification. Regulations require posting signs to be made of a durable material and printed in English and Spanish. They must contain a skull and crossbones at the center of the sign and the word "Danger" in letters large enough to be read from a distance of 25 feet. If the restricted-entry interval is greater than 7 days, the sign must also list

- the date the restricted-entry interval expires
- the property operator's name
- any field identification

Check pesticide labels and current federal, state, and local laws to determine requirements for posting. Local offices of county agricultural commissioners have this information.

To post a treated area, place signs at usual points of entry and along unfenced areas next to roads and other public rights-of-way. Signs should be no more than 600 feet apart. Post the area before you make an application (but no sooner than 24 hours before the application). Signs have to remain in place throughout the restricted-entry interval. Remove them within 3 days after the end of the restricted-entry interval and before you allow workers to enter the field.

PUBLIC AND ENVIRONMENTAL SAFETY

Prevent the public from accidentally becoming exposed to pesticides during an application or from encountering treated areas after you make the application. Notify people in the area about the planned pesticide application. Explain the potential hazards and possible exposure symptoms. Tell them what you are doing to reduce these hazards. Explain what they should do to avoid exposure. Try to make pesticide

FIGURE 6-34.

Some pesticide labels require treated areas to be posted. Also, an area must be posted if the restricted-entry interval is more than 7 days. All greenhouse applications must be posted unless access is carefully controlled throughout the restricted-entry interval.

applications at times when people are not present. Prevent drift of pesticide materials outside the treatment area.

Check pesticide labels and material safety data sheets for environmental hazards. These include hazards to wildlife, endangered species, honey bees, or groundwater. Become familiar with wildlife in the area. For information and help, contact the California Department of Fish and Game. Obtain specific information on groundwater conditions at the application site. For help, consult with the pesticide coordinator at the local agricultural commissioner's office. Use selective pesticides whenever possible. Also, make pesticide applications at times when honey bees and other beneficial insects are not present in the treated area. Do not allow sprays to drift into waterways, because many pesticides are toxic to fish or other aquatic life.

HANDLING PESTICIDES SAFELY

Undiluted pesticides are a greater risk to people and the environment than diluted spray mixtures. The safe handling and transporting of undiluted pesticides can prevent many environmental and human health hazards.

Along with toxic hazards, pesticides have a high dollar value and may be subject to theft. Part of your safe handling program should include security measures to prevent theft.

Manufacturer's Packaging

Manufacturers package pesticides in several different ways, depending on the formulation. The type of packaging and formulation affects the hazards of handling, transporting, and storing. Pesticides are available in paper bags, water-soluble bags, and plastic and metal containers (Figure 6-35). Most packages are in convenient units of size for ease in measuring and mixing. Manufacturers usually pack quantities of these units in larger cardboard boxes for shipping and handling. The U.S. Department of Transportation must approve these shipping containers.

Paper and plastic bags are common packages for powder and granule formulations. For safety, manufacturers package some highly toxic or otherwise hazardous powders in water-soluble plastic bags. However, if you do not handle them carefully, paper or plastic containers may tear or puncture. Opened paper and plastic bags may be difficult to reseal, presenting possible future problems with leaking. Spilled

FIGURE 6-35.

Pesticides are packaged in a number of different types of containers. Most packaging is in convenient units of size for ease in measuring and mixing.

powders scatter easily and are difficult to clean up. To prevent tearing and reduce the danger of spilling, cut bags open with scissors or a sharp knife. This also makes the bags easier to close after use.

Manufacturers use plastic bottles and pails for packaging liquid and granular formulations. If improper handling results in one of these containers being punctured, there will be a pesticide spill. Uncapped containers are also subject to spilling. Spilled liquids are difficult to contain or clean up because they soak into wood, cloth, paper, and nearly everything else they contact. Granular formulations are easier to contain and clean up should a spill occur. Also, granules do not soak into porous surfaces.

Manufacturers use metal containers for liquid and dust aerosols and many liquid formulations. However, metal containers are not suitable for some corrosive chemicals. Manufacturers package fumigants (usually liquids under high pressure) in reuseable steel cylinders (Figure 6-36). Metal containers probably are the safest packaging materials for pesticides because they resist puncturing and do not break. They are resealable and you can either recycle empty containers or dispose of them at an approved disposal site. However, take special precautions with metal aerosol containers. If you puncture, overheat, or burn them, they may explode or cause injury.

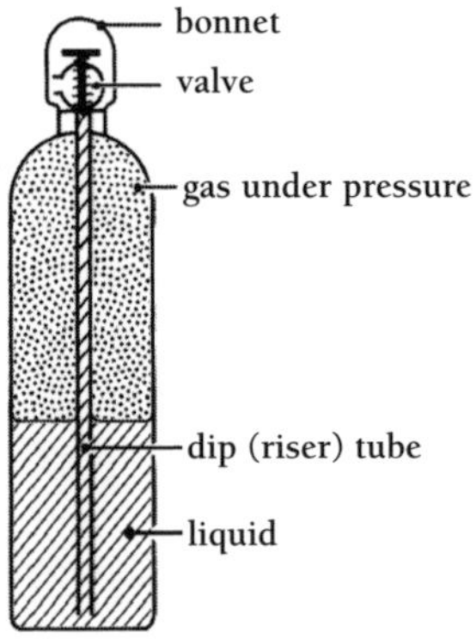

Service Containers

Service containers are any container, other than the original labeled packaging, that holds pesticides. Manufacturers design these for applying, storing, or transporting pesticide concentrates or use-diluted preparations. If you are transporting a service container, label it with the following information:

- common name of the pesticide
- the signal word
- name and address of the person responsible for the container

Transporting

Many pesticides are subject to state and federal hazardous materials transportation requirements, including

- incident reporting
- packaging—including container maintenance and retesting
- labeling
- marking
- placarding
- emergency actions in the event of an accident
- loading
- vehicle safety equipment
- routing

There is always a risk of an accident while transporting undiluted or diluted pesticides in a vehicle. Spilled materials may cause serious human exposure and environmental damage. Some pesticides are flammable, adding dangers of fire and toxic fumes. There is a risk that passing vehicles will scatter pesticides spilled on public roads. This will further endanger people, animals, residential areas, or nearby crops. Spilled chemicals may wash into ditches, streams, and rivers during rainstorms, creating the potential for serious damage, including groundwater contamination. Spilled pesticides may also contaminate the vehicle, its occupants, or other cargo. It may be impossible to completely remove all residue from a vehicle.

Never carry pesticides in the passenger compartment of any vehicle. The safest way to transport pesticide is in the back of a truck (Figure 6-37). Secure all pesticide containers in the cargo area and protect them from rain and other potential damage. Never stack pesticide containers higher than the sides of the transporting vehicle. Secure fumigant cylinders in the vehicle in an upright position. Be sure these cylinders have screw-on steel bonnets to protect the valve mechanisms. When transporting any pesticides, never allow children, adults, or animals to ride in the cargo area. Also, never transport food, animal feed, or clothing in the same compartment. Do not leave pesti-

FIGURE 6-36.

Most gas fumigants are supplied in large steel cylinders. These are capable of withstanding the high pressures of the gases they contain.

Labels in figure: bonnet, valve, gas under pressure, dip (riser) tube, liquid

SIDEBAR 15

Where to Get Information and Regulations on Transporting Pesticides

▦ FOR INTERSTATE MOVEMENT OF PESTICIDES

U.S. Department of Transportation
Office of Motor Carrier Safety
980 9th Street, Suite 450
Sacramento, CA 95814-2724
(916) 498-5050
or
U.S. Department of Transportation
Western Resource Center
201 Mission Street, Suite 2100
San Francisco, CA 94105
(415) 744-3088

For Southern California:
U.S. Department of Transportation
Office of Motor Carrier Safety
22690 Cactus Avenue, Suite 250
Moreno Valley, CA 92553
(909) 653-2299

▦ FOR TRANSPORTATION OF PESTICIDES WITHIN THE STATE OF CALIFORNIA

California Highway Patrol
Commercial Vehicle Section
444 N. 3rd Street, Suite 310
Sacramento, CA 95814
(916) 445-1865

Contact the California Highway Patrol
Motor Carrier Safety Unit Supervisor
at one of the Division Offices listed below:

Northern Division:
2485 Sonoma Street
Redding, CA 96001-3026
(530) 225-2715

Valley Division:
11336 Trade Center Drive
P.O. Box 640
Rancho Cordova, CA 95741-0640
(916) 464-2090

Golden Gate Division:
1551 Benicia Road
Vallejo, CA 94591-7568
(707) 648-4180

Central Division:
4771 West Jacquelyn Avenue
Fresno, CA 93722-6406
(559) 445-6992

FIGURE 6-37.

Transport pesticides only in the back of a truck. Secure containers in the cargo area and protect them from moisture and damage. Never carry people, animals, food, animal feed, or clothing in the same area.

(continued)

Southern Division:
437 North Vermont Avenue
Los Angeles, CA 90004-3590
(323) 664-1108

Border Division:
9330 Farnham Street
San Diego, CA 92123-1284
(858) 637-7158

Coastal Division:
4115 Broad Street, Suite B-10
San Luis Obispo, CA 93401-7963
(805) 549-3261

Inland Division:
847 E. Brier Drive
San Bernardino, CA 92408-2820
(909) 383-4811

■ FOR LOCAL INFORMATION
County Agricultural Commissioner's Office

FIGURE 6-38.

Sometimes the transporting vehicle must display specific placards when it carries certain quantities of pesticides. Check with local authorities for placarding requirements.

cides unattended in a vehicle unless they are inside a locked compartment. To assist emergency workers in case of an accident, carry a manifest or list of the pesticides being transported.

For information on transporting pesticides on public highways, contact the following agencies:

- California Highway Patrol
- California Public Utilities Commission

These agencies will provide you with current regulations and help you determine whether you need special licenses or permits. They will tell you if these materials are subject to hazardous materials transportation requirements. Your vehicle may require placards signifying the type of hazardous material being carried (Figure 6-38). If your vehicle requires placards, place them on all four sides of the vehicle. Always remove placards from vehicles when the hazardous material is not being transported. Sidebar 15 lists where to get information and regulations on transporting pesticides. Regulations require that some vehicles have devices that protect the pesticide cargo in the case of a rear-end collision. Secure fumigation cylinders so they will not rupture or fall out of the vehicle if there is an accident.

Should you have an accident involving spilled pesticides, alert the highway patrol, county sheriff, city police, or local fire department at once. Keep people and vehicles away. Never leave the scene of a spill until responsible help arrives. For advice on cleaning up spills, contact CHEMTREC (Chemical Transportation Emergency Center) at 800-424-9300. *Call this number only in the case of an actual emergency.* There are times when the person or company transporting the material cannot quickly and safely clean up a spill. In these cases, municipal agencies provide or contract for cleanup of roadways within their jurisdiction. These agencies include CalTrans (on state highways) and designated city or county agencies, including some fire departments.

Handling

Handle bulk pesticide containers carefully. Do not drop or throw containers or packages, because this may cause damage and leaks. Check for contamination or leaks on all packages being handled. Do not let damaged packages or spilled pesticides contact your skin or clothing. Wear rubber gloves and protective clothing, such as an apron, when handling pesticide packages. If a leak is present, you may also need respiratory and eye protection. Check the label for all precautions and required safety equipment. Never walk through a spilled pesticide. If you discover a damaged and leaking container, transfer the pesticide to another container. Use a container labeled for that pesticide or another properly labeled container (see Chapter 7 for more information).

Prevent theft or danger to children

and animals. Never leave pesticide containers unattended or stored in unlocked areas (Figure 6-39). Always keep pesticides away from food and water and away from sources of heat and fire. Never allow paper containers to get wet.

Do not eat, drink, or smoke while handling pesticides or pesticide containers. Wash thoroughly when finished and before eating, drinking, smoking, or using the bathroom.

Storage

Store pesticides in their original, tightly closed containers. Whenever possible, wipe or wash pesticide residue off outsides of containers. Protect pesticides from extremes in temperature and from becoming wet. A pesticide storage area should be a separate building, away from people, living areas, food, animal feed, and animals. The area must have good ventilation and lighting. Be sure it is dry and secure, with lockable doors and windows. Post signs near all primary entrances to warn others that the building contains pesticides (Figure 6-40).

Keep a record of all pesticides being stored. Indicate on this record the date of purchase and the date you placed

FIGURE 6-39.

Keep pesticides in a lockable area of the vehicle to prevent unauthorized access while the vehicle is unattended.

FIGURE 6-40.

Store pesticides in a separate building, away from people, living areas, food, animal feed, and animals. Make sure the storage area is well ventilated, well lighted, dry, and secure. Securely lock doors and windows. Post the primary entrances with signs that warn that the building contains pesticides.

each chemical in the building. Keep this record, or a copy of it, separate from the building. To prevent injury during a fire or other emergency, give this information to emergency workers. Before an emergency arises, provide the local fire protection agency with an inventory of the pesticides being stored. Also provide them with Material Safety Data Sheets. Update these records periodically and whenever you put additional types of pesticides in the storage area.

Check stored pesticides on a regular basis. Inspect the condition of containers and look for leaks or spills. Immediately clean up any spilled pesticide in the storage area (see cleanup procedures in Chapter 7).

Some pesticides do not store well for long periods of time. Pesticides may change chemically during extended storage, especially if exposed to temperature extremes. These changes may cause some products to lose their effectiveness or others to become more toxic. Sometimes moisture and air picked up during storage alters the composition of some pesticides. Pesticides in unsealed containers are most susceptible. Solvents and petroleum-based chemicals deteriorate some types of containers after a time.

Keep packages on shelves or on pallets to reduce exposure to excess moisture. Do not store most chemicals for longer than two years. Before pesticides exceed their shelf-life, use them in an appropriate application or transport them to an approved disposal site.

Never store certain pesticides such as 2,4-D and other hormonal herbicides with other pesticides. Vapors from these herbicides may combine with other pesticides. These vapors contaminate the other pesticides and could result in potential damage to treated plants. Always check the label for special storage precautions to prevent such problems.

Liquids expand when heated or frozen. Liquid pesticides in sealed containers may expand enough to rupture the containers under extremely hot or cold conditions. Therefore, keep the storage area well ventilated to prevent overheating. When storing pesticides in locations subject to winter freezing, be sure to insulate the storage building.

MIXING PESTICIDES

Techniques for mixing pesticides are the same for large and small volumes— thoroughly mix the proper amount of pesticide with a measured amount of water or other solvent. Before beginning, read the mixing directions on labels of all pesticides you will be using. Then, choose the proper order to add chemicals to the spray tank (see page 94). When the mixture needs adjuvants, add these before pesticides unless label instructions give a different order.

Determine what protective clothing you need for mixing and application. Check the spray equipment for cracked hoses or leaks. Make sure the filters, screens, and nozzles are clean. Have a supply of fresh water nearby for washing in case of an accident.

The water used for filling a spray tank should look clean. Be sure it is free of sand, dirt, algae, or other foreign matter. Sand or dirt causes excessive wear on pumps and nozzles and clogs filters, screens, and nozzles. Algae may clog filters and nozzles and can react with some pesticides to reduce their effectiveness. Smell the water to see if you can detect any chemical odor. Chemicals in the mixing water may react unfavorably with some pesticides. For example, chlorine (used in domestic water supplies for controlling bacteria) reduces the effectiveness of some pesticides. High levels of dissolved salts deactivate certain pesticides and may even damage treated foliage. If possible, check the water's pH as described on page 102. High pH (alkaline water) causes hydrolysis, or breakdown, of many pesticides before you spray them onto the target surface. Use a buffer or acidifier if the pH is too high. Whenever you have any doubts about the water quality, locate another source.

Measure pesticides carefully, accurately, and safely. Inaccurate measuring can cause serious problems. For instance, certain herbicides require application rates of ⅙ to ¾ ounce of formulated material per acre. Small inaccuracies in measuring produce gross errors in application rates.

California laws require that employees use a closed mixing system when mixing, loading, diluting, or transferring liquid formulations of pesticides with the signal word *Danger* being used for the production of an agricultural commodity. They must also use closed systems when loading or transferring dry formulations of *Danger* pesticides after mixing these formulations with water or other diluents.

Closed mixing systems allow you to accurately and safely measure the amount of pesticide you put into the spray tank. (The closed-system requirement does not apply if you handle 1 gallon or less of *Danger* pesticide per day and the liquid pesticide is in an original container of 1 gallon or smaller.)

Measuring. Liquids and some granular pesticides are measured by volume, while dusts, powders, and most dry formulations are measured by weight. Pesticide labels use the English system of measurement. You use fluid ounces, pints, quarts, and gallons for liquids, and pounds and ounces for dry materials. You need an assortment of glass or plastic measuring utensils, from 1 cup to 1 gallon, for accurately measuring liquids. Some pesticides react with metal, especially aluminum and iron, so avoid using metal measuring utensils. Use an eyedropper to measure small quantities of liquids. Use an accurate scale and a set of measuring cups and spoons for measuring and weighing dry pesticides (Figure 6-41). To avoid mistaking some measuring equipment for kitchen utensils, identify these in a very obvious manner. For instance, paint handles with brightly colored waterproof paint or attach waterproof labels. When not being used, keep all measuring and weighing equipment locked in the pesticide storage area. This prevents these items from being used for other purposes. Clean and wash utensils before storing them to prevent contaminating future mixtures.

FIGURE 6-41.

Measuring and weighing pesticides requires a variety of calibrated utensils and an accurate scale.

Pesticide packages are available in different units of weight or volume. Whenever possible, plan a mixture that uses an even, preweighed amount of pesticide. The unit cost may be greater when you buy pesticides in smaller packages. However, this disadvantage can be minimal compared to the convenience and added safety of not having to weigh or measure. Do not open pesticides packaged in water-soluble packets, since these contain highly hazardous formulations. Calibrate application equipment to use the entire packet or a number of whole packets.

Select a mixing location that you can clean easily should an accident occur. When not using premeasured packets, measure and weigh chemicals in a clear, open area. If outdoors, stand upwind to reduce chances of exposure. Wear an approved dust-mist respirator or cartridge respirator while weighing and mixing dry pesticides to prevent inhaling dust. Protect your hands and clothing with appropriate outerwear. Because liquids spill and splash easily,

wear suitable gloves and a rubber apron, or a waterproof suit. Refer to the pesticide label for specific protective clothing and equipment for mixing and loading pesticides. However, you must wear a faceshield, goggles, or other protective eyewear, even if the requirement is not on the pesticide label. Reduce chances of spills or splashes into your face and eyes by always measuring and pouring pesticides below eye level (Figure 6-42).

Begin mixing by filling the spray tank at least half full with clean water. To allow room for the pesticide, adjuvants, and residues from triple rinsing, avoid filling the tank more than ¾ full. Check and adjust the pH of the water in the spray tank at this time. Start agitators if the equipment has them.

Open pesticide containers carefully to prevent spilling and to make resealing easier. Cut paper containers open with a sharp knife or scissors rather than by tearing. Metal and plastic containers all have protective seals that you must break before use. Most of these contain-

FIGURE 6-42.

Always pour and measure pesticides below eye level. If measuring outdoors, stand upwind. Wear the label-mandated personal protective clothing for mixers when measuring pesticides.

ers have screw caps that allow you to easily reseal them.

After measuring or weighing the correct amount of pesticide, carefully pour it into the partially filled spray tank (Figure 6-43). Rinse the measuring container and pour the rinse solution into the spray tank also. Use caution while rinsing to prevent splashing. Many closed mixing systems have container rinsing devices that pump the rinse solution into the pesticide tank. Unless rinsed automatically, drain liquid containers into the spray tank for 30 seconds after you empty them. Rinse and drain the containers three more times (triple rinse). After each draining, fill the container about ¼ full of water and put the cap on again. Shake the container for several seconds to mix the residue with water. Pour each rinse solution into the spray tank. Sidebar 16 illustrates how much pesticide you can remove from the container by triple rinsing. You do not have to send containers that have been triple

rinsed to a Class 1 disposal site. Instead, take them to a pesticide container recycling center or a Class 2 disposal site.

For bags that hold dry pesticides, follow these emptying guidelines:

- Open and empty the bag so that no pesticide material remains in the bag that can be poured, drained, or otherwise feasibly removed.
- Empty the pesticide bag completely and hold the bag upside down for five seconds after continuous flow ceases.
- Straighten out the seams so that the bag is in its original "flat" position.
- Again, hold the bag upside down for five seconds after continuous particle flow ceases—shake the bag twice and hold for five seconds or until continuous flow ceases.
- Follow the guidelines on page 201 for burning empty pesticide bags.

FIGURE 6-43.

Carefully pour pesticides into the spray tank. Rinse measuring containers and empty and triple rinse liquid pesticide containers. Pour the rinse solutions into the spray tank.

SIDEBAR 16

Triple Rinsing Procedures for Pesticide Containers

■ PROCEDURE

1. When container is empty, let it drain into spray or mixing tank for at least 30 seconds.

2. Add correct amount of water to container as follows:

Container Size	Rinse Solution Needed
5 gallons or less	¼ of the container volume
More than 5 gallons	⅓ of the container volume
28 gallons or more	Do not require triple rinsing— return to dealer

3. Close container.

4. Shake container or roll to get solution on all interior surfaces.

5. Drain container into sprayer or mixing tank. After empty, let drain for an additional 30 seconds.

6. Repeat steps 2 through 5 *two* additional times.

■ AMOUNT OF ACTIVE INGREDIENT REMOVED FROM A 5-GALLON CONTAINER BY TRIPLE RINSING

Rinse Step	Amount of Active Ingredient Remaining*
Drain	14.1875 grams a.i.
1st Rinse	0.2183 gram a.i.
2nd Rinse	0.0034 gram a.i.
3rd Rinse	0.00005 gram a.i.

*After draining, a 5-gallon container is assumed to still contain 1 ounce of formulated pesticide. This would amount to 14.1875 grams of a.i. if the formulation contained 4 pounds of a.i. per gallon.

FIGURE 6-44.

When filling a spray tank, be sure there is an air gap between the filler pipe and the top level of the water in the tank. This prevents backflow of pesticide-contaminated water into the water supply.

After adding the pesticide, fill the spray tank to its final volume. Do not allow the tank to overflow during filling. Also, never let the hose, pipe, or other filling device come in contact with liquid in the tank. If you fill the tank through a top opening, leave an air gap between the spray tank and filling device. This space should equal at least twice the diameter of the filling pipe. It prevents siphoning of the spray mixture back into the water supply after you stop the water flow (Figure 6-44). Side or bottom filling systems require check valves to prevent backflow of pesticides into the water supply. Recheck the pH of the tank mixture and adjust if necessary.

APPLYING PESTICIDES EFFECTIVELY

To use pesticides safely and effectively, confine them to the treatment area and apply them in the proper amounts. Pesticide coverage often must be uniform to be most effective. For example, to control some plant-feeding pests, the pesticide spray must coat both sides of leaf surfaces. If you improperly aim the spray at the foliage it may cause *shingling*. This is a condition in which leaves clump together and prevent droplets from reaching some leaf surfaces (Figure 6-45). Using an air blast sprayer or oscillating boom sprayer produces *ruffling* of the plant foliage. This allows spray droplets to contact all surfaces.

Spills, leaks, and drift waste the pesticide and may leave residues in nontarget areas. Improper equipment calibration results in too little or too much pesticide reaching the target site. Safe pesticide applications require

- using proper equipment
- developing good application techniques
- reducing or eliminating drift
- being aware of all potential hazards

FIGURE 6-45.

Spray that is improperly aimed at foliage causes leaves to stick together and prevents proper coverage—a condition known as shingling. *Air blast and oscillating boom sprayers cause* ruffling *of foliage and improve distribution of spray droplets.*

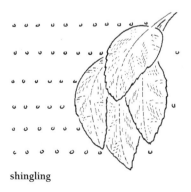

shingling

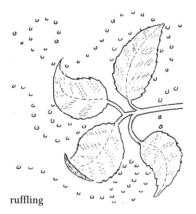

ruffling

FIGURE 6-46.

Be sure tank covers fit tightly to prevent pesticide mixtures from splashing out during operation or while transporting the equipment. If tanks are ever unattended, their covers must be lockable.

Selecting Application Equipment

Be sure the equipment you use to apply pesticides is suited to the location and conditions of the treatment area. Equipment that is too big or powerful may be as much of a problem as equipment that is too small. Most pesticide application equipment works efficiently only in a limited number of situations. Some conditions require that the spray be moved to target surfaces with a blast of air to improve coverage.

Choose application equipment that is comfortable to work with and easy to use. Be sure the equipment is easy to repair and parts are readily available. Hand-held equipment must be light-weight so that it is convenient to use. Motor-powered units should be quiet enough to prevent operator stress yet powerful enough to do the job properly. Moving parts need shields and guards to prevent accidents and injuries. Powered equipment must have accurate gauges so you can monitor spray pressure and other functions.

Pesticide application equipment has to be durable to withstand the long hours of operation. Make sure that filler covers on spray tanks close properly, seal well, and are lockable (Figure 6-46). Hoses and fittings should be strong and durable to prevent loss of pesticide mixtures and environmental contamination.

Safe Application Techniques

Safe application techniques require
- working with the weather
- controlling droplet size and deposition
- being aware of the application site and its hazards
- developing special application patterns for the site to accommodate hazards and environmental conditions
- leaving buffer zones to protect sensitive areas

Working with the Weather. Weather has significant influence on pesticide applications in outdoor areas. Its effect on pesticide applications in greenhouses and other confined spaces is more subtle. Temperature affects the phytotoxicity of certain pesticides. Label directions usually warn against using these products when temperatures are above or below critical limits. High temperatures accelerate pesticide degradation and volatilization. Clear, sunny weather produces warm temperatures. Ultraviolet light, which is most intense during these times, rapidly breaks down many pesticides.

Air temperature is responsible for the inversion phenomenon that may often cause pesticide drift. Inversions occur when the air 20 to 100 or more feet above the ground is warmer than the air

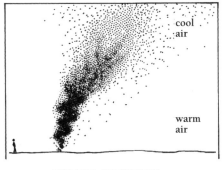 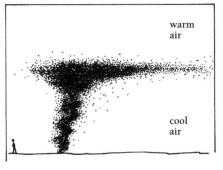

NORMAL CONDITION—
SMOKE RISES AND DISPERSES.

INVERSION CONDITION—
SMOKE CONCENTRATES.

FIGURE 6-47.

A temperature inversion is caused by a layer of warm air occurring above cooler air close to the ground. This warm air prevents air near the ground from rising, similar to a lid.

below it. The warm air forms a cap that blocks vertical air movement. To detect a temperature inversion, observe a column of smoke rising into the air. (Black smoke from a burning tire or diesel fuel is easy to see. However, check with local air quality authorities to be sure such burning is permissible.) If the smoke begins moving sideways or collects in one area a few hundred feet above the ground, an inversion condition probably exists (Figure 6-47). Inversion conditions are dangerous during a pesticide application. The inversion layer traps fine spray droplets and pesticide vapors. These become concentrated, similar to the smoke column. Rather than dispersing, the pesticide often moves as a concentrated cloud away from the treatment site.

Honey bees forage only during certain temperature ranges. Therefore, make applications when temperatures are not suitable for bee activity if you are using pesticides that might injure bees.

Rainfall, fog, and even heavy dew affect pesticide applications. This is because the moisture dilutes and degrades pesticides and may wash the material off treated surfaces. Rainwater washes pesticides into the soil, producing possible groundwater and surface water contamination. Water movement after heavy rains carries pesticides away

from the application site. Fog plays a role in offsite pesticide movement.

Wind influences pesticide drift and affects volatilization. Strong air movements are responsible for uneven pesticide deposition. However, some air movement has advantages in getting good coverage over treated surfaces.

Controlling Droplet Size and Deposition. The following factors influence how spray droplets cover the treated surfaces:
- droplet size
- pressure of the spray stream
- force and volume of the air used to distribute spray
- speed of travel of the application equipment

Droplet size is a factor of nozzle size, style, and condition combined with spray volume, spray pressure, and weather influences. Most application equipment emits a spray with a wide range of droplet sizes. However, the best spray applications result from applying uniform-sized droplets evenly to all treated surfaces. Increase the uniformity of spray droplets by selecting nozzles designed for the working pressure and volume of your sprayer. Inspect and replace worn or defective nozzles. The type of application equipment used must be suitable for the physical and environmental features of the location. Application speed is critical. Adjust your speed to the type and size of the area being treated. You must travel more slowly when spraying large trees and shrubs. This is because spray droplets must travel farther, and larger surface areas require more volume for adequate coverage.

Site Characteristics and Environmental Hazards. Before beginning a pesticide application, observe the physical characteristics of the terrain, greenhouse, building, or other application site. Look for all potential hazards. Check for organisms or structures that the spray mixture might damage. Be aware of possible damage caused by the physical movement of the equipment and operator through the area. In outdoor areas, ditches, embankments, steep slopes, electrical wires, and electric fences are potential hazards. In confined areas, electrical outlets, motors, sources of sparks, and improperly ventilated spaces can be hazardous to operators or equipment.

Application Pattern. An application pattern is the route you follow while applying a pesticide. The purpose of any application pattern is to provide an even distribution of pesticide over the treated area. To do this, you must avoid overlaps or gaps. Pesticide application speed usually determines the uniformity of the application pattern. At higher speeds, the equipment bounces more. With air blast sprayers, as you increase travel speed you reduce the volume of displaced air. When establishing an application pattern, consider

- prevailing weather conditions
- what is being sprayed
- hazards in or near the application site

Design a pattern that eliminates the need to travel through airborne spray or walk or drive through freshly treated areas. Operating the application equipment (such as boom applicators) during turns produces an uneven application. Figure 6-48 illustrates how to make a uniform application by shutting the sprayer off during turns. Watch for clogged nozzles that will also produce uneven applications.

FIGURE 6-48.

Shut off spray nozzles during turns to avoid uneven applications. After spraying the main part of the treatment area, finish by spraying the edges.

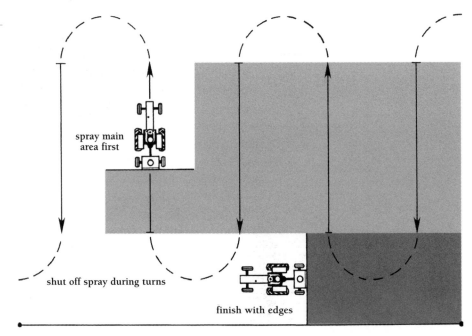

spray main area first

shut off spray during turns

finish with edges

SENSITIVE AREA

BUFFER AREA
(DO NOT SPRAY)

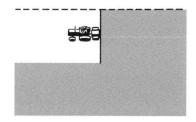

FIGURE 6-49.

Leave untreated buffer areas when an application site adjoins sensitive areas. The buffer should be no less than the width of one spray swath.

Leave untreated buffer strips when a treatment area adjoins sensitive areas. These are locations where applications might expose organisms, people, or structures to pesticides (Figure 6-49). As a general rule, the buffer should be no less than the width of one spray swath. The size of the buffer strip depends on the

- type of application equipment you are using
- prevailing weather conditions
- nature of pesticide being applied
- type of pest problem being treated
- sensitive nature of adjoining areas

Pesticide Drift

Pesticide drift refers to the movement of pesticides away from the treatment site. Drift is most serious when you make applications during windy conditions, especially while using high pressure and small nozzle sizes. Wind carries away spray droplets intended for a specific treatment area (Figure 6-50). Another form of drift occurs when sprayed pesticides partially evaporate before reaching the target. The resulting vapor can drift away from the treatment area through air movement, often traveling several miles.

Table 6-2 lists some of the factors that influence drift. There are many steps that you can take to reduce this problem. Eliminating very small droplets significantly reduces drift. Increase droplet size by using larger nozzles and by lowering the output pressure of the sprayer. Certain adjuvants, called deposition aids, assist in increasing spray droplet size or reducing evaporation potential. Add one of these to the spray tank to help avoid drift.

Do not spray during windy conditions. Usually, winds less than 5 miles per hour help provide good pesticide distribution in trees and leafy plants. Stronger winds, however, increase drift potential. In some cases, spraying may be illegal if the wind speed is over a designated rate. Contact the local agricultural commissioner for information on pesticide application restrictions during windy conditions.

Other conditions, such as a temperature inversion, also promote drift of small droplets and vapors. High temperatures and low humidity increase the evaporation rate, which reduces the size of droplets before they reach their target. The resulting smaller droplets may be highly subject to drift.

FIGURE 6-50.

Pesticide sprays and dusts drift when you apply them during windy periods. Drift is also the result of small droplet size caused by high pressure and small nozzle orifices.

TABLE 6-2.

Factors Influencing Pesticide Drift.

MATERIAL OR CONDITION	FACTORS
pesticide	volatility of active ingredient solvent used to dissolve or suspend active ingredient (formulation) solvent used to dilute pesticide in spray tank
adjuvants	deposition aids, thickeners, and stickers (reduce drift by making droplets larger or less volatile)
application equipment	operating pressure of spraying system nozzle size distance from nozzles to target surface height from which spray is released speed of travel of application equipment application pattern and technique
target surfaces	size of target area location of target area nature of target surfaces
weather conditions	wind intensity wind direction air temperature humidity

Special Hazards in Treatment Areas

Pesticides containing petroleum-based carriers may be flammable. Never use these in areas where open flames or other ignition sources are present. Gas-fired water heaters and electric motors may ignite flammable pesticides. When applying pesticides in areas where such hazards exist, use a nonflammable water-based spray. Otherwise, shut off all ignition sources.

The spray from water-based pesticides usually conducts electricity. If the spray contacts an electrical source, you risk a potentially fatal electric shock. Never direct any spray onto power transmission lines, electrical cords, outlets, or motors or appliances. Disconnect motors and appliances and shut off electricity in areas where you are applying pesticides to prevent chances of electrocution.

CLEANUP AND DISPOSAL

Disposal of Surplus Diluted Pesticide. To avoid problems associated with leftover pesticide mixtures, calculate the exact size of the treatment area. Then, mix only enough pesticide for the job. If you have some leftover spray mixture, use it in another appropriate location. Otherwise, you must send the leftover material to a Class 1 disposal site. There are private companies that specialize in collecting and transporting pesticide wastes to Class 1 disposal sites.

Never indiscriminately dump excess pesticide. Such dumping is a potential source of environmental and groundwater contamination. It is also illegal. People convicted of dumping are subject to large fines and possible jail terms.

Pesticide Container Disposal. Regulations concerning the disposal of pesticide containers vary from county to county. Obtain specific disposal information from local Water Quality Control Boards, the Department of Health Services, and local agricultural commissioners.

Some localities allow you to burn paper and plastic containers as part of an agricultural burn permit. For burning pesticide bags, follow the instructions in Sidebar 17. In nonagricultural

SIDEBAR 17

Guidelines for Emptying and Burning Pesticide Bags

■ EMPTYING AND BURNING PESTICIDE BAGS

Obtain an agricultural burn permit from your local air pollution control district.

■ EMPTYING GUIDELINES

- ☐ Open and empty the bag so that no pesticide material remains in the bag that can be poured, drained, or otherwise feasibly removed.
- ☐ Empty the pesticide bag completely and hold the bag upside down for five seconds after continuous flow ceases.
- ☐ Straighten out the seams so that the bag is in its original "flat" position.
- ☐ Again, hold the bag upside down for five seconds after continuous particle flow ceases—shake the bag twice and hold for five seconds or until continuous flow ceases.

■ PESTICIDE BAG BURNING GUIDELINES

- ☐ Burn the pesticide bags only at the location specified on the agricultural burn permit.
- ☐ Select a location that will minimize the amount of smoke blowing over areas where people or domestic animals may be located. To select a site, consider distances to homes, parks, schools, businesses; wind speed and direction; inversions; and length of time to burn the bags.
- ☐ Place a rock, brick, or similar noncombustible weight on top of the stack of bags to be burned.
- ☐ Light the bottom-most bag.
- ☐ Stand upwind of the burn site to avoid breathing the smoke.
- ☐ Control the site until burning is completed and the fire is extinguished.

areas, contact local authorities to work out arrangements for disposing of plastic and paper pesticide containers. Unrinsed empty containers are hazardous wastes. Dispose of these according to provisions of Water Quality Control Board and Department of Health Services regulations.

You can recycle triple-rinsed metal and plastic containers or take them to an approved Class 2 disposal site. If these containers have not been triple rinsed, you can send them only to a Class 1 disposal site. Check with the Water Quality Control Board or agricultural commissioner in your area for the locations of approved disposal sites.

Cleaning Application Equipment. After each use, you must clean and decontaminate application equipment. Otherwise, residues remaining in tanks may contaminate a subsequent pesticide mixture and alter its toxicity. Pesticide residue on the outside of application equipment can be hazardous to

people who must operate or repair this equipment. Therefore, wash the outside of spray equipment with water, using a small amount of detergent if necessary. Clean equipment in an area where you can contain runoff. Otherwise, clean the equipment at the application site.

Rinse the inside of the tank with water. If necessary, decontaminate it by using an appropriate pesticide tank cleaning material (or 1 quart of household ammonia to each 25 gallons of water). Prepare a tank washing solution by mixing ½ pound of detergent with 30 gallons of water. Buy commercial pesticide tank cleaning and neutralizing compounds from chemical suppliers and farm equipment dealers. Be sure to check the pesticide label for any precautions regarding the use and disposal of cleaning and decontaminating chemicals. Follow the directions for the amount of cleaner to use for your spray tank. Be sure to run pumps and agitators and flush all hoses.

Personal Cleanup

After using pesticides, clean your personal protective equipment, shower thoroughly, and change into clean, uncontaminated clothing. When showering, take special care to wash your hair and clean your fingernails. Place clothing that you wore during the pesticide application into a plastic bag until you can launder it. Never eat, drink, smoke, or use the bathroom until you have thoroughly washed.

RECORD KEEPING

Maintain records of every pesticide application you make and other activities associated with your use of pesticides. Keep records of the following pertinent information.

The Pesticide Application

- name, manufacturer, and EPA Registration Number of the pesticide
- total amount of pesticide used
- amount of water used
- calibration adjustments
- adjuvants added to the mixture
- type of equipment used or method of application
- severity of pest infestation
- stage of development of the host (if applied to crops or animals)
- restricted-entry interval
- date and time when the application was completed

Other Records

- posting requirements
- pesticides handled by employees
- handler training specific to classes of pesticides handled
- fieldworker training

Also note temperature and general weather information at the time of application. Write down any other conditions that might have an influence on the effectiveness of the pesticide. Keep a record of the names of people you spoke to regarding each pesticide application. Include any follow-up information and notes of application results. See Figure 8-12 on page 237 for a pesticide application follow-up checklist. Figure 6-51 is an example of a pesticide application record. Keep copies of written recommendations with your application records.

Application records are helpful as a history of pesticide use, especially when there are *plantback restrictions*. Even more important, this information is vital in case problems associated with the application should develop. Good records may also be important to your defense in any legal action.

LIABILITY

You assume personal responsibility for accidents and injuries that arise as a result of each pesticide application. You may be subject to fines, jail sentences, and loss of your applicator certificate or license if you are negligent in your application of pesticides or have broken state or federal laws. Also, courts may hold you responsible in lawsuits for personal injury or damages. If you are working for someone else, your actions may result in lawsuits against and fines to your employer. Should someone bring a claim of negligence against you, accurate records of all your pesticide applications help in your defense.

Should the pesticide you are applying drift and damage plants, animals, or someone's belongings, or cause human injury, you may incur personal liability. The pesticides you apply can potentially damage the intended crops or surfaces. Damage might result from

- improper mixing
- using the wrong adjuvants
- improper application
- applying the wrong pesticide
- poor timing
- using a pesticide that has been contaminated with impurities

Someone may sue you for destroying beneficial insects such as honey bees. If the bees are essential for pollinating a crop, you could be liable for the loss of

	Date:	Applicator:
APPLICATION SITE	Owner/Responsible Party:	Location:
	Size of Treatment Area:	Plant Age and Condition:
	Description (Turf, Ag Crop, etc.):	Soil Conditions:
	Surrounding Sensitive Areas:	
	Previous Pesticides Used:	
PEST PROBLEM	Primary Pest:	Damage Observed:
	Other Pests Present:	Location of Damage:
	Beneficials Present:	
	Severity of Pest Problem:	

PESTICIDE(S) USED

Pesticide(s):	Formulation:	Rate:	Total Amount Used:
(1)			
(2)			
(3)			

Adjuvants
Type: _____ Amount: _____

Total Gallons of
Diluted Spray Used:

APPLICATION

Date(s) of Application: _____

Equipment used: _____

Equipment Calibrated By: _____
Pesticides Mixed By: _____
Pesticides Applied By: _____

Persons Notified or Spoken to Regarding Application:
(1) _____
(2) _____
(3) _____

Weather Conditions
Temperature: _____
Cloud Cover: _____
Wind Speed: _____
Wind Direction: _____
Other: _____
Travel Speed: _____
Total Hours for Application: _____

FOLLOW UP

Effectiveness of Application: _____ Beneficials Present: _____ Pest Resurgence Noted: _____

Injury to Nontarget Plants or Surfaces:

COMMENTS _____

FIGURE 6-51.

Pesticide application record.

the crop as well. There have been instances where applicators were sued because they applied pesticides to the wrong location.

Pesticides and pesticide application equipment are attractive nuisances. Children, fascinated with what you are doing, may be injured or even killed by chemicals and equipment if you leave these unattended.

Often, taking prompt action greatly reduces the extent of damage (and therefore liability) from a pesticide accident or application error. See the following chapter for information on how to deal with pesticide emergencies.

Liability Insurance

Commercial pesticide applicators usually buy liability insurance to protect themselves from claims associated with pesticide use. Clients of professional applicators may require the applicators to have liability insurance. Policies cover the costs of damages from accidents and improper use. This type of insurance often is expensive and sometimes difficult to obtain due to the nature of pesticide injury claims. Insurance companies consider as better risks applicators who maintain complete records and are conscientious in their efforts to use pesticides responsibly.

Some professional organizations representing pesticide applicators have information on insurance companies and policies. Some provide opportunities to participate in group policies. Select insurance suitable to your operation and specialty. Be sure you understand the extent of coverage and policy liability limits.

REVIEW QUESTIONS

1. **How are you able to avoid most pesticide accidents?**
   - ☐ a. Through carelessness
   - ☐ b. By ignoring safe work habits
   - ☐ c. By failing to maintain your equipment
   - ☐ d. By following the pesticide label and obeying the laws and regulations dealing with pesticides

2. **Which of the following is *not* part of the mandatory training for employees handling pesticides as part of their work?**
   - ☐ a. How to handle, open, and lift containers
   - ☐ b. How to confine spray to the target area
   - ☐ c. How to bury pesticide containers
   - ☐ d. Recognizing pesticide poisoning symptoms

3. **Why is training on recognizing and avoiding heat stress important for pesticide handlers?**
   - ☐ a. Many heat stress symptoms are similar to pesticide poisoning symptoms
   - ☐ b. All pesticide poisoning is caused by heat stress
   - ☐ c. Heat stress is a new type of problem that has never before existed
   - ☐ d. For information only, because heat stress never occurs in California

4. **Which agricultural workers must receive pesticide information training under provisions of the federal Worker Protection Standard?**
   - ☐ a. All agricultural workers
   - ☐ b. Workers entering treated areas within 30 days of the expiration of any restricted-entry interval
   - ☐ c. Workers entering any area treated with pesticides during the current growing season
   - ☐ d. Only workers who directly handle or apply pesticides

5. **Who is responsible for providing personal protective equipment to pesticide handlers?**
   - ☐ a. The University of California
   - ☐ b. County agricultural commissioners
   - ☐ c. Pesticide handlers are required to provide their own equipment
   - ☐ d. The employer of the pesticide handler

6. **Why is it important to keep current on new information about pesticides with which you work?**
   - ☐ a. To learn how to use more pesticides
   - ☐ b. To learn ways to use pesticides more frequently
   - ☐ c. To keep up-to-date on improvements in pesticides and pesticide application technology
   - ☐ d. To learn the best ways of avoiding new laws that affect pesticide use

7. **What information will you *not* find on a Material Safety Data Sheet (MSDS)?**
   - ☐ a. Information on fire and explosion hazards of the pesticide
   - ☐ b. Emergency spill or leak cleanup procedures
   - ☐ c. Personal protective equipment requirements for application situations
   - ☐ d. Information about health hazards of the pesticide

8. **While applying pesticides, which is the most common way you might be exposed?**
   - ☐ a. Breathing the fumes and spray droplets
   - ☐ b. Splashing of spray material onto your face and into your mouth
   - ☐ c. Pesticide material getting onto your skin
   - ☐ d. Stepping into a puddle of pesticide liquid

9. **What criteria do you use to select the personal protective equipment for applying a pesticide?**
   - ☐ a. Use whatever PPE is available
   - ☐ b. Follow the pesticide label requirements
   - ☐ c. Avoid using PPE whenever possible
   - ☐ d. Follow the guidelines of the Material Safety Data Sheet (MSDS)

10. **When applying pesticides, what is the advantage of wearing coveralls over your work clothing, even if this is not required by the pesticide label?**
    - ☐ a. Coveralls can be easily removed if they become contaminated
    - ☐ b. Coveralls keep you cooler
    - ☐ c. They are more professional in appearance
    - ☐ d. No advantage—they increase your exposure potential

11. **What is the *disadvantage* of leather or fabric gloves when handling pesticides?**
    - ☐ a. They are too expensive
    - ☐ b. They absorb pesticides
    - ☐ c. They promote uncomfortable sweating of the hands
    - ☐ d. They become stained from the pesticides

12. **In which of the following pesticide application situations *must* you wear eye protection?**
    - ☐ a. While working inside an enclosed cab
    - ☐ b. While applying a solid bait form of a rodenticide
    - ☐ c. Injecting pesticides into the soil
    - ☐ d. Spraying an orchard from an open cab tractor

13. **While mixing or applying certain pesticides, you must select and use an appropriate respirator based on:**
    - ☐ a. Recommendations of the county agricultural commissioner
    - ☐ b. Your personal preferences
    - ☐ c. The current weather conditions
    - ☐ d. The pesticide label requirements

14. **Why must the facepiece of a cartridge respirator fit tightly?**
    - ☐ a. To prevent parts of your face from being exposed to pesticide vapors
    - ☐ b. To channel the air through the cartridges so you breathe only filtered air
    - ☐ c. To avoid irritating the skin on your face
    - ☐ d. So straps need not be tightened too much

15. **How often must you clean personal protective equipment, including body wear?**
    - ☐ a. At the end of each work period, before using the equipment again
    - ☐ b. At least once per week if the equipment is used more than two days
    - ☐ c. At least once per week if the equipment has visible residues on it
    - ☐ d. Before the beginning of each spray season

16. **In applying pesticides to an agricultural crop, when *must* you use a closed mixing system?**
    - ☐ a. While mixing any liquid pesticide
    - ☐ b. While using a liquid *Danger* pesticide from an original pint container
    - ☐ c. While using a liquid *Danger* pesticide from an original 5-gallon container
    - ☐ d. While transferring a 50-gallon tank of a *Warning* pesticide that has been mixed with water

17. **Which *is not* an appropriate way of notifying workers on an agricultural property of a pesticide application?**
    - ☐ a. Posting signs around the treated area
    - ☐ b. Verbally telling workers about the application
    - ☐ c. Enclosing a notice about the application with the workers' next paychecks
    - ☐ d. Posting signs around the treated area *and* verbally telling workers about the application

18. **When transporting pesticides in a vehicle:**
    - ☐ a. Secure the packages inside the passenger compartment
    - ☐ b. Carry them in the cargo area of a truck, but have someone ride in that area to keep the packages safe
    - ☐ c. Secure containers in the cargo area and never allow anyone to ride in this part of the vehicle
    - ☐ d. Strap the containers to the top of the vehicle

7 Pesticide Emergencies

*Pesticide-related injuries often require
immediate medical attention.*

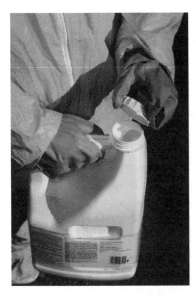

FIGURE 7-1.

Any time you work around pesticides, you should be prepared to handle an emergency. Pesticide emergencies may be the result of leaks, spills, fires, thefts, misapplication, or improper storage or handling.

ACCIDENTS MAY OCCUR while you are handling or applying pesticides, even if you are working under the most careful conditions. Many pesticides diluted with water are hazardous, but undiluted pesticides are usually much more dangerous (Figure 7-1). Pesticide emergencies may be the result of

- leaks
- spills
- fires
- thefts
- misapplication
- lack of care in storage or handling

Whenever you use pesticides, carry with you the names and locations of nearby medical facilities capable of treating pesticide-related injuries. If an accident happens and you have been exposed, seek medical care.

Be prepared to offer first aid to accident victims who get exposed to pesticides. Then, insist they receive prompt medical attention. To help employees locate medical facilities, post the notice shown in Figure 7-2 in a conspicuous place at the worksite.

FIRST AID

First aid is the help you give a person exposed to pesticides before they reach professional help. However, first aid is not a substitute for professional medical care. The *precautionary statements* section of each pesticide label provides specific first aid information.

Poisoning or exposure can occur if pesticides are splashed onto your skin or into your eyes, if you accidentally swallow them, or if you inhale vapors,

dusts, or fumes. The type of exposure determines what first aid and medical treatments are required. Serious pesticide poisoning may stop breathing or cause convulsions, paralysis, skin burns, or blindness. Applying the proper first aid treatment for pesticide exposure may reduce the extent of injury and even save lives. To prepare yourself for such emergencies, enroll in an American Red Cross first aid course that includes cardiopulmonary resuscitation (CPR) training.

Protect yourself when administering first aid to a person suffering from pesticide exposure. Avoid getting pesticides onto your skin and do not inhale vapors. Do not enter a confined area to rescue a person overcome by toxic pesticide fumes unless you have the proper respiratory equipment. Remember, the pesticide that affected the injured person can also injure you.

Get professional medical care *at once* for anyone who was exposed to a highly toxic pesticide or who shows signs of pesticide poisoning. Call an ambulance or transport the injured person to a medical facility for treatment. In addition to the first aid measures listed below, speed in obtaining medical care often controls the extent of injury. Provide medical personnel with complete information about the pesticide suspected of causing the injury.

Pesticides on Your Skin or Clothing

Concentrated pesticides spilled on your skin or clothing can cause serious injury (Figure 7-3). Some pesticides

FIGURE 7-2.

Post a notice like this one in a conspicu-ous place at the worksite. Be sure all employees are shown where this notice is posted.

Emergency Medical Facility

Name of facility:

Location:

Telephone number:

Medical Monitoring for Employees

Name of physician or facility:

Location:

Telephone number:

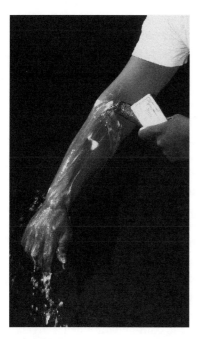

FIGURE 7-3.

If pesticides spill on you, the first step is to remove contaminated clothing and wash the affected parts of your body with soap and plenty of water. Do this quickly to avoid serious injury.

may cause skin burns or rashes or, through skin absorption, produce internal poisoning. Immediately remove contaminated clothing and wash the affected areas with clean water and soap. Follow the sequence of first aid steps listed in the next section.

First Aid for Skin Exposure

Follow these steps in case you or someone else receives skin exposure to pesticides:

Leave the Contaminated Area. Get away (or remove the victim) from the fumes, spilled pesticide, and further contamination. Do this quickly!

Restore Breathing. If the victim has stopped breathing, begin artificial respiration (rescue breathing) at once and continue until breathing resumes or until professional help arrives. If the person has stopped breathing and has no pulse, begin cardiopulmonary resuscitation (CPR) and continue until professional help arrives.

Prevent Further Exposure. Remove the contaminated clothing and thoroughly wash the affected skin and hair areas. Use soap or detergent and large amounts of water.

Get Medical Attention. Call an ambulance or have someone transport the injured person to the nearest medical facility as quickly as possible.

Pesticides in Your Eyes

Many pesticides are caustic and cause serious damage if they get into your eyes. Prompt first aid, followed by medical care, helps reduce damage.

First Aid for Eye Exposure

To treat eye exposure, you must:

Flush the Eyes. Immediately flush the affected eye or eyes with a gentle stream of clean, running water. Hold eyelids open to assure thorough flushing (Figure 7-4). Continue flushing for at least 15 minutes. When flushing your eyes, do not use any chemicals or drugs in the water, since this may increase the extent of injury.

If running water is not available, slowly pour clean water from a glass, water cooler, or other container onto the bridge of your nose, rather than directly into your eyes.

Obtain Medical Care. Always get medical attention if irritation persists after the flushing. Let medical providers

FIGURE 7-4.

If you get a pesticide into your eyes, wash them with clean, running water for 15 minutes. Then, if irritation persists, seek medical care.

know the name of the pesticide that caused the injury.

Inhaled Pesticides

Inhaled chemicals, such as fumigants, pesticide dusts, vapors from spilled pesticides, and fumes from burning pesticides, can cause serious lung injury and may be absorbed into other parts of the body through the lungs. Take first aid measures immediately to reduce injury or prevent death.

Wear a supplied-air respirator when entering an enclosed area to rescue a person who has been overcome by pesticide fumes. Cartridge respirators are not suitable for high concentrations of pesticide vapors or deficient oxygen conditions. If you do not have a supplied-air respirator, call for emergency help. You will be of more assistance to the injured person by seeking proper emergency help than if you are overcome by the pesticide fumes yourself.

First Aid for Pesticide Inhalation

Follow these steps if you need to provide first aid to someone overcome by pesticide fumes:

Leave the Contaminated Area/ Remove an Exposed Person from the Contaminated Area. Anyone overcome by pesticide vapors must get to fresh air immediately. Avoid physical exertion because this places an extra strain on the heart and lungs.

Loosen Clothing. Loosening clothing makes breathing easier and also releases pesticide vapors trapped between clothing and the skin.

Restore Breathing. If breathing has stopped, or is irregular or labored, begin artificial respiration (rescue breathing). Continue assisting until breathing has improved or until medical help arrives. If the person has stopped breathing and has no pulse, begin cardiopulmonary resuscitation (CPR) and continue until help arrives.

Treat for Shock. Inhalation injury often causes a person to go into shock. Keep the injured person calm and lying down. Prevent chilling by wrapping the person in a blanket after removing contaminated clothing. Do not administer alcoholic beverages.

Watch for Convulsions. If convulsions occur protect the victim from falls or injury and keep air passages clear by making sure the head is tilted back.

Get Immediate Medical Care. Call an ambulance or transport the person to the nearest medical facility. Provide medical personnel with as much information as possible about the pesticide.

Swallowed Pesticides

Two immediate dangers are associated with swallowed pesticides. The first is related to the toxicity of the pesticide and the poisoning effect it will have on a person's nervous system or other internal organs. The second involves physical injury that the swallowed pesticide causes to the linings of the mouth and throat and to the lungs. Corrosive materials, those which are strongly acid or alkaline, can seriously burn these sensitive tissues. Petroleum-based pesticides can cause lung and respiratory system damage, especially during vomiting. Never induce vomiting if you suspect that the swallowed pesticide is corrosive or petroleum-based.

You can reach regional poison information centers, located in Sacramento, San Francisco, Fresno, and San Diego, by telephone 24 hours a day and 7 days a week. In a poisoning emergency, call the Poison Control System anywhere in California by using a single toll-free number: 1-800-876-4766 (1-800-8-POISON). These centers provide quick, lifesaving information on poisoning treatment.

First Aid for Swallowed Pesticides

Act quickly when a pesticide has been swallowed. Follow the pesticide label or poison information center instructions or these guidelines:

Dilute the Swallowed Pesticide. If the person is conscious and alert, give large amounts (1 quart for an adult or a large glass for a child under 7) of water or milk. Do not give any liquids to an unconscious or convulsing person.

Induce Vomiting. If you are certain that neither a corrosive nor petroleum-based pesticide has been swallowed (check the pesticide label), induce vomiting. Make sure the person is kneeling or lying face down or on their right side. If in doubt, do not induce vomiting.

Obtain Medical Care. Call an ambulance or transport the poisoning victim to the nearest medical facility. Provide medical personnel with as much information as possible about the swallowed pesticide.

PESTICIDE LEAKS AND SPILLS

Treat all pesticide leaks or spills as emergencies. Concentrated pesticide spills are much more dangerous than pesticides diluted with water, but both types should be dealt with immediately. Leaks or spills can occur during transporting, storing, or while using pesticides. Pesticides may be spilled indoors, in enclosed areas, or outside.

When spills occur on public roadways, immediately contact the California Highway Patrol and the State of California Office of Emergency Services. These agencies will take charge of coordinating the cleanup and protecting the public. When pesticides are spilled on public roadways, a report is required to be filed with the Office of Emergency Services. If leaks or spills should occur in areas other than public roadways, follow the emergency procedures listed below. Report all leaks or spills of pesticides, no matter where they occur, to the local county agricultural commissioner as soon as possible.

Put materials that have been cleaned up and anything that was contaminated by the spill into a sealable drum. Label the drum to indicate it contains hazardous waste. Include the name of the pesticide and the signal word (*Danger, Warning,* or *Caution*).

Because local regulations vary, contact the county agricultural commissioner or Water Quality Control Board for instructions on how to dispose of the sealed drum and its contents. Under most circumstances, you must send the residue from a pesticide spill to a Class 1 disposal facility.

Spills on cleanable surfaces such as concrete require thorough decontamination. Commercial decontamination preparations are available for this purpose, or you can prepare a solution that contains 4 tablespoons of detergent and 1 pound of soda ash dissolved in each gallon of water. (Soda ash cannot be used for detoxification of a few pesticides, so check the label or MSDS before using this solution. Contact the pesticide manufacturer if you have any questions.)

If anyone has been injured or contaminated, administer first aid. Send for medical help if necessary.

Barricade. Rope off the area or set up barricades to keep everyone away from the contaminated site.

Ventilate the Area. If the spill is indoors, get out of the building. Open doors and windows. Set up a portable fan.

Cleaning up Pesticide Leaks or Spills

Cleaning up major pesticide spills requires the help of professionals. It is extremely difficult and costly to remove contaminated soil or to prevent or clean up groundwater contamination. The types of pesticide leaks and spills you will most likely encounter will be controllable quantities—such as when a container is damaged or slips to the ground or when diluted pesticide leaks from application equipment. Proper and immediate response to even these types of small leaks and spills is necessary to minimize damage to human and environmental health.

There are certain basic steps you should follow in cleaning up a pesticide leak or spill.

Clear the Area. Keep people and animals away from the contaminated area. Provide first aid if anyone has been injured or contaminated. Send for medical help if necessary.

Some liquid pesticides are flammable or are formulated in flammable carriers. Pesticide powders are potentially explosive, especially if a dust cloud forms in an enclosed area. Do not allow any smoking near a spill. If the spill occurs in an enclosed area, shut off all electrical appliances and motors that could produce sparks and ignite a fire or explosion.

Wear Personal Protective Equipment. Before beginning any cleanup, put on the personal protective clothing listed on the label for handling the concentrated material. Check the pesticide label for additional precautions. If you are uncertain what has been spilled, wear the maximum protection. This includes chemical-resistant boots and gloves, waterproof protective clothing, goggles, and a respirator.

Contain the Leak. Stop the leak by transferring the pesticide to another container or by patching the leaking container (repair paper bags and cardboard boxes with strong tape). Use soil, sand, sawdust, or absorbent clay to form a containment "dam" around liquid leaks. Common cat litter is a good absorbent material for pesticide cleanup. If the wind is blowing pesticide dusts or powders, lightly spray the area with water or cover the spill with a plastic tarp to prevent offsite movement.

Clean Up the Pesticide. Proceed to clean up the spill or leak (Figure 7-5). Brush the containment dam of

FIGURE 7-5.

Cover pesticide spills with an absorbent material and shovel it into a sealable container. When the cleanup is completed, seal and label the container and send it to a Class 1 disposal site. Wear personal protective equipment (required by the pesticide label) during the cleanup.

absorbent material toward the center of a liquid spill. Add additional absorbent material if necessary. If the spill is on soil, shovel out contaminated soil for disposal. Place the absorbent or spilled dry product and any contaminated soil in a sealable container. Containers for holding contaminated materials must be suitable for transporting. Label the container with the pesticide name and signal word.

Clean Nonporous Surfaces and Safety Equipment. If the spill occurred on a cleanable surface such as concrete or asphalt, use a broom to scrub the contaminated surface with a strong detergent solution. Clean this up again with absorbent material and place it in the container. Equipment such as brooms, shovels, and dust pans must be cleaned or disposed of. When you finish, clean your personal protective equipment.

Dispose of the Material. Local regulations on disposal of hazardous materials may vary. Check with the local county agricultural commissioner or Water Quality Control Board for instructions on how to dispose of the container and its contents.

PESTICIDE FIRES

Fighting pesticide fires requires special care because smoke and fumes generated by burning pesticides cannot be contained; areas endangered by these fumes must be evacuated. Toxic fumes hamper fire-fighting efforts and require the use of supplied-air respirators and protective clothing. Water must be used with caution when fighting pesticide fires. Use it primarily to cool containers and prevent overheated chemicals from exploding. Do not splash or spread toxic chemicals with high-pressure water.

Once the fire has been brought under control, all hoses and equipment, including personal protective clothing, must be decontaminated. Residue remaining at the fire site must be removed and disposed of.

How to Deal with a Pesticide Fire

Follow this sequence if a pesticide fire breaks out.

Call the Fire Department. Contact the nearest fire department as quickly as possible (call 9-1-1). Inform them that there is a fire involving pesticides. Provide them with the names of the chemicals contained in the structure or vehicle. If possible, provide Material Safety Data Sheets to the arriving fire units.

Clear the Area. Get people out of the immediate area of the fire; there may be considerable risk of toxic fumes and explosion.

Evacuate and Isolate the Area Around and Downwind of the Fire. Protect animals and move equipment and vehicles that could be damaged by the fire or fumes or that would impair fire fighting efforts. Keep spectators from being exposed to smoke from the fire and runoff from fire fighting. Contact the police or sheriff and have downwind residences, schools, and buildings evacuated until the danger has passed.

MISAPPLICATION OF PESTICIDES

Another form of emergency may exist when pesticides have been misapplied.

Intentional misapplication involves intentional use of a pesticide on an unregistered site or knowingly applying pesticides in a manner inconsistent with label directions.

Accidental misapplication involves unknowingly applying a pesticide to a site not on the label.

Negligent application involves improper calibration of application equipment as well as improper use and disposal of the pesticide; it also involves applying pesticides at the wrong time or in any other way inconsistent with label requirements.

Making an application mistake is a serious problem; do not compound the damage by failing to take responsible corrective action once the mistake is discovered. You may be financially responsible for damages, both physical and legal, caused by your misapplication of a pesticide. You may be able to reduce the amount of damage and liability by taking prompt action once you discover the error. Of primary importance is the protection of people, animals, and the environment.

Incorrect Amount of Pesticide Used

Although using insufficient quantities of pesticides usually does not give adequate control of the target pest and is a waste time and money, it generally presents no immediate problems to people or the environment. Using excessive amounts of pesticide, however, can be an environmental threat as well as a danger to human health. This type of problem occurs as a result of

- poor calibration of your application equipment
- faulty mixing of chemicals in your spray tank
- not understanding the label statement regarding application rates

Residues from the pesticide may last longer than expected, or a concentrated application may cause damage to the treated area.

Correcting the Problem. Once an improper application has been discovered, take immediate action. Notify the county agricultural commissioner of the problem and seek information and advice on what remedies to take. Contact the pesticide manufacturer to find out what corrective measures they suggest. Remember, speed is of the utmost importance when trying to reduce damage.

Applying the Wrong Pesticide

Lack of attention to your mixing operation or giving the wrong instructions to an employee may result in the wrong pesticide being applied. Besides possible damage to plants or surfaces in the treatment area, using the wrong pesticide exposes you and your workers to unanticipated hazards. Mixing and application might take place without the required personal protective equipment, resulting in possible injury to the applicator.

Correcting the Problem. When you discover that you have mixed or applied the wrong pesticide, contact the county agricultural commissioner for help, and then call the pesticide manufacturer. Notify people in the application area and keep them away until it can be made safe again.

Pesticides Applied to the Wrong Site or Crop

Another form of accident involves pesticides being applied to the wrong site. This can be a serious problem if the site (or crop) is not listed on the pesticide label or if there are workers at the site who are performing cultural operations.

Correcting the Problem. Contact the county agricultural commissioner and the pesticide manufacturer for assistance. Keep people and animals out of the sprayed area until it has been determined that it is safe to return.

REVIEW QUESTIONS

1. **The name, address, and location of a medical facility capable of treating pesticide-related injuries should be available:**
   - a. In a prominent file folder at your farm office
   - b. At the pesticide mixing site whenever pesticides are used
   - c. At the local county agricultural commissioner's office
   - d. At the pesticide dealer's facility

2. **First aid and other emergency information for pesticide accidents is found:**
   - a. In the front section of the local telephone directory
   - b. On the second page of the pesticide manufacturer's informational brochure
   - c. On the bottom of the pesticide container
   - d. In the precautionary statements section of the pesticide label

3. **First aid for pesticide on the skin includes:**
   - a. Removing contaminated clothing and washing with soap and water
   - b. Changing out of the contaminated clothing at the end of the work period
   - c. Lying down for 20 minutes, then removing contaminated clothing
   - d. Immediate transport to a medical facility for assistance in washing the affected areas of skin

4. **If pesticides get into your eyes, you should always:**
   - a. Keep eyes shut tightly and covered with a damp cloth until irritation stops
   - b. Wipe eyes thoroughly with a clean cloth before returning to work
   - c. Flush eyes with clean water for 15 minutes before returning to work
   - d. Flush eyes with clean water for 15 minutes and seek medical attention

5. **If pesticide vapors are inhaled, first aid procedures include:**
   - a. Having victim breathe rapidly for 15 minutes
   - b. Send victim home for remainder of the work day
   - c. Loosen clothing, restore breathing if necessary, and seek medical care
   - d. Have victim drink a large quantity of alcoholic beverage

6. **When someone swallows a pesticide you should:**
   - a. Have victim stop work and rest for at least one hour
   - b. Get immediate medical care for victim
   - c. Have victim eat several pieces of fruit
   - d. Watch for signs of illness and seek medical care if symptoms appear and last for more than an hour

7. **When cleaning up a spilled pesticide, the absorbent and all contaminated materials must be:**
   - a. Buried at least 2 feet below the soil surface
   - b. Put into bags or containers and taken to the local dump site
   - c. Put into sealed containers and shipped to a Class 1 disposal site
   - d. Taken to the local agricultural commissioner's office for disposal

8. **Information on cleaning up spilled pesticides can be found in the:**
   - a. Front section of the local telephone book
   - b. Directions For Use section of the pesticide label
   - c. Accidental release measures section of the material safety data sheet
   - d. Leaks and spills section of the pesticide manufacturer's brochure

9. Dealing with fires involving pesticides requires:

☐ a. Large amounts of water to disperse the burning materials

☐ b. Professional help, equipped and trained to fight pesticide fires

☐ c. Seeking immediate help from neighbors and family members

☐ d. Waiting until the burning has nearly stopped before calling the fire department

10. If the wrong pesticide has been accidentally applied to a site, you should:

☐ a. Notify the county agricultural commissioner at once

☐ b. Notify the Water Quality Control Board at once

☐ c. Call the nearest Poison Control Center for advice

☐ d. Watch for adverse effects and, if any appear, notify the county agricultural commissioner

8 Using Pesticides Effectively

The uniform-sized spray droplets produced by controlled droplet applicators (CDAs) enhance the safety and effectiveness of some pesticide applications.

YOU MUST USE pesticides *effectively* as well as safely. The results of a pesticide application should usually be worth any financial or labor investment by

- yielding a profit or quality advantage in crops
- reducing health hazards to people and livestock or poultry
- improving health, appearance, and growth of turf and ornamental plants
- eliminating annoying pests from buildings, workplaces, and homes

This chapter discusses several ways for you to improve pesticide application effectiveness.

PEST DETECTION AND MONITORING

Monitoring, identifying, and timely detection of pests are your primary keys to effective pest management. Detection verifies the presence of pests and helps you anticipate when and where pests will occur. Correct identification helps you get information about a pest's life stages and habits. Also, you need this information to choose a pesticide and to know when, where, and how to apply it. Establishing a monitoring program not only allows you to detect pests, it also lets you

- observe seasonal changes in pest populations
- properly time control applications
- assess the effectiveness of control measures

Predicting Problems

Early detection lets you plan a program for following pest development and activity. This helps you predict if or when treatment is necessary. To help you predict pest problems, review the pest history of the farm, landscaped area, building, right-of-way, or other location. This will let you know what pests to expect at different times of the year. If this information is not available, try to get pest history information from a similar location nearby.

Look for conditions that favor pest buildup. For example, some pest insects overwinter in crop residues or field borders. If you see these pests in such areas, there is a strong likelihood they will eventually move into the crop. Weeds that produce seed provide a seed reservoir for the following year. If this is the case, anticipate large populations of these weeds in following seasons.

Vertebrates, such as squirrels, may not be problems while other food supplies are adequate. However, if conditions change, they may move into cropped or landscaped areas for food. Cockroaches, ants, and rodents need food sources, water, and often shelter before they can seriously infest an area.

Chapter 1 describes how to identify many types of pests. The sidebars in Chapter 1 show you how to use pest identification services. They also describe how to package and ship pests to experts or identification laboratories.

After a while, you will learn to recognize the more common pests found in your work situation. When you come across pests you do not recognize, collect samples using traps, nets, or other appropriate methods. If weeds are your problem, dig up samples so roots are included with the rest of the plants. Collect seedlings and/or flowering specimens if they are present.

Be careful when handling birds and rodents because they may be diseased. For instance, some flea-infested rodents can vector the plague organism. Birds often carry lice, mites, or biting bugs. Rabies is prevalent in some skunks, bats, and other small mammals. Handle these animals with tongs or heavy gloves to avoid being bitten. Do not contact their urine or feces.

Be sure you recognize *natural enemies* of pests. Natural enemies may be contributing to the control of the pest problem, eliminating or reducing the need for a pesticide application. Do not mistake natural enemies for pests.

Using Life History Information. Knowing something about the life history of a pest is useful when planning how to control it. Some of the things you might learn include

- where to look for nesting sites
- the pest's food preferences
- what types of natural enemies help control the pest
- the pest's seasonal occurrences or life cycles

Plan pesticide applications and other control measures that are most appropriate to the pest. This includes applying pesticides during the pest's most susceptible life stage. For instance, successful weed control often occurs when weed seeds are germinating or plants are in the seedling stage. Once past the seedling stage, perennial weeds are usually most susceptible to herbicides when they are flowering. Eggs of insects and mites are often resistant to pesticides. In addition, adult scale insects have hard, waxy outer coverings that protect them from pesticides.

Find out what the pest is feeding on when using poison baits for birds or rodents. Once you know this, select a bait that contains that food. If possible, time control measures around breeding seasons to prevent vertebrate pests from reproducing.

Establishing a Monitoring Program

Frequent monitoring provides information on the day-to-day populations of pests. This is the information you need to make intelligent decisions. Information you collect may include the density, life stages, and species composition of pest populations. Also include your observations of factors controlling or favoring the pest. You will find that it is difficult to monitor pests while their populations are low and damage is minimal. However, this monitoring is worth the effort. If chemical treatment is necessary, you may learn enough information to be able to use less-toxic pesticides. The monitoring information may also help you limit applications to a more restricted area.

Visual monitoring is the most common method. It includes any systematic method of searching for pests, pest damage, or evidence of the presence of pests. Generally, this requires thoroughly examining a representative portion of an area in a uniform way. It may include sampling foliage, pulling up a certain number of plants, or walking a prescribed transect. Look for patterns of distribution, damage, or activity. Then check for evidence of natural enemies or other mortality factors. Sometimes other organisms may indicate the presence of pests, such as fleas in the area of rodent nests or ants climbing trees or shrubs to collect honeydew from aphids and scale insects.

The following indicators may provide clues to the presence and identity of some pests:

- seeds
- weed remains from the previous season

- animal burrows
- tracks
- feeding damage
- fecal droppings
- webbing
- insect or mite eggs

Table 8-1 lists some of the useful tools that help you to monitor and observe pests.

Weeds. The most important field information needed for making weed management decisions includes

- what species are present
- the stage of development (seedling, flowering, postflowering)
- whether the relative abundance of different species is changing from previous seasons

TABLE 8-1.

Equipment Used for Collecting and Monitoring Pests.

EQUIPMENT	USE	COMMENTS
hand lens	locating, examining, and identifying insect, mite, fungal, and other pests	Magnification range of 7× to 14× most useful. Hold lens close to eye and bring object to be examined up to lens for focus.
insect net	monitoring and collecting many types of insects	Essential piece of equipment. Three types available. *Aerial net:* made of lightweight net material; used for flying insects. *Beating net:* made of heavier cloth such as muslin; used for sampling insects on plants and shrubs. *Aquatic net:* specially designed net to collect aquatic specimens.
beating tray	monitoring plant-feeding pests	Especially useful on larger trees and shrubs. Easy to make; design for own special applications.
pheromone traps	monitoring flight activity of many insects	Several styles of traps are available for different insect species.
light traps	attracting mostly night-flying insects	Only useful in indoor or enclosed areas. Some have electric grid to kill attracted insects.
animal traps	helpful in detecting small animals such as rodents and birds	Traps usually have to be carefully located. Several types available: *Live traps:* animals are usually attracted by baits, captured animals are unharmed. *Spring traps:* injures or kills trapped animals. *Sticky traps:* animals get caught in sticky substance, may die.
pitfall traps	detecting walking insects	Very effective in landscape and nursery areas.
other traps	detecting insects and pathogens	Often attract by shape or color. Lure traps with bait other than pheromones. Types include sticky yellow traps, spherical sticky traps, and spore traps for scab and other diseases.
pyrethrum test	insect detection in turf	Applied primarily as a 1–2% solution in water. Irritates cutworms and other subterranean pests which then come to the surface.
microscope	examining plants and other objects for pests and very helpful in identifying insects, mites, and fungi	Low-power dissecting microscope that provides magnification in the range of 10× to 50× is the best.
binoculars	helpful in spotting and identifying birds, but also useful for rodents; sometimes helpful in examining crop damage and infestations	Magnification range should be 6× to 7× with an objective lens size between 35 mm and 50 mm. Porro prism or Dach prism binoculars are best.

EQUIPMENT	USE	COMMENTS
tracking powder	monitoring movement of rodents; sometimes used to monitor insects	Use only on floor surfaces to prevent powder from falling from upper areas.
containers	holding and transporting collected specimens: plant parts, insects, mites, nematodes, fungi, and weeds	Types include glass vials, plastic bags, and paper bags.
knife	cutting open plants, fruits, nuts, wood, and other objects to locate pests and examine for damage	Should be strong and sharp.
shovel	sampling weeds; helpful in digging around plant roots or in removing plants for examination	Clean after each use to avoid transporting soil pests to other locations.
ice chest	keeping collected specimans fresh until they can be examined; also used to ship materials to identification labs	Inexpensive foam plastic chests work very well.
identification aids	assisting in pest identification	Includes books, photos, keys, and preserved specimens. Obtain these from libraries, bookstores, and biological supply houses.

Monitor for weeds in the late fall or early winter (after the first rains) to detect emerging winter annuals. Monitor in the late spring to detect emerging summer annuals. Monitor at other times as needed to detect perennial and biennial weeds. Identify all the weed species found growing in an area, preferably while they are in the seedling stage. Watch for any new species.

Use a form similar to Figure 8-1 to keep records of the different weed species and their locations. Map the locations of perennial weeds. Try to estimate the percentage of each weed species relative to the total weed population. Count the numbers and varieties in one or more randomly selected areas of 1 square yard. Note areas where weeds have produced seeds. Also, keep records of all herbicides used for weed control in the area. This information is useful when plantback restrictions apply. It also helps you evaluate the effectiveness of previous control efforts. Include in these records the types of cultural methods that were used for weed control.

Look for adjacent weedy areas such as roadsides or ditchbanks that may be a reservoir for seeds. Other ways that weeds move into an area include

- Cultivation equipment may move weed seeds or vegetative structures from one site to another.
- Flooding may carry weed seeds into an area in the flood water.
- Birds and mammals can move seeds or vegetative structures on their coats, in their feces, and with their nesting materials.

Nematodes. Usually, you must manage nematodes before the crop or other plants are in the ground. Early detection allows enough time to apply a soil treatment before planting. Therefore, take soil samples in autumn for winter- and spring-planted crops or plants. If fumigation is not an option, early detection allows you to select nematode-resistant plant species.

You can use a simple method to determine if nematodes are present. Check susceptible crops or weeds by digging up plants that look stressed. Inspect the roots for galls, cysts, or swollen root tips. Monitor sandy soils regularly for rootknot nematode infestations when susceptible plants are grown there. If you detect nematodes or know that nematodes have been a problem, arrange for more detailed

ORCHARD LOCATION _____   CONTROL METHODS _____

CONTROL DATES _____

COMMENTS _____

	NOV _____		FEB _____		MAY _____	
	% of total weeds		% of total weeds		% of total weeds	
	treated	untreated	treated	untreated	treated	untreated

ANNUAL GRASSES
annual bluegrass
barnyardgrass
crabgrass
sprangletop
wild barley
wild oat
_____
_____
_____

ANNUAL BROADLEAVES
cheeseweed (mallow)
clovers
groundsel
filaree
fiddleneck
knotweed
lambsquarters
mustards
pigweeds
puncturevine
purslane
_____
_____
_____
_____
_____

PERENNIALS
bermudagrass
dallisgrass
johnsongrass
curly dock
field bindweed
nutsedge
_____
_____

FIGURE 8-1.

Keep records of the weed species present in an area to help select appropriate herbicides or other control measures. The form illustrated here was developed for weeds found in walnut orchards.

quantitative sampling. One sample per year should be sufficient.

Take soil samples for nematodes along a long continuous strip through the area. Keep each sample separate. Sample the soil within the root zone of the plants. Also look for stunted or damaged plants. If you find any, include the infected plants, with roots, in the sampling. Prepare the samples and send them to an identification laboratory as instructed in Chapter 1. Draw a map of the area that shows locations of healthy and infected plants, soil types, water drainage, and other important features. Look for ways in which nematodes might be introduced to an area such as through contaminated cultivation equipment.

Pathogens. Monitor pathogens by observing plant symptoms or damage or, with certain fungi, by looking for fruiting bodies and other structures. Remember that damaged plant material may serve as an inoculum source for healthy plants. Look for inoculum sources *before* conditions favor the spread of pathogens. This is important since the most successful control of plant disease pathogens involves suppressing them before infection occurs. Environmental conditions such as temperature, rainfall, or heavy dew are often the controlling factors for pathogen infection or development. Look for any *pattern* of symptoms:

- Do symptoms occur only on scattered plants?
- Are symptoms concentrated in certain parts of the field?
- Are symptoms generally distributed?

Also, monitor for the presence of insects or nematodes that are capable of transmitting certain pathogens—aphids, for instance.

Identifying most plant pathogens requires laboratory analysis. Collect damaged plant material according to the instructions in Chapter 1.

Arthropods. You can observe most insects, mites, and other arthropods by visual monitoring. You can also collect plant foliage and examine it with a hand lens or microscope (Figure 8-2). Use a sweep net to collect certain pest insects found on foliage (Figure 8-3). However, avoid using sweep nets on tender plants because you can damage them by this technique. Beat foliage onto a white sheet, tray, or pan for a simple way of detecting certain plant-feeding insects. Use these methods to estimate the size of an arthropod pest population or evaluate its rate of increase or decrease. Sometimes the decision to apply a pesticide is based on the number of insects or mites found on a sample of leaves taken from different plants or from sweep net samples. Control decisions are often based on studies that show that until the pest population builds up to a certain size, no *economic* damage will occur.

Light, especially the ultraviolet spectrum (black light), attracts many night-flying insects. Some pest managers use black light traps to attract and kill certain nocturnal insect pests in small areas. These traps also serve as monitoring devices for particular types of insect pests in enclosed areas such as warehouses.

Use sticky traps for catching and monitoring some insect pests. These cardboard or plastic traps have a surface coated with a thick, sticky paste. You can do several things to make sticky traps attractive to target insects. Where you place the traps and the color and shape of the traps attract certain insects. For example, put sticky traps along wall bases or other normal pathways to monitor cockroaches. Use a bright yellow color to attract whiteflies. Hang sticky red or green spheres in trees to catch apple maggot adults or walnut husk flies. You can add attractants to sticky traps or sticky surfaces to attract flies, cockroaches, and other pest insects. Effective attractants include various

FIGURE 8-2.

A hand lens is often needed for detecting, identifying, and monitoring insects, mites, and other arthropods on plant foliage. Hold the lens close to your eye and bring the object being examined up to it until it is in focus.

FIGURE 8-3.

Use a sweep net to monitor the presence of certain pest insects on plant foliage.

foods, sugar syrups, or chemicals with odors resembling certain foods.

Pheromones lure some insects into sticky traps. Pheromones are chemicals produced by insects that attract individuals of the same species. Most pheromone traps use a chemical that mimics the pheromone produced by female insects to attract males for mating. A few mimic pheromones released by males to attract females. As you monitor these traps, you will notice that trap catches increase during the time when insects emerge from their pupal stage and begin to mate. Knowing when adults are emerging gives you a good idea of when to apply insecticides for optimal control. For some agricultural pest insects, you can use *phenology models* to accurately predict egg hatch. This allows you to precisely time insecticide applications. These models use pheromone trap catch information and daily high and low temperatures in the calculations.

The University of California Statewide Integrated Pest Management Project develops phenology models for many insect pests. These are available on the internet at:
http://www.ipm.ucdavis.edu/.

Vertebrate Pests. Monitoring for vertebrates requires some understanding of the habits of potential pests. Many species are active only at certain times of the day or night. Other species cease their activities when people are around. Often the best way to monitor for them is to check for evidence of their presence. This includes gopher or ground squirrel burrows, feces of rats or rabbits, or mouse trails. Use animal traps and tracking powders to monitor the activities of vertebrate pests when it is too difficult or time-consuming to watch continually for the pests. Some animal traps are spring-loaded devices, such as rat traps, that kill the target animals. Use live traps, which resemble cages, when it is important not to harm the captured pests (Figure 8-4).

Use tracking powders to monitor rodent activity in buildings (Figure 8-5). Spread the powder (cornstarch or flour works well) over an area suspected of being a rodent trail or runway. Tracks left in the dust reveal information about the population size, age of individuals, and areas of activity. This technique is useful in planning the placement and timing of traps or rodenticides. Keep tracking powders on floor surfaces to prevent contaminating counters, furnishings, or other objects in an area. Certain tracking powders contain toxicants that kill rodents. The rodents ingest the poison while cleaning themselves.

FIGURE 8-4.

Live traps can be used to monitor the presence of small animals such as birds or rodents without injuring the animals. Domestic animals, such as this cat, may be accidentally trapped on occasion.

FIGURE 8-5.

Tracking powders are used to monitor the activity of small rodents and insects. Toxicants sometimes are added to the powder to kill the animal when it cleans itself.

MAKING PESTICIDE USE DECISIONS

How do you decide when to use a pesticide and what pesticide to use? Health codes require controlling certain pests in restaurants and other public places. In residential and urban situations, you take action when the people living and working in these areas can no longer tolerate the pests. Pesticides used in these situations are often selected according to their safety, speed, and effectiveness. In agriculture and other commercial ventures, however, the economics of pest control is also important.

In most cases, a few individuals of a particular pest probably will not cause economic losses, but as their numbers increase, so does their damage. For some pests—mostly insects, nematodes, and mites—*action thresholds* or *treatment thresholds* have been established. These indicate what population levels can be tolerated without loss and at what level a pesticide application will pay for itself. Such treatment thresholds must be flexible. If the market price for a crop fluctuates, for instance, the threshold of allowable pest damage can be changed to accommodate for this. When the price of pesticides increases or decreases, the tolerable pest injury is adjusted accordingly.

Action thresholds, based on extensive sampling, pest monitoring, and life history information, are designed to help people not to spend more money to control a pest than the economic loss the pest might cause if not controlled. These thresholds may not always be practical, however, because many of the factors that go into the calculations cannot always be accurately predicted.

The tolerance for weeds, vertebrates, and pathogens may be very low due to the potential these pests have for building up over time and the difficulty in controlling them at later stages of infestation. For plant pathogens, it may be necessary to apply pesticides when environmental conditions favor disease outbreak. This could be long before any signs of disease are present. Usually once you see disease symptoms, the damage has already taken place. Control at this time may not be economical if plants are seriously injured or are no longer susceptible to further damage. To determine if suppression is necessary, use indicators such as
- inoculum source
- history of disease infection
- favorable conditions for the pathogen to develop

For weeds, the most effective time to apply herbicides is when weeds are in the seedling stages. Often it is significantly easier and cheaper to apply herbicides before planting or when crop plants are very young. There is no "wait and see" time to allow higher populations to develop. Usually, weeds most seriously affect new, small crop plants. The young plants are more susceptible to competition for light, water, and nutrients. For this reason, the crop stage may be as important as weed numbers in determining treatment needs.

Factors that influence herbicide use decisions include

- favorable weather conditions
- weed species
- growth stage of problem weeds
- growth stage of the crop
- amount of damage being caused by weeds
- resistance of certain weed species to herbicides
- soil type and condition
- herbicide persistence in the soil
- the economics of chemical control versus mechanical methods such as mowing or tilling

Other Factors Influencing Pesticide-Use Decisions

Other factors besides cost, effectiveness, and pest susceptibility often have an influence on your decision to use pesticides to control pests. These include

- potential for air pollution and groundwater contamination
- protecting endangered species
- produce packer, handler, or processor restrictions (for agricultural crops)
- cost of training pesticide handlers
- requirements to protect workers in treated areas
- compatibility of restricted-entry and preharvest intervals with necessary cultural practices
- limitations imposed by plantback restrictions

SELECTING THE RIGHT PESTICIDE

Choosing the right pesticide can be a difficult task. Often you can choose from several pesticides to control a pest in a particular situation. To get information about pesticides for specific uses, consult

- pesticide label books (available by writing to the manufacturers)
- farm advisors and agricultural commissioners
- licensed pest control advisers
- pesticide chemical handbooks
- University of California publications, treatment guides, and pest management guidelines (Figure 8-6)

The University of California Statewide Integrated Pest Management Project's agricultural and urban pest management guidelines, including pesticide recommendations, are accessible through the Internet at http://www.ipm .ucdavis.edu/ (Figure 8-7). Up-to-date pesticide use guidelines, pesticide toxicology information, and other pest management techniques are accessible through this website. You can buy many UC IPM pest management publications from DANR Communication Services, 6701 San Pablo Ave., 2nd Floor, Oakland, CA 94608-1239, telephone 1-800-994-8849 (a catalog of publications is available upon request). University of

FIGURE 8-6.

Pest management manuals are published by the University of California for many different types of crops. These are useful for selecting the proper chemical and other control methods.

FIGURE 8-7.

The University of California Statewide Integrated Pest Management Project maintains an up-to-date listing of pest management guidelines that can be accessed through the Internet.

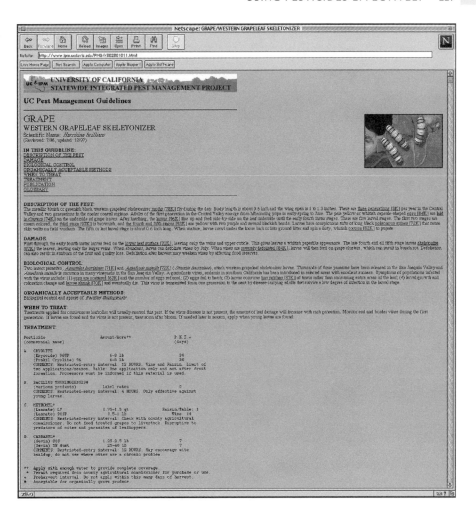

California county Cooperative Extension offices can also order these publications for you.

Pest Species

Select a pesticide or pesticide combination that is suitable for the pest species or range of pest species being controlled. Be sure the materials chosen are capable of controlling the current life stage of these pests. Determine the suitability of the pesticides by reading pesticide labels. If the target site is not on the label, do not use the material.

Toxicity of the Pesticide to Be Used

Each pesticide has a signal word that indicates the relative hazard of the pesticide. Hazards are modified by such factors as formulation type, persistence in the environment, and amount of pesticide used. For example, microencap-

sulated formulations are safer for applicators to use than wettable powders.

As a rule, and if you have a choice, select pesticides with the signal word that indicates the lowest level of hazard. *Warning* is preferable to *Danger,* and *Caution* is preferable to both *Warning* and *Danger.* These will usually be safer for you to work with. Also, they will often be less harmful to the environment, beneficial insects, natural enemies, and animals.

Pesticide Persistence

Depending on the nature of the pest control problem, consider persistence characteristics when selecting a pesticide. Residuals are desirable in situations where reinfestations are constantly a problem, such as for termite control. Persistent pesticides may be more hazardous in areas where people live and work. Persistence also influences how pesticides move off the target site through leaching and runoff. To protect beneficial insects such as honey bees, low persistence is often as important as low toxicity. Persistence is an important consideration when choosing herbicides, because residues may damage subsequent crops.

Certain types of pesticides, such as some chlorinated hydrocarbons, persist in the environment for a long time. Other pesticides, such as many organophosphates, break down rapidly under normal environmental conditions. The persistence of a pesticide is its *half-life*. This is the measure of how long it takes for the material to be reduced to half of the amount originally applied. Besides the type of pesticide, there are other factors that influence persistence. For instance, the amount of pesticide applied determines how much of the active ingredient remains after a time.

Pesticide formulation types affect persistence. Microencapsulated and granular formulations tend to release the active ingredient over a longer period. Therefore, only part of the material begins to break down at the moment of application. Pesticides dissolved in oils or petroleum solvents may volatilize more slowly than water-soluble materials and therefore persist longer. Wettable powders have a longer persistence to insects than do emulsifiable concentrate mixtures.

The pH of the water used for mixing pesticides affects the breakdown speed. The pH of the soil or plant or animal tissues may have a similar influence. Tissue or soil that is highly alkaline tends to cause more rapid breakdown of some pesticides than neutral or *acidic* tissue or soil.

The physical nature of the surface being treated also influences pesticide persistence. Porous surfaces or soil with high organic matter absorbs pesticide, reducing the amount of active ingredient available for pest control. Oily surfaces and waxy coatings on leaves and insect body coverings prevent uptake of the pesticide. The oils or waxes may even combine with the active ingredient, reducing toxicity and persistence.

Soil microorganisms break down many pesticides and influence the persistence of pesticides in the soil environment. These organisms include
- bacteria
- fungi
- protozoans
- algae

Water-soluble pesticides that percolate deeper into the soil break down more slowly than those that remain near the surface. This is mainly because fewer microorganisms are present at greater soil depths. Many pesticides break down faster in soils that have diverse populations of microorganisms. High levels of organic matter in the soil often slow degradation because the organic matter binds to the pesticide. This makes the pesticide unavailable to the microorganisms. Repeated use of the same pesticide in the soil can increase the breakdown rate. This increase is apparently the result of either
- a greater soil microorganism population
- an enzyme change in the microorganism population that makes the microorganisms more efficient in decomposing the specific pesticide

Weather affects persistence. For instance, wind and rain remove or dilute pesticides from target surfaces, lessening their effectiveness. High temperatures and humidity cause chemical changes in some compounds, accelerating breakdown. Sunlight produces photochemical reactions that decompose many pesticides. Cooler soil temperatures usually increase pesticide persistence.

Cost and Efficacy of Pesticide Materials

The cost of a pesticide is an important factor, but be careful not to base selection on cost alone. Check labels to see what rates of active ingredient are required. Convert the cost per pound of active ingredient into cost per unit of area treated. You must balance cost with the degree of effectiveness that can be expected. A pesticide that costs 30% more but gives 60% better control is often the better bargain unless you need a less effective pesticide to protect natural enemies.

Unfortunately, the effectiveness of a pesticide is hard to measure, and unbiased opinions are difficult to obtain. Local environmental conditions and methods of application also influence efficacy. Often you must make a value judgment based on personal experience. Keep a notebook and evaluate the results after each application to increase your knowledge of pesticide efficacy.

Weather influences the quality of an application and the efficacy of pesticides. Rainfall shortly after an application can wash off or dilute sprays, while windy conditions produce drift. Some pesticides are more effective in controlling target pests when temperatures are within an optimal range. High temperatures cause some pesticides to be phytotoxic. Effective pesticide use, therefore, involves

- timing to coincide with optimal weather conditions
- pest susceptibility
- protecting natural enemies

Ideal conditions are not always possible during pesticide application. Often you must make some compromises that affect efficacy.

Ease of Use and Compatibility with Other Materials

Pesticides that are simple to use and are compatible with other pesticides have an advantage. Compatibility and ease of use also depend on

- how the pesticide is being used
- what the pesticide is mixed with
- the nature of the treatment area

Effects on Beneficial Insects and Natural Enemies

Always try to conserve beneficial insects and natural enemies. If you are using an integrated pest management program, consider how the selected pesticide will work within the goals of the program. This sometimes means compromising for less immediate control of the pest to achieve greater long-term control.

Restricted-Entry Intervals and Harvest Limitations

The pesticide selected must work within constraints of legally established restricted-entry intervals and the allowable days before harvest. These limitations protect workers, consumers, and the public from excessive residues.

SELECTIVE PESTICIDES

Selectivity refers to the range of organisms affected by a pesticide. A *broad spectrum* pesticide kills a large range of pests as well as nontarget species. A *selective* material controls a smaller group of more closely related organisms, often leaving beneficials and nontarget organisms unharmed. However, selectivity is not always desirable. There are some definite advantages to controlling multiple pests with a single broad spectrum pesticide. These include cheaper pesticides (due to a larger market for the manufacturer) and reduced application time and costs.

Pesticide selectivity is controlled by factors such as

- the penetration rate through an organism's outer body covering (or the cuticle of plant tissue)
- the speed at which the toxicant is excreted by organisms
- how the toxicant binds to tissues of different organisms

Some organisms have metabolic ways of altering or detoxifying pesticides, and these pesticides are therefore ineffective against them. Also, many organisms avoid pesticide exposure through their behavior or by being repelled by the pesticide material.

THE SELECTIVE USE OF PESTICIDES

The way you mix and apply pesticides can also improve selectivity. Ways to make broad spectrum pesticides more selective include
- application timing
- application techniques
- dosage level
- types of formulations
- adjuvants
- ability to keep the pesticide on target

Application Timing

Proper application timing is important for controlling target pests as well as protecting natural enemies and beneficial insects. Because some pesticides are more effective at different life stages of the pest, time applications with the most susceptible stage. Understanding the biology of the pest will help you determine its susceptible life stages and decide if a pesticide application will work.

The life stage of nontarget plants in the treatment area is another important consideration. Some herbicides, for example, may be toxic to crop plants as well as weeds once the crop plants have reached a certain growth stage. Check pesticide labels for precautions on using pesticides during inappropriate life stages of nontarget plants.

Whenever possible, avoid injuring nontarget organisms by timing applications to periods when they are not present in the area. This technique works well for honey bees because they forage only during warm, daylight hours. Pesticides applied during the early morning, late afternoon, or on cold and cloudy days usually reduce hazards to honey bees. Insecticides and miticides applied while perennial plants are dormant may also protect nontarget and

beneficial organisms. This technique is often an effective control method for some species of plant-feeding mites, aphids, scales, and other insects that overwinter in dormant plants.

Pesticide Application Techniques

Use specific pesticide application techniques to improve coverage, reduce drift, and achieve better control of pests. Sometimes you can lower the amount of pesticide applied without sacrificing the quality of pest control. Choosing the right application techniques can also reduce human and environmental hazards.

Equipment Operation. Learn how to properly operate pesticide application equipment. For example, the ground speed must always remain constant to assure even pesticide coverage. Check the nozzles frequently to make sure none have become clogged. Shut off all nozzles during turns to prevent an uneven spray pattern. When injecting pesticides into the soil, shut off nozzles and raise the boom before making a turn. Leave enough room after the turn to bring equipment up to specified ground speed before restarting the pesticide flow.

Uneven ground causes booms on tractors or other equipment to bounce unless they are well supported and ground speed is slowed. Make sure the boom is always parallel to the ground during application. A tilted boom produces an uneven spray pattern. Adjust boom height to the recommended range specified by the type of nozzles being used (Figure 8-8).

When using hand spray guns with high-pressure sprayers, keep the application uniform on all parts of the surfaces being treated. Make sure the spray reaches upper foliage or branches of trees or shrubs. Direct the spray to all sides of the plants, but avoid excessive runoff.

Keep the ground speed of air blast sprayers in balance with the volume of

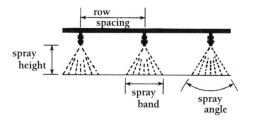

FIGURE 8-8.

Boom height must be adjusted to correspond to the type of nozzle being used.

air being moved by the fans. This improves even dispersion of pesticide droplets. Traveling too fast will result in poor coverage because the sprayer blower cannot displace the air surrounding the plants fast enough.

When operating backpack sprayers, walk at a regular pace and avoid uneven steps. Hold the nozzle steady and keep it a constant distance from the target surface.

Preventing Gaps or Overlaps. Pesticide swaths have to be uniform, without overlaps or gaps, to make the best economic use of spray materials. In some agricultural settings, there are furrows or rows the operator can follow to keep the application uniform. In open, unmarked areas, the operator needs to depend on some other method to prevent overlap or gaps. One method involves using foam markers to mark sprayed areas to prevent overlap or gaps in the application pattern. These markers, attached to the ends of a spray boom, intermittently leave a deposit of long-lasting foam. The operator aligns the application equipment to the foam trail left from a previous pass. In some situations, you can add colored dyes to the spray mixture to visualize where spraying has taken place.

Remembering the exact point where spraying stopped when leaving the application site to refill spray tanks is a problem. Unless you return to this location, there will be an uneven application. Marking devices help you avoid such problems. In some situations, tie colored surveyor's tape to plants to locate where the spraying stopped. In open areas, use marking flags to indicate the location. However, when applying hazardous pesticides, use a marking method that does not require you to contact treated surfaces. Remote-operated foam markers work well.

Electronic positioning devices, such as global positioning systems (GPS), are an accurate way of guiding pesticide application equipment. As the cost of this equipment becomes more reasonable, its usefulness as an application tool increases. You enter swath width and direction of travel into a control unit mounted on the tractor near the operator. The positioning device monitors the location of the sprayer and, through readout instruments, guides the operator. When you move the application equipment out of the treatment area for refilling, maintenance, or repairs, the positioning unit electronically records its last location. Then it guides you back to the exact spot.

Spot Treatments. You can increase selectivity if you apply pesticides as spot treatments rather than to an entire area. In addition, you can reduce the amount of pesticide used by 70 to 90% through spot treatment methods. For example, some weeds may grow in clumps scattered throughout a field after controlling all the other weeds by cultivation or with herbicides. Spot treatment involves treating just these clumps or patches rather than the whole field. Periodically, insects and mites congregate in a few areas before dispersing more generally, especially if the infestation is just beginning. Control these pests by treating only the infested plants. In landscaped areas, pests may occur only on certain plant species. Avoid applying pesticides to uninfested plants. Frequently, you just need to treat the edges of fields or landscape areas for invading pests.

You can use some special types of application equipment to improve the effectiveness of spot treatments. Field crop sprayers equipped with chemical injection pumps allow the operator to mix several different pesticides for the same application. The equipment automatically meters concentrated, liquid formulations and dilutes these with appropriate amounts of water.

If you adjust rope wick applicators to wipe herbicides onto target weeds growing above the crop, these become selective, spot treatment devices. Compact, hand-held sprayers allow operators to efficiently apply pesticides as spot treatments to small areas. All-terrain cycles (ATCs) eliminate tedious walking and speed up spot treatment applications.

Band Treatments. In orchards and vineyards, you can apply herbicides as bands within the tree or vine rows. This leaves an area between the rows with a groundcover of weeds that you can mow or cultivate. You use only about one fourth as much herbicide per acre with this method (Figure 8-9). Mowed weeds between trees or vines reduce soil compaction, prevent erosion, reduce dust, and lower orchard or vineyard floor temperatures. However, weeds in untreated strips may compete with the trees or vines for water and nutrients under certain circumstances.

Treating Alternate Rows or Blocks. Spraying alternate rows or blocks in orchards, vineyards, or field crops reduces the amount of pesticide applied. This technique provides some protection to natural enemies in the untreated sections. Use this technique when you need to make frequent treatments for the same pest. Examples include sprays for disease organisms, insects, or mites that occur over an extended period. Spray the untreated rows or blocks during the following application (Figure 8-10). You use only half as much material per application, although the pesticide dilution rate does not change.

Low-Volume Applications. Techniques using low-volume and ultra-low-volume sprays improve the efficiency of pesticide application in certain situations. Because low-volume applications

FIGURE 8-9.

Strip spraying is a way of controlling weeds in tree or vine rows while reducing the use of herbicides. Only about ¼ of the actual acreage needs to be treated. The area between rows is usually mowed and maintained as a ground cover.

FIGURE 8-10.

Applying pesticides to alternate rows or alternate blocks is a method that is sometimes used when several sprays are required for control of the same pest. This technique reduces the amount of pesticide used each time by 50%; it also provides locations in the treatment area for the protection of natural enemies.

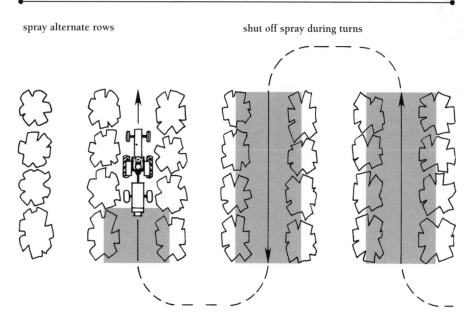

spray alternate rows   shut off spray during turns

use only about one fourth as much water carrier, spray mixtures are more concentrated. Ultra-low-volume applications involve highly concentrated mixtures of pesticide combined with a carrier such as vegetable oil. You need special application equipment for ultra-low-volume applications. Sometimes you can lower pesticide amounts by about one third with low-volume applications and by as much as one half with ultra-low-volume applications. However, keep the application consistent with label instructions or current University of California recommendations. You can also realize savings of time, fuel, labor, and water. Pesticide applications must be more accurate and calibration more precise when making low-volume applications. Operators using ultra-low-volume equipment work with more concentrated mixtures. This increases the hazards and emphasizes the need to wear label-prescribed personal protective equipment.

Pesticide Dosage Level

Sometimes you can lessen the injury to natural enemies by reducing the amount of active ingredient applied to the treatment area for control of certain insects or mites. Use this technique only if the lower dosages are effective against target pests. Be sure the rate is consistent with pesticide label instructions, current University of California recommendations, or a PCA's written recommendation. The number of target pests controlled may be less, but you might improve overall control by protecting natural enemies. Protecting natural enemies helps in long-term management of some insect and mite pest problems. This further reduces the need for additional pesticides. Lowering dosage levels only works when adequate numbers of certain species of natural enemies are present before treatment.

Type of Formulation Used

The pesticide formulation influences its selectivity. Granular formulations, for example, do not stick to foliage, increasing their selectivity to soil or aquatic pests. Applying a granular *systemic* formulation to the soil so plant roots take it up is a selective application practice. Pests feeding on plant tissue die, but most natural enemies and beneficial

FIGURE 8-11.

Use of a bait station, like this one being used for control of ground squirrels, is a method of selectively using pesticides. The bait station excludes most nontarget organisms.

insects do not contact the pesticide. (If the pesticide translocates to the nectar, it may destroy nectar feeders like honey bees and many parasitic wasps, however.) Liquid sprays and baits containing attractants improve the chances of target pests finding the pesticide. These substances make the pesticide more selective. Putting toxic baits in feeding stations to exclude nontarget animals increases selectivity. You can control squirrels with poisonous bait, for example, but the design of the bait station excludes dogs and livestock and protects children (Figure 8-11).

Using Adjuvants

You can use some adjuvants to improve selectivity as well as the effectiveness of certain pesticides. Use stickers, spreaders, and drift control agents to keep spray mixtures on target. Use surfactants to enhance uptake by target pests, and use attractants to make pesticides attractive specifically to target organisms.

KEEP THE PESTICIDE ON TARGET

Preventing drift improves the effectiveness of a pesticide application because more active ingredient reaches the target. Drift factors include

- the skill of the operator
- type of application equipment used
- droplet size of the spray being applied
- operating pressure of the sprayer
- physical properties of the pesticide formulation
- general weather conditions
- unique local weather conditions (microclimate)

Operator Skill and Knowledge of Options Available. Learn to use application equipment in ways that reduce or prevent drift problems. Use the lowest amount of pressure that will still produce an adequate spray pattern. Be sure nozzles are in good condition and are properly aligned. Thickeners added to the spray mixture reduce the number of fine droplets. Apply pesticides only during times when there is positive air movement away from a sensitive area. Leave a buffer strip between the treatment site and sensitive downwind areas. Shut off nozzles during turns.

Application Equipment. Your choice of application equipment can have an impact on how much pesticide drifts away from the treatment area. Sprayers that produce extremely small droplets increase drift. Lower the working pressure of the sprayer to reduce the quantity of small-sized droplets. Use low-pressure nozzles to maintain a suitable spray pattern. Apply herbicides with low-pressure nozzles whenever possible. Use shields around nozzles to confine the spray and reduce drift problems. Rope wick applicators used for weed control wipe herbicides onto leaves of weed plants, thus eliminating drift.

Electrostatic sprayers emit electrically charged spray droplets. These are attracted to the oppositely charged treatment surface. Because of the attraction between the spray particle and the treatment surface, fewer droplets drift away. Electrostatic sprayers seem to be most effective in situations where spray droplets travel only short distances.

Controlled droplet applicators (CDAs) produce more droplets of a uniform size. This reduces the quantity of very small and very large droplets and lowers some of the drift potential.

Droplet Size. Droplet size, a factor in drift, is determined by spray pressure, nozzle size, and spray solution characteristics. Most conventional sprayers produce a wide range of droplet sizes, averaging between 40 to 500 microns (μm) in diameter. Sidebar 18 compares the relative sizes, in microns, of different types of droplets. In a typical

SIDEBAR 18
Droplet Size Comparison

■ DROPLET SIZE COMPARISON
in microns

1,000 _____	
moderate rain	
500 _____	
light rain	
300 _____	average range of
drizzle	droplets produced
200 _____	by pesticide
mist	sprayers*
100 _____	
50 _____	
cloud	
30 _____	
20 _____	
coarse aerosol	
10 _____	
sea fog	
5 _____	
smoke	
0 _____	

*Most sprayers produce droplets ranging in size between 40 and 500 microns; droplets smaller than 100 microns are most effective for the control of insects and mites but are highly subject to drift.

sprayer, about 70% of the droplets will be in the 100 to 250 μm diameter range. An additional 20% will be larger than this, while about 10% are smaller than 100 μm. Larger droplets drift less because they are heavier and fall quickly. However, they are usually less effective for many types of pest control because they bounce or run off target surfaces. Although a 400 μm droplet is only 10 times larger in diameter than a 40 μm droplet, it contains 1,000 times more pesticide. Therefore, large droplets bouncing off or missing the target surface results in a considerable loss of active ingredient.

Smaller droplets, those below 100 μm, are the most efficient size for controlling many types of pests. Most of the droplets that actually reach insects and mites are smaller than 50 μm. Droplets of 100 μm or less in diameter are also best for effective penetration of dense foliage. However, these smaller droplets are the ones most likely to drift.

Physical Properties of the Pesticide Formulation. Factors such as the viscosity and volatility of pesticide formulations influence drift potential. Viscosity relates to the thickness of the liquid. The thicker or more viscous a liquid is, the more difficult it is to break it up into smaller droplets. Deposition aids include adjuvants used to increase the viscosity of a spray mixture, reducing drift by increasing droplet size. Volatilization is the process by which the pesticide changes from a liquid into a vapor. It takes place during application or occurs within several hours after spraying. Volatilization increases with higher temperatures. Pesticide vapors may drift many miles on slight air currents.

Evaporation of the carrier (usually water) in the spray droplet causes concentration of the pesticide and reduces droplet size. This happens while droplets travel between the sprayer and target surfaces. Hot, dry weather favors droplet evaporation, while high humidity and cool temperatures retard this process.

Weather Conditions. Wind is the most important component of weather contributing to pesticide drift. Slight winds of about 3 to 5 miles per hour help to distribute pesticide droplets and improve coverage. This air movement contributes to the mixing of pesticide spray with surrounding air. When air movement is below 2 miles per hour, spray may not mix evenly with the air. This can result in an uneven application. Winds greater than 10 miles per hour are too strong for safe pesticide application. High winds promote drift and increase evaporation. Table 8-2 describes ways to judge wind speed. You can use a small, hand-held device known as an *anemometer* to measure wind speed more accurately.

Besides wind, which is mostly horizontal air movement, vertical air movement contributes to mixing and dispersion of pesticide droplets. Air temperature influences vertical movement since warm air rises. You can detect the horizontal and vertical air movements and wind direction by burning a pot of oil or an old tire. However, this practice may be illegal in some areas due to air quality standards.

Temperature inversion is a weather condition that may promote pesticide drift. It occurs when the air from 20 to 100 or more feet above the treatment location is warmer than the air at ground level. This warm air forms a cap, preventing vertical air movement and pesticide dispersion (see Figure 6-47 on page 197). This layer traps fine droplets and spray vapor. They become concentrated as an invisible cloud under these conditions. A mild wind moves this pesticide cloud away from the treatment location. Eventually the pesticide falls to the ground or surfaces of nontarget plants or other objects. This condition may be dangerous because the concentration of small droplets moves together downwind instead of dispersing widely into the atmosphere.

Treatment areas may have microclimates that are different from surrounding areas. An irrigated field has higher

TABLE 8-2.

Method of Calculating Wind Speed.

For a practical means of estimating low wind velocities near the ground, toss a handful of dust into the air and walk downwind with the cloud of dust. If you can keep up with it in a slow walk, the wind is approximately 2 mph. If you can just barely keep up with it in a fast walk, the wind is approximately 4 mph. A lively run is approximately 10 mph, and only a well-trained athlete can dash 20 mph.

WIND VELOCITY (mph)	OBSERVATIONS
Less than 1	Smoke rises almost vertically.
1–3	Direction of wind shown by smoke drift, but not by wind vanes.
4–7	Wind felt on face; leaves rustle; ordinary wind vane moved by wind.
8–12	Leaves and small twigs in constant motion, wind extends light flag.
13–18	Raises dust and loose paper, small branches are moved.
19–24	Small trees in leaf begin to sway; crested wavelets form on inland water.

humidity and lower temperatures than dry areas nearby. This produces a localized, low-level temperature inversion that influences the concentration and movement of airborne pesticides.

FOLLOW-UP MONITORING

Follow up after every pesticide application to determine if the application was successful. Figure 8-12 is a follow-up checklist. Begin by comparing the amount of pesticide actually used with the anticipated amount. This should vary by no more than 10%. If more or less pesticide was applied, determine the cause. Check sprayer calibration, check tank mixing procedures, and recalculate the size of the target area. Look for clogged or worn nozzles and wear or blockage in the sprayer pumping system.

Inspect the application site to make sure coverage was adequate and uni-form. (Wear personal protective equipment if necessary.) Look for

- signs of pesticide runoff
- lack of penetration into dense foliage
- shingling
- uneven coverage from the top to bottom of large plants

After an application of insecticides or acaricides, make a second follow-up visit to the treatment area a day or so later. (If the restricted-entry interval has not lapsed, be sure to wear personal protective equipment and avoid unnecessary contact with plant foliage.) At this time look for signs indicating control of the target pest. Check for damage to natural enemies in the area. In addition, look for other problems, such as phytotoxicity or spotting of painted surfaces. Watch for pest resurgence and secondary pest outbreaks.

Follow up fungicide applications with an inspection to verify that the fungicide suppressed the pathogen.

After applying herbicides, follow up to see which weed species were controlled and which were partially or not controlled. Also look for damage to nontarget plants. Record this information on the treatment record and use it to determine if you need an additional herbicide treatment.

Record your follow-up observations in the same notebook used to record other aspects of the pesticide application. This information will be useful when you plan future applications for the same pest or in similar target locations.

AMOUNT OF PESTICIDE USED
(a) Calculated amount required for job: _____
(b) Actual amount used: _____
(c) Variation—divide (a) by (b) then multiply by 100.
   Subtract answer from 100. (This should be between + 10 and – 10.)
_____

COVERAGE
(a) Uniform _____   or uneven _____
(b) Runoff? _____
(c) Penetration into all areas? _____

EFFECTIVENESS
(a) Target pests controlled or reduced below economic injury level?
_____
(b) Condition of natural enemies: _____
(c) Secondary pest outbreak? _____

PROBLEMS
(a) Spotting or staining of surfaces? _____
(b) Injury to plants? _____
(c) Other: _____

COMMENTS _____
_____
_____

FIGURE 8-12.

Pesticide application follow-up checklist.

REVIEW QUESTIONS

1. **Which of the following is *not* a benefit of a pest monitoring program?**
   - ☐ a. Observing seasonal changes in pest populations
   - ☐ b. Ability to use more pesticides and apply these more frequently
   - ☐ c. Proper timing of pesticide applications
   - ☐ d. Assessing the effectiveness of pest control measures

2. **Knowing something about the life history of a pest will help you to:**
   - ☐ a. Impress your friends
   - ☐ b. Plan pesticide applications and other control measures that are most appropriate to the pest
   - ☐ c. Schedule pesticide applications without monitoring for the pest
   - ☐ d. Avoid all uses of pesticides or other control measures

3. **Which of the following indicators *would not* help you identify a pest?**
   - ☐ a. Feeding damage
   - ☐ b. Webbing
   - ☐ c. Fecal droppings
   - ☐ d. Barometric pressure

4. **When making weed management decisions, which of the following information about the field is *the least* useful?**
   - ☐ a. Species of birds present in the area
   - ☐ b. The stage of development of weeds (seedling, flowering, postflowering)
   - ☐ c. Species of weeds present
   - ☐ d. Whether the relative abundance of different weed species is changing from previous seasons

5. **A common use of a pheromone monitoring trap is to:**
   - ☐ a. Reduce the populations of specific insect pests
   - ☐ b. Collect large numbers of different insect species
   - ☐ c. Determine what beneficial insects are present
   - ☐ d. Time insecticide sprays for optimal control

6. **Pesticides that move deeper into the soil (percolate) have a tendency to break down:**
   - ☐ a. More quickly than pesticides on the soil surface
   - ☐ b. About the same as pesticides on the soil surface
   - ☐ c. More slowly than pesticides on the soil surface
   - ☐ d. Rapidly except during freezing temperatures

7. **How do high levels of organic matter in the soil sometimes influence pesticide breakdown?**
   - ☐ a. Organic matter binds the pesticide, making it unavailable to microorganisms, slowing the breakdown
   - ☐ b. Organic matter rapidly breaks down the pesticide
   - ☐ c. Organic matter increases microorganism activity in the soil, speeding up the breakdown
   - ☐ d. Organic matter lowers soil temperature, reducing the microorganism activity and slowing pesticide breakdown

8. **Three factors that make for effective pesticide use are:**
   - ☐ a. Cost of the pesticide, size of area to be treated, and location of pests
   - ☐ b. Hot weather, adequate rainfall or irrigation, and concentration of the spray mixture
   - ☐ c. Timing application to optimal weather conditions, pest susceptibility to the pesticide, and ability to protect natural enemies
   - ☐ d. Volume of spray used, method of application, and capacity of the spray tank

9. **Which of the following *would not* be a selective way of using a pesticide?**
   - ☐ a. Using the maximum label rate of broad spectrum pesticide and applying it uniformly
   - ☐ b. Using spot treatments
   - ☐ c. Making band treatments
   - ☐ d. Using a systemic formulation to protect natural enemies

10. **One way to reduce the chances of pesticide drift is to:**
    - ☐ a. Make applications when wind speed exceeds 10 mph
    - ☐ b. Lower pressure in the system and use large-orifice nozzles
    - ☐ c. Make applications during hot, dry weather
    - ☐ d. Use nozzles that create the smallest droplet sizes

11. **Which type of application equipment would produce the *least* amount of pesticide drift?**
    - ☐ a. Rope wick applicator
    - ☐ b. Backpack sprayer with one size "02" (²⁄₆₄ inch) nozzle
    - ☐ c. Boom spray with 14 size "04" (⁴⁄₆₄ inch) nozzles
    - ☐ d. Orchard air blast sprayer with 12 size "05" (⁵⁄₆₄ inch) and 8 size "06" (⁶⁄₅₄ inch) nozzles

9

Pesticide Application Equipment

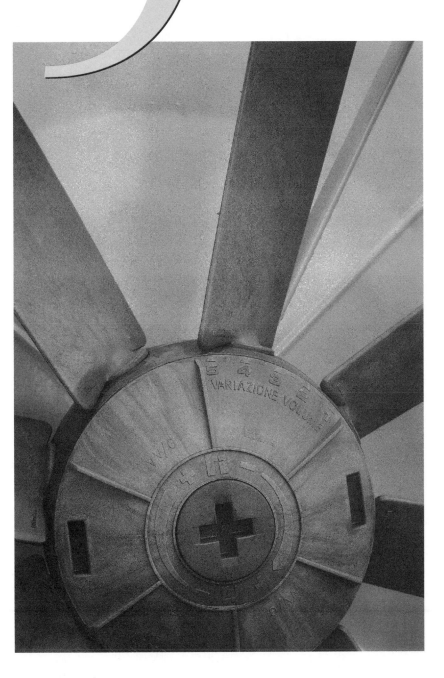

Air blast sprayers use powerful fans to propel
spray droplets to target surfaces.

PESTICIDE APPLICATION
equipment ranges from simple devices
attached to garden hoses to elaborate
machines mounted on self-propelled
ground applicators, fixed-wing aircraft,
and helicopters. Some equipment
specifically applies dusts, while other
types apply granules. You can select
from many different types of equipment
designed for applying liquids. Special
equipment is available for
- weed control
- applying pesticides to orchards,
  vineyards, row crops, and field
  crops
- injecting pesticides into the soil
- applying pesticides to animals
- controlling aquatic pests
- controlling pests in buildings and
  residences
- many other special purposes

This chapter describes the different
types of pesticide application devices,
except those used with aircraft. It
explains and illustrates features of components, such as tanks, pumps, and
nozzles. It also discusses maintenance
procedures.

LIQUID APPLICATION EQUIPMENT

Most liquid application equipment
uses hydraulic pressure or air to propel
pesticide droplets to the target. This
equipment is either hand-operated or
powered by mechanical sources such as
a tractor power take-off (PTO) or electric, gasoline, or diesel motor. Liquid
application equipment consists of several components, including

- a tank for mixing and holding the
  pesticide
- a pump or other device for creating pressure to move the liquid
- one or more nozzles for breaking
  the spray up into small droplets
  and directing it toward the target
- on some equipment, fans, pressure
  regulators, filter screens, control
  valves, agitators, booms, hoses,
  and fittings to improve pesticide
  handling, mixing, and application
  (Figure 9-1)

Components of Liquid Application Equipment

Before considering a pesticide application machine as a whole unit, look at all
the individual components. Make sure
they meet your application needs. Some
components, such as nozzles, are easy to
replace when worn or damaged or if
your application needs change. Other
parts, such as tanks, are expensive to
replace, and may be difficult to repair if
they become damaged. Select these with
care to be sure they are compatible with
the pesticides you plan to use.

Pesticide Tanks

Manufacturers produce tanks for
mixing and holding liquid pesticides
from metal, fiberglass, and thermoplastic materials such as polyethylene
and polypropylene. Choose a nonab-
sorptive material so you can easily
clean the tank of pesticide residues.
Tanks must be corrosion- and rust-
resistant to protect them from reacting
with corrosive pesticides. They should

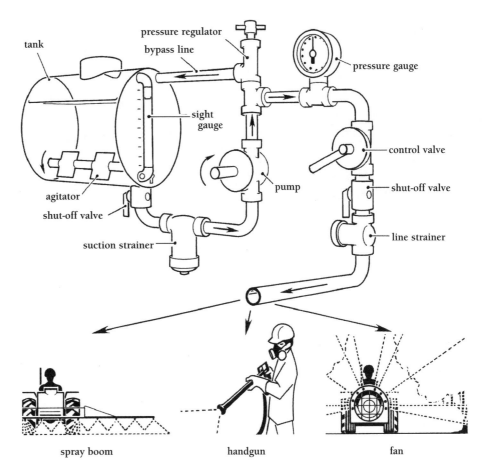

tank
pressure regulator
bypass line
pressure gauge
sight gauge
control valve
agitator
shut-off valve
pump
shut-off valve
suction strainer
line strainer

spray boom   handgun   fan

FIGURE 9-1.

Liquid application equipment usually includes a tank for mixing and holding pesticides (often equipped with an agitator) and a pump for creating hydraulic pressure, and may also include a pressure regulator, pressure gauge, control valve, and several types of strainers. Spray is emitted through nozzles on a spray boom, manifold, or hand spray gun, and may be dispersed by a fan.

have a large opening for easy filling and cleaning (Figure 9-2). A tight-fitting cover prevents pesticides from spilling or splashing.

Many counties require that tank covers be lockable. Although not always required by law, a lockable cover is a worthwhile safety feature. It prevents unauthorized or accidental exposure to the tank contents. Larger tanks need a bottom drain so you can completely empty them. All 40-gallon or larger tanks must have a sight gauge or other accurate means to determine the amount of liquid in the tank. Equip external sight gauges with shut-off valves to prevent leaking if they become damaged (Figure 9-3).

Tanks are commonly available in capacities from 3 to 1,600 gallons. Table 9-1 is a guide for selecting tanks based on your pesticide application needs.

Metal Tanks. Manufacturers produce tanks from one of several different grades of stainless steel. They also make steel tanks with epoxy or other coatings to prevent them from rusting or corroding. Stainless steel has superior qualities for rust and corrosion resistance, so you can use most pesticides in them. Stainless steel cleans easily and is strong and durable. If damaged, you can repair stainless steel tanks, although repairs may require considerable skill. These tanks are more expensive than tanks

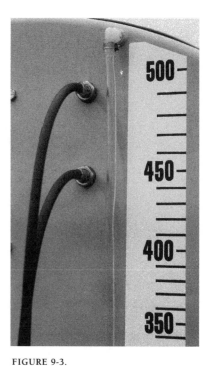

FIGURE 9-2.

Pesticide tanks must have a large top opening for ease in filling. The opening should be fitted with a splash-proof cover.

FIGURE 9-3.

A sight gauge enables the operator to tell how much pesticide is contained in the tank at all times. External tubes must be equipped with a shut-off valve to prevent leaks if the gauge becomes damaged.

TABLE 9-1.

Pesticide Tank Selection Guide.

CHARACTERISTIC	TANK TYPE				
	COATED METAL	STAINLESS STEEL	FIBERGLASS	POLYPROPYLENE	POLYETHYLENE
acid resistance	fair to good	depends on grade	fair to good	good	good
alkali resistance	excellent	excellent	fair	good	good
organic solvent resistance	excellent	excellent	poor to fair	good	fair
rust and corrosion resistance	fair to good	excellent	excellent	excellent	excellent
absorbs pesticides	if scratched	no	if scratched	no	no
easily cleaned	good	excellent	fair	excellent	excellent
easily repaired	yes	yes	yes	no	no
strength and durability	good to excellent	excellent	good	good	good
weight	heavy	heavy	medium	light	light
requires external reinforcement	no	no	no	yes	yes
cost	moderate	high	moderate	low	low

FIGURE 9-4.

Pumps for powered sprayers are available in many different styles and capacities. Be sure to select a pump that is suitable to the type of pesticide being used and one that can supply the pressure and volume requirements of your application needs.

made from other materials, but they generally last longer.

Galvanized or coated metal tanks require more care and attention. Scratches or chips in the protective coating expose bare metal and may cause serious corrosion problems. You cannot use some pesticides in coated metal tanks. Glyphosate, for example, reacts with metal to produce hydrogen gas, resulting in an explosion hazard. Epoxy coatings have fair to good resistance to acids and excellent resistance to alkaline materials and organic solvents. You must inspect epoxy coated metal tanks regularly and touch up chips and scratches to prevent corrosion.

Fiberglass Tanks. Fiberglass tanks are strong and durable and you can easily repair small damaged areas. They are lighter than metal tanks. Fiberglass is highly resistant to organic solvents. It has good to fair resistance to acids, but only fair resistance to alkaline materials. The fiberglass material absorbs pesticide liquids if there are scratches or abrasions on the interior tank walls. This absorption may cause contamination of future tank mixes. Therefore, you must repair scratched areas with resin to protect against this problem.

Thermoplastic Tanks. Most thermoplastic materials have good resistance to acids and alkalis. Polyethylene is a common material used for spray tanks, although low-density polyethylene does not resist organic solvents well. Manufacturers produce most thermoplastic sprayer tanks from either high-density polyethylene or polypropylene. These plastics are lightweight and durable. However, when these plastics get warm they become flexible and will deform unless they are reinforced or supported. Minor scratches or abrasions do not cause absorption problems. However, polyethylene and polypropylene are difficult to repair if they become punctured or cracked.

Pumps

Most liquid sprayers use pumps to move the pesticide from the tank to the nozzles. The pump must generate adequate pressure to propel spray droplets to the target (Figure 9-4). Small, hand-operated sprayers use simple bellows or piston pumps. You operate these pumps by squeezing a trigger or moving a lever. Some compressed air sprayers have a piston-type air pump, similar to a bicycle tire pump. The pump compresses air in the sealed pesticide tank. When you open a valve, the compressed air forces liquid out of the tank. Some sprayers use cartridges of compressed carbon dioxide gas to pressurize the spray. Powered sprayers have more complex mechanical pumps designed for liquid pesticides.

Selecting the appropriate pump for a particular application depends on the formulations of pesticides you use. You must also consider the volume and pressure needed to apply these pesticides. Water-soluble and emulsifiable concentrate pesticide formulations are less abrasive to pumps than wettable powder, flowable, or dry flowable formulations. Construction materials and type of pump also affect how well pumps perform and wear. When choosing a sprayer pump, consider the following features.

Output capacity. The pump must supply enough volume for all nozzles under every use condition. If the sprayer has hydraulic agitation, the pump must have sufficient output to recirculate liquid in the tank while spraying. Pump output capacity is given in gallons per minute (gpm).

Pressure. A pump must produce the desired capacity at a pressure suitable for the work you perform. Some high-capacity pumps are only able to produce low pressures. You can regulate most high-pressure pumps so they are suitable for low-pressure work as well. Pressure is measured in pounds per square inch (psi).

Resistance to corrosion and wear. The materials used to construct the pump, as well as pump design, affect its ability to resist corrosion and wear. Pumps with the fewest parts contacting spray chemicals are the most suitable for corrosive pesticides. Pump design is also important in reducing the amount of wear due to wettable powder abrasion.

Ease of repair. An important feature of any pump is the ease with which you can repair it. Be sure parts are readily available.

Type of drive. Pumps require different operating speeds depending on their design. Most tractor power take-off shafts rotate at 540 and/or 1,000 rpm. Gasoline and diesel engines and electric motors all have specific operational rpm ranges. Because each pump also has particular horsepower requirements, match it with the speed and horsepower of the drive unit. If a pump needs to operate at higher speeds, you may need a special transmission.

Table 9-2 is a guide for selecting common pump designs. Other types of pumps not included in this table may also be available and suitable for certain applications.

Diaphragm Pumps (Figure 9-5). Diaphragm pumps are a popular style used on several types of spray equipment. Manufacturers produce these pumps from durable materials, including aluminum, steel, and high-impact plastic. You can use these for low- and high-pressure applications. Diaphragm pumps handle abrasive and corrosive chemicals well because only the chemical-resistant diaphragm contacts pumped liquids. They are also simple to maintain and repair.

Diaphragm pumps have a low- to medium-volume capacity of between 5 and 40 gallons per minute. They can produce pressures in the range of 200 to 700 psi. These pumps operate in the range of 500 to 800 rpm.

A cam that moves one to three diaphragms produces the pumping action. Moving a diaphragm in one direction creates a negative pressure inside the pumping chamber. This negative pressure forces open a one-way valve, pulling liquid pesticide from the tank into the chamber. As the diaphragm reverses direction, the one-way valve seals shut. Positive pressure in the chamber forces open a second one-way valve,

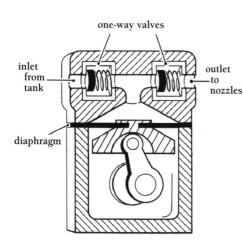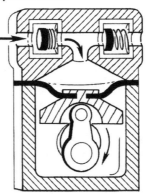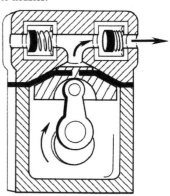

FIGURE 9-5.

In a diaphragm pump, a flexible diaphragm is moved up and down by a cam mechanism. This oscillation moves liquid through one-way valves. Some diaphragm pumps incorporate two or three diaphragms moved by the same cam.

TABLE 9-2.

Guide to Selecting the Proper Pump for a Pesticide Sprayer.

PUMP TYPE	PRESSURE RANGE (psi)	OUTPUT VOLUME (gpm)	OPERATING SPEED (rpm)	SUITABLE PESTICIDE FORMULATIONS	COMMENTS
CENTRIFUGAL	5–200	>200	1,000–5,000	all	Used on large, heavy duty sprayers. Common on air blast sprayers. Best for high-volume uses.
DIAPHRAGM	20–700	5–40	500–800	all (organic solvents may deteriorate some parts)	Often used on low-volume weed sprayers. Also used with some high-pressure equipment.
GEAR	20–100	5–65	500–2,000	nonabrasive	Limited uses. Good for low volume and low pressure.
PISTON	20–1,000	2–60	500–800	nonabrasive unless equipped with wear-resistant cups	Excellent for high-pressure applications. Very versatile.
ROLLER	10–300	8–40	300–2,000	nonabrasive only; may be damaged by organic solvents	Limited low-volume uses. Can produce moderate pressure.

pushing the liquid pesticide out another opening. Pressure in the system may pulsate due to this action. However, more expensive pumps have two or three diaphragms working opposite each other that minimize pulsating pressure. Manufacturers equip some diaphragm pumps with surge chambers to reduce pulsating pressure.

Diaphragm pumps have only a few moving parts. Diaphragms usually wear out after a while, so you must replace them when they begin to leak. Replace the rubber valves when they fail to seal properly. The petroleum-based solvents in emulsifiable concentrate formulations accelerate the deterioration of these rubber components.

Low-pressure diaphragm pumps are suitable for most herbicide applications. You can use the high-pressure styles in hydraulic and air blast sprayers.

Roller Pumps (Figure 9-6). Roller pumps are among the least expensive pump types. They are capable of producing moderate volumes, between 8 and 40 gpm. Low to moderate pressures, in the range of 10 to 300 psi are possible with roller pumps. They operate in the speed range of 300 to 2,000 rpm.

In these pumps, a series of rollers fit into slots around the circumference of a rotating disc or *impeller*. The impeller spins off-center to its housing. This allows the rollers to move further in or further out of their slots. Liquid is picked up at the point where rollers are furthest out. The impeller rotation forces the rollers back into their slots and pressurizes the liquid.

Roller pumps are subject to considerable wear, especially from abrasive materials like wettable powders. Rollers made of rubber last longer. However, you must use nylon or Teflon rollers to pump petroleum-based pesticides such as oils or emulsions, because petroleum-based pesticides deteriorate rubber. Usually, you can easily replace worn out rollers. Roller pumps are most suitable for herbicide applications, especially if you use flowable, emulsifiable concentrate, soluble powder, or other nonabrasive formulations.

Gear Pumps (Figure 9-7). Gear pumps are suitable for low-pressure applications between 20 and 100 psi. They can produce spray in a range of 5 to 65 gpm. They operate in the range of 500 to 2,000 rpm.

Manufacturers produce two types of gear pump designs. The *external gear* design has two identical gears that mesh with each other and move fluid

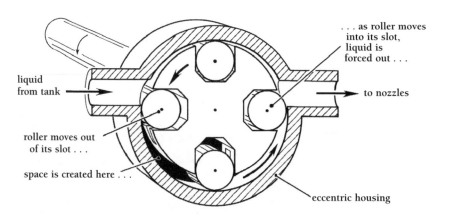

FIGURE 9-6.

Roller pumps consist of cylindrical rollers that move in or out of slots in a spinning rotor. This action creates space for liquid during half of the rotor rotation and discharges the liquid out of the pumping chamber during the remainder of the rotor rotation.

through the pumping chamber. An *internal gear* design has a smaller gear meshing inside a larger gear, producing the pumping action.

Manufacturers build gear pumps from brass, bronze, or alloy steel. These usually are molded parts, making them difficult to repair. You can use lubricating liquids, such as oil sprays or emulsi-fiable concentrates in gear pumps. However, wettable powders and similar abrasive formulations create wear in these pumps.

Centrifugal Pumps (Figure 9-8). Manufacturers produce centrifugal pumps out of high-impact plastic, aluminum, cast iron, or bronze. These

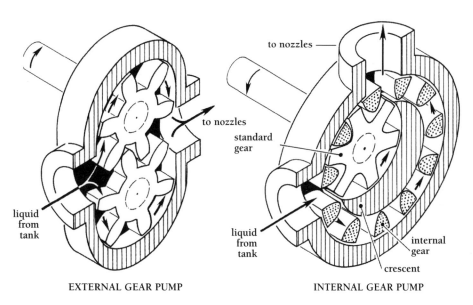

EXTERNAL GEAR PUMP   INTERNAL GEAR PUMP

FIGURE 9-7.

The external gear pump moves liquids by a meshing action of two identical gears. The internal gear pump consists of a standard gear that meshes with and drives an internal gear to move liquids. The close meshing of the gears in both of these designs forces fluids to move in only one direction through the pumping chamber.

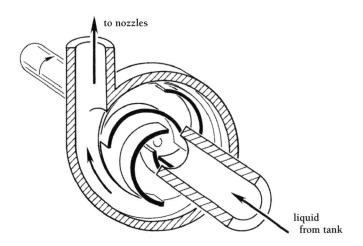

FIGURE 9-8.

In a centrifugal pump, liquid enters near the center of a vaned rotor. As the rotor spins, the liquid is moved away from the center by centrifugal force. Rotors must turn at a high rpm in order to build up sufficient pressure for most spray applications.

pumps are heavy duty and adaptable to a wide variety of spray applications. They produce volumes in excess of 200 gpm at pressures ranging between 5 and 200 psi. Centrifugal pumps require operating speeds between 1,000 and 5,000 rpm. A high-speed impeller creates the pumping action that forces liquids out of the pump. Manufacturers produce high-pressure centrifugal pumps by adding one or more stages of impellers. In these, fluids pass from one impeller to the next.

Centrifugal pumps have a wide range of applications. You can use them for spraying abrasive materials because there is no close contact between moving parts. They are often easy to repair and work well for high-volume air blast sprayers.

Piston Pumps (Figure 9-9). Piston pumps produce pressures in the range of 20 to 1,000 psi at volumes between 2 and 60 gpm. They operate between 500 and 800 rpm. These are generally the most expensive pumps. However, you usually need this type for high pressures or if you use both high and low pressures.

One or more pistons travel inside cylinders, forcing fluids through one-way valves. This action is similar to that of diaphragm pumps. However, piston displacement is usually greater than diaphragm movement. Pulsating pressure may be a problem with piston pumps, as it is in diaphragm pumps. Abrasive chemicals cause wear in piston pumps, although most have easily replaceable cylinder liners and piston cups. More expensive piston pumps have stainless steel or ceramic cylinder liners to resist wear.

Agitators

Spraying equipment needs an agitator for initial mixing of pesticides and to keep insoluble mixtures from settling inside spray tanks. Use a sprayer with an agitator whenever you use wettable powders, water-dispersible granules, flowables, or emulsions. There are hydraulic and mechanical agitators available.

Hydraulic Agitators (Figure 9-10). Hydraulic agitators circulate spray material back through jets located in the bottom of the spray tank. In some designs, this fluid comes from a bypass on the pressure side of the pump. Other sprayers have a separate pump to circulate fluid for tank agitation. Jets located in the bottom of the tank must be at least 1 foot from tank walls. This pre-

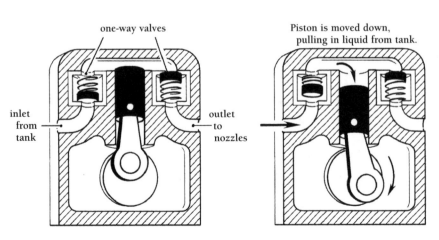
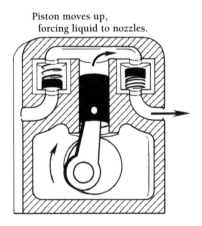

one-way valves

Piston is moved down, pulling in liquid from tank.

Piston moves up, forcing liquid to nozzles.

inlet from tank

outlet to nozzles

FIGURE 9-9.

This sequence shows how a piston pump functions. The downward movement of a piston draws liquid through a one-way valve into the cylinder. When the piston moves up, liquid is forced out through another one-way valve. Some pumps consist of several pistons working opposite each other.

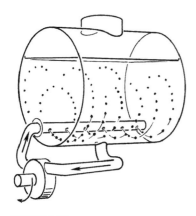

FIGURE 9-10.

Hydraulic agitators recirculate spray material back into the spray tank, providing continual mixing of the solution.

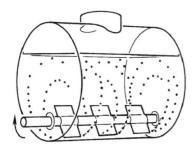

FIGURE 9-11.

Mechanical agitators consist of paddles or propellers that continually stir the liquid in the spray tank.

vents the spray from weakening or making holes in the tank.

The main disadvantage with hydraulic agitators is that they are not able to break up settled spray material when you shut the pump down for a while. Severe settling requires mechanical agitation to suspend insoluble particles.

Mechanical Agitators. Mechanical agitators are propellers or paddles mounted on a shaft near the bottom of a spray tank (Figure 9-11). The shaft passes through the tank wall and connects to the drive line by belts or chains. Mechanical agitators provide constant mixing in the tank as long as the sprayer is running. They are usually effective in suspending settled formulations. Mechanical agitators require some maintenance, especially where shafts pass through tank walls. Packings and grease fittings prevent leaks but need periodic tightening and servicing. Be sure to use a marine-grade grease on bearings and seals exposed to liquids. Also, periodically tighten and service belts or chains.

Filter Screens and Strainers

Filter screens and strainers protect pumps and prevent clogged nozzles. They remove undissolved clumps of pesticide formulation, sand, soil, and other debris from the spraying system. Filter screens and strainers help prevent clogged nozzles when using water that may contain small quantities of sand.

Strainers. Strainers (Figure 9-12) are devices containing filter screens that remove foreign particles that would otherwise clog nozzles or damage pumps. Manufacturers usually put strainers between the tank and pump (*suction strainer*), between the pump and nozzles (*pressure strainer*), and at the nozzles (*nozzle strainer*).

A simple *suction strainer* connects to the end of the intake hose near the bottom of the spray tank. Use this type of strainer in low-capacity systems, usually with roller pumps. Other systems use low-capacity suction strainers, sometimes called *line strainers*. Manufacturers install these into a section of the hose connecting the tank to the pump. Both the suction and low-capacity line strainers have an effective straining area of about 3 to 5 square inches.

Larger capacity sprayers have a Y or T line strainer located between the tank and pump. These contain screens providing from 7 to 30 square inches of filter surface. A capped opening on the line strainer allows removing and

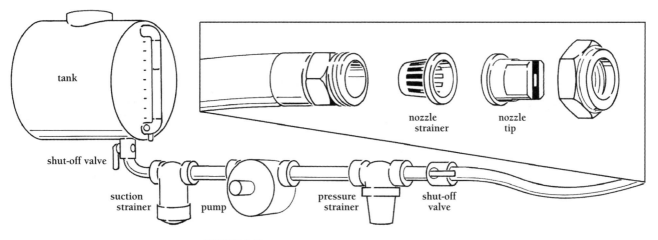

FIGURE 9-12.

Strainers hold filter screens and are located in different parts of the system. The suction strainer is positioned between the tank and pump. The pressure strainer is located between the pump and nozzles. Nozzle strainers are located adjacent to nozzles.

cleaning the filter screen. You do not have to disassemble any plumbing or disconnect hoses. Shut-off valves between the strainer and the tank prevent spray material leaks when you remove the filter for servicing.

The *pressure strainer* is similar to the suction strainer, but it is located between the pump and nozzles. It also contains a capped opening so you can remove the filter screen for cleaning. The sprayer should have a shut-off valve between the pressure strainer and the pump. This prevents leaks while cleaning filters.

Use *nozzle strainers* to protect nozzle orifices from smaller particles missed by the suction and pressure strainers. These go between the nozzle and nozzle retainer. Some nozzle strainers have spring-loaded check valves. These keep the nozzles from dripping when you shut off the spray. These check valves usually lower the pressure at the nozzle, however. You may need to increase the system pressure to accommodate them.

Filter Screens. Filter screens range in size from 10 to 200 mesh. A 10 mesh size has 10 openings per inch. The larger the mesh number the finer the screen. For most spraying equipment, the suction strainer should have a coarse screen

in the range of 10 to 20 mesh. Smaller mesh restricts liquid flow to the pump and also plugs easily. This results in a pressure drop within the system and increases strain on the pump.

For the pressure strainer, use a finer screen in the range of 40 to 50 mesh. This allows the pressure strainer to collect particles missed by the suction strainer.

Screens of nozzle strainers most commonly range from 50 to 200 mesh. Use smaller mesh screens when equipping your sprayer with smaller nozzle orifices. Match filter screens with nozzle orifice dimensions to prevent clogging. However, the filter size should never be much smaller than the orifice. You do not need nozzle strainers if the nozzle orifice is larger than the pressure strainer screen mesh.

Nozzles

Spray nozzles control the application rate, drop size, and spray pattern. They also contribute to the thoroughness and safety of the pesticide application (Figure 9-13). Several different nozzle types are available, depending on the type of application. Nozzles are one of the most important parts of the sprayer. If you do not carefully select and maintain the nozzles, you can waste all your efforts

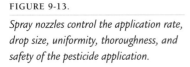

FIGURE 9-13.

Spray nozzles control the application rate, drop size, uniformity, thoroughness, and safety of the pesticide application.

for pest control. Base your nozzle selection on several criteria, including the

- type of material the nozzle is made of
- style of nozzle
- nozzle orifice size

Nozzle Construction and Wear.
Manufacturers produce nozzles out of several different materials, all of which are subject to wear. The design of the nozzle, the kinds of materials being sprayed, and the spray pressure influence nozzle wear. Flat-spray styles with sharp-edged orifices wear much faster initially than, for example, a flooding tip with a circular orifice. Also, as the spray pattern angle increases, the wear on the nozzle increases. Further, the size of the orifice affects wear—larger orifices wear more slowly than smaller ones.

Spray materials influence wear differently depending on the amount of dissolved or suspended solids in the liquid. True solutions cause the least amount of wear, while suspended solids cause different degrees of wear. Wear caused by suspended solids depends on

- particle size
- size distribution
- shape
- hardness
- concentration

The solids that influence wear may be the pesticide or may be an inert carrier in the formulation. Rate of nozzle wear, even when using the same type of pesticide over a time, varies. Sometimes chemical companies make small changes in inert ingredients in their formulations. These have no effect on the performance of the pesticide but may influence nozzle wear. Also, formulations of the same pesticide can vary from one manufacturer to another. Some pesticides form crystals under certain conditions of water pH, water temperature, and the presence of other chemicals. These crystals often increase wear on nozzles. Higher liquid pressure increases the rate of nozzle wear.

As a nozzle wears, the volume and pattern of spray changes and affects the quality of application. Replace nozzles when they fail to deliver an accurate amount and the desired spray pattern. The output from nozzles of the same size, used together on a boom, should not vary from each other by more than 10%. To ensure uniform wear, be sure to use nozzles made from the same material. Manufacturers produce nozzles from the following materials:

Brass. Brass nozzles are moderately inexpensive but wear quickly from abrasion. Brass is an acceptable material if you do not use abrasive sprays or if you replace nozzles frequently.

Stainless steel. Stainless steel nozzles do not corrode and they resist abrasion. Although hardened stainless steel wears exceptionally well, these nozzles are more expensive than most others.

Aluminum and monel. Aluminum and monel nozzles resist corrosion but are highly susceptible to abrasion because they are such soft metals. Avoid using aluminum and monel nozzles unless you need specific corrosion resistance.

Plastic. Plastic nozzles are the least expensive. The plastic material resists corrosion, but when made totally of plastic they may swell if exposed to organic solvents. Plastics also have low abrasion resistance. Use solid plastic nozzles only with selected pesticides. Some plastic nozzles have stainless steel orifice inserts, making them much more resistant to wear. The inserts also reduce problems of swelling.

Tungsten carbide and ceramic. Tungsten carbide and ceramic nozzles are highly resistant to abrasion and corrosion. To reduce costs, manufacturers use tungsten carbide or ceramic inserts with brass or plastic nozzle bodies. Use these types of nozzles for high-pressure and abrasive sprays.

Nozzle Types. Different applications require nozzles adapted to specific requirements. Nozzles used to apply

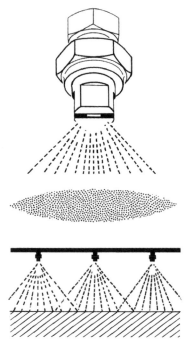

FIGURE 9-14.

Flat-spray nozzles produce a fan-shaped pattern that has more droplets in the center part of the fan than at either edge. This allows for overlap of the spray, eliminating gaps and providing an even pattern when multiple nozzles are used.

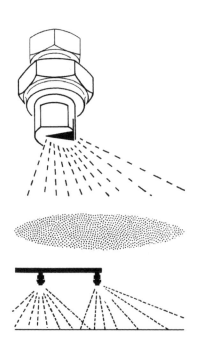

FIGURE 9-15.

Off-center flat-spray nozzles emit a full pattern of spray to one side of the nozzle. These are used on the ends of spray booms to extend the reach of the nozzle.

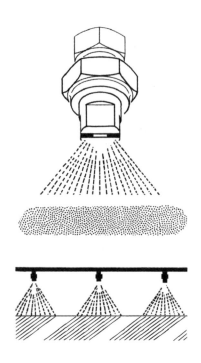

FIGURE 9-16.

Even flat-spray nozzles provide a uniform distribution of spray throughout the fan pattern. The spray from these nozzles is not overlapped; these nozzles are used to apply separate bands of pesticide without overlap.

herbicides in a field may be unsuitable for applying insecticides or fungicides to foliage. Spraying weeds along a roadside may require different nozzles than spraying weeds in a corn field. Orchard sprayers have different nozzle requirements than row crop sprayers. Residential, industrial, and institutional applications need nozzles suitable for confined spaces.

Flat-spray nozzles (Figure 9-14). Flat-spray nozzles distribute pesticide in a flat fan shape, with fan angles ranging between 50 and 160 degrees. Flat-spray nozzles produce a pattern with more spray droplets in the center of the fan. The pattern tapers off at each end. This allows you to evenly space a series of flat-spray nozzles on a boom, allowing an overlap of the spray pattern of each nozzle. If you operate the nozzles at the correct height, the spray patterns combine into an even swath with nearly uniform deposits between nozzles. Use flat-spray nozzles for herbicide, fungicide, and insecticide soil applications.

An off-center flat-spray nozzle emits a pattern of spray more to one side than the other (Figure 9-15). Use this nozzle style at the end of a boom to increase the spray swath width. Use this nozzle on orchard and vineyard soil for applying herbicide to both sides of the plant row.

Low-pressure flat-spray nozzles provide an acceptable spray pattern at pressures as low as 10 psi. Use these nozzles for the same types of applications as conventional flat spray nozzles. However, they have fewer problems with drift because they produce larger drops at a lower pressure.

Even flat-spray nozzles (Figure 9-16). Manufacturers produce even flat-spray nozzles in 40, 80, and 95 degree fan angles. They are similar to flat nozzles,

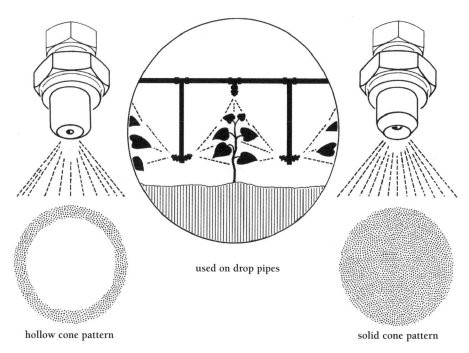

used on drop pipes

hollow cone pattern   solid cone pattern

FIGURE 9-17.

Cone nozzles are used for applying insecticides and fungicides to foliage, especially when larger volumes are required to assure complete coverage.

except there is no tapering of spray volume at the pattern ends. Use these when applying one or more separate bands that do not overlap.

Cone nozzles (Figure 9-17). Use cone nozzles for applying insecticides and fungicides to dense foliage. These produce spray in either a hollow cone or solid cone pattern, with spray angles between 20 and 110 degrees. Use *hollow cone spray nozzles* for most applications. If you need larger, heavier droplets to reduce drift or if you require greater volume, use solid cone nozzles.

Use *disc-core nozzles* (Figure 9-18), which are a type of cone nozzle, in air blast sprayers. They are suitable for high pressure and high flow rate applications of insecticides and fungicides. Standard disc-core nozzles produce a hollow-cone spray pattern, while full-cone spray patterns produce greater volume output. The orifice is in a disc made of brass, hardened stainless steel, ceramic, or tungsten carbide. Fitted behind this disc is a core, sometimes called a *spinner plate*. This core pro-

duces a high rotation speed of the liquid into the whirl chamber. Manufacturers make cores out of brass, aluminum, nylon, hardened stainless steel, and tungsten carbide. Using different combinations of discs and cores provides a wide range of volume output and droplet size.

Solid stream nozzles (Figure 9-19). Solid stream nozzles produce a single solid stream of pesticide. Use these in hand spray guns for spraying distant objects. They are also suitable for crack and crevice treatments in and around buildings and for banding fluids in row crops. Different orifice sizes determine the volume of output.

Flood nozzles (Figure 9-20). Flood nozzles produce a relatively wide fan angle of up to 160 degrees. Use these to apply large volumes of liquid at low pressure. People commonly use these for liquid fertilizers. Operators rarely use flood nozzles for pesticide application because it is usually unnecessary to apply large volumes of liquid. Because of the large fan angle, use a wide spacing on the boom.

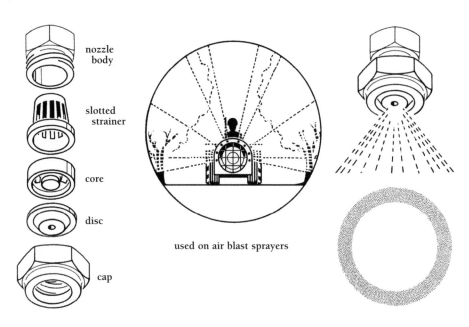

used on air blast sprayers

FIGURE 9-18.

Disc-core nozzles are used in high-pressure applications that have a high flow rate, such as air blast sprayers. They are also used for some low-volume applications with air blast sprayers. Cores (or spinner plates) break up spray droplets and improve the deposition pattern.

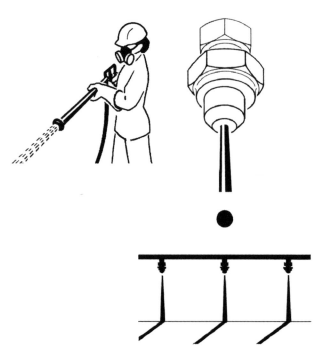

FIGURE 9-19.

Solid stream nozzles are used in high-pressure hand spray guns and in low-pressure crack and crevice units. They are also used on boom sprayers for applying fluids in bands.

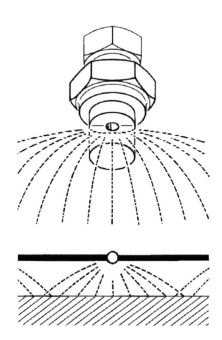

FIGURE 9-20.

Flood nozzles are used to apply large volumes of liquid under low pressure. They are occasionally used for pesticide application but are more commonly used for liquid fertilizers.

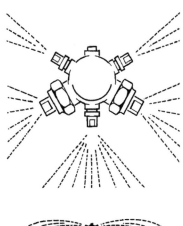

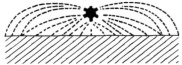

FIGURE 9-21.

Broadcast nozzles enable a wide swath to be sprayed without using a series of nozzles on a boom. Swath widths from 30 to 60 feet can be produced.

Broadcast nozzles (Figure 9-21). Use broadcast nozzles on boomless sprayers. They consist of a cluster of nozzles all attached at one point. They produce a swath of between 30 and 60 feet. These nozzles are useful where you cannot use a spray boom but need a wide swath. People use broadcast nozzles, like flood nozzles, when large volumes of liquid need to be applied. It is more difficult, however, to be accurate with broadcast nozzles than with a series of evenly spaced flat nozzles on a boom.

Bifluid nozzles. Bifluid nozzles break liquids up into extremely fine droplets, such as in a mist or fog. To do this, they use a high-velocity airstream. Use these on some types of aerosol generators for fogging enclosed areas such as greenhouses and warehouses. They also work for fogging confined outdoor areas.

Nozzle Tip Numbers. Most manufacturers have a method of coding nozzle tips, and they print identification numbers on the face of the nozzle. For example, for flat spray nozzles, a common nozzle is number 8004. The first two digits indicate that the nozzle produces an 80 degree fan spray. The last two numbers indicate the volume of spray (0.4 gallons per minute) output at 40 psi. Nozzle number 65155 is a 65 degree fan spray producing a volume of 1.55 gallons per minute at 40 psi. Check the manufacturer's catalog to determine the rated operating pressure for the nozzles you use. Some nozzle styles operate at higher or lower pressures. For example, manufacturers commonly rate flood nozzles at 10 psi.

Manufacturers code solid stream, flood, broadcast, bifluid, and disc nozzles in a similar way. For example, some assign disc core nozzles numbers such as 4, 6, 7, and 10. Sometimes the letter "D" precedes this number to indicate a disc nozzle. The number represents the size, in 64ths of an inch, of the orifice (except for the smallest sizes). A D7 nozzle has an orifice diameter of $7/64$ inch. You can match several sizes of cores to discs to regulate the output capacity of the nozzle at different pressures. Follow the manufacturer's instructions for the proper installation of discs and cores.

When selecting nozzles, read the manufacturer's catalog. Learn about the nozzle sizing, their proper application, and the optimal pressure range. Manufacturers have charts for selecting spray volume or determining nozzle size. Table 9-3 is a guide for selecting different styles of nozzles.

Hand Spray Guns

Use hand spray guns to apply a high-pressure stream or spray of pesticide (Figure 9-22). Use these for applying insecticides and fungicides to trees, vines, and shrubs in landscape, nursery, aquatic, and greenhouse settings. Also use hand spray guns to apply herbicides along roadsides, rights-of-way, and fencerows. Applicators also use them to apply insecticides to livestock for control of external parasites.

You can attach hand spray guns to many different types of spraying equipment. Often orchard sprayers or low-pressure row crop sprayers have connectors for attaching a hand spray gun for occasional touch up or specialized spraying. Operators of some greenhouses put pesticide pumps and tanks in a separate room. This equipment pumps pesticides through permanent plumbing to different outlets within the greenhouse. These provide convenient locations for connecting flexible hoses and hand spray guns. You can also connect hand spray guns to portable sprayers by a flexible hose. Long hoses let you spray areas farther from the pumping equipment. However, be sure the system accommodates for pressure drop due to the long hose.

A spray gun usually has a handle, a valve, and a nozzle (or a small boom with several nozzles). The valve is part

FIGURE 9-22.

Hand spray guns usually produce high-pressure streams or sprays; they are used for applying insecticides and fungicides to trees and shrubs and are also used for spraying aquatic areas, livestock, buildings, and roadsides.

FIGURE 9-23.

A pressure regulator is a spring-loaded valve that controls the pressure of fluid going to the nozzles. If pressure increases, excess pesticide is bypassed back into the spray tank.

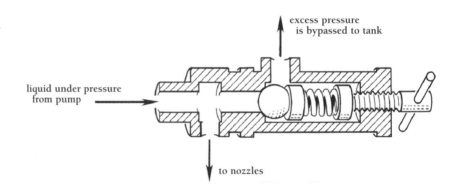

of a trigger mechanism or connects to a knob at the end of the handle. Nozzles are usually interchangeable so you can use the hand spray gun for different types of applications. In some models, you can adjust the pressure and spray pattern with a valve mechanism.

Pressure Regulators

A pressure regulator is a spring-loaded valve that controls the pressure of liquid going to the nozzles. Put the pressure regulator between the pump and the nozzle, spray boom, or manifold (Figure 9-23). To change the pressure, adjust the amount of tension on the valve by turning the pressure regulating screw or handle. Increasing the spring tension (turning the screw clockwise) increases the liquid pressure going to the nozzles. When the pressure in the system exceeds the pressure of the spring-loaded valve, the valve opens. This forces some spray material back into the tank and prevents pressure in the system from going any higher. Should the pump output pressure drop (by slowing the pump down, for example), the regulator reduces or stops the flow of liquid into the tank.

TABLE 9-3.

Guide to Selecting Different Styles of Nozzles.

	STYLE OF NOZZLE	SUGGESTED USES	RECOMMENDED PRESSURE	TYPE OF SPRAY PATTERN
	FLAT-SPRAY NOZZLES	Preemergence and postemergence herbicides, insecticides, and fungicides. Used on a boom.	20–60 psi. Keep pressure as low as possible when spraying weeds.	Fan-shaped pattern with fewer droplets at sides than in center of fan pattern. Suitable for overlapping with other nozzles to produce wide spray swath.
	OFF-CENTER FLAT-SPRAY NOZZLES	Used on ends of spray booms to extend reach of spray pattern.	Same as flat-spray nozzles.	Fan-shaped with angle to one side.
	EVEN FLAT-SPRAY NOZZLES	Preemergence and postemergence herbicides, insecticides. and fungicides. Use on boom. Do not overlap spray pattern.	20–40 psi. Keep pressure low when used for weed control.	Fan-shaped pattern with even distribution of spray across width of fan.
	CONE NOZZLES	Insecticides and fungicides applied to foliage. Often used with air blast sprayers.	40–120 psi	Hollow or solid cone pattern. Fine spray droplets, good penetration.
	SOLID STREAM NOZZLES	All types of pesticides. Used on booms or hand guns.	5–200 psi	Low- or high-pressure solid stream. High pressure breaks spray into fine to medium droplets.
	FLOOD NOZZLES	Herbicides and fertilizers. High volume and low pressure to reduce drift. Used on booms.	5–20 psi	Wide, fan-shaped pattern of coarse droplets.
	BROADCAST NOZZLES	Weed and brush control in pastures and turf. Nozzles are clustered without boom.	10–30 psi	Wide, fan-shaped pattern ranging from fine to coarse droplets.
	BIFLUID NOZZLES	Used for developing extremely fine, airborne droplets. Flying insect control in enclosed spaces.	None. Uses air pressure to move liquids.	Fog or mist.

For an accurate reading, adjust pressure regulators while the system is operating and nozzles are spraying. When you shut off the nozzles, pressure in the system increases slightly and the pressure regulator sends all the liquid through the bypass.

Unloaders

An unloader is a device that senses pressure changes that occur when turning on or shutting off the flow of liquid to the nozzles. When you shut off the nozzles, the unloader bypasses all the pumped liquid back into the spray tank. Once the flow to the nozzles starts, the unloader redirects the liquid at the pressure set by the pressure regulator. Unloaders are an important part of high-pressure systems because they protect pumps, valves, hoses, and other components from excessive and sudden pressure surges.

FIGURE 9-24.

A pressure gauge is used to monitor the pressure of spray going to the nozzles and will alert the operator to problems in the system.

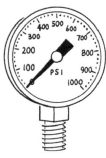

suitable for 30 psi

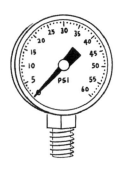

suitable for 500–700 psi

FIGURE 9-25.

Select a pressure gauge that is compatible with the pressure range of the sprayer. It should have a higher maximum pressure than the sprayer to prevent damage due to unexpected pressure surges.

Pressure Gauges

Equip your liquid sprayers with pressure gauges so you can monitor the fluid pressure in the system (Figure 9-24). A change in pressure also warns you of potential malfunctions such as leaks or clogged nozzles. Usually, install the pressure gauge between the pressure regulator and the nozzles. Here, it monitors pressure in the system while spray is being emitted through the nozzles.

Proper equipment calibration depends on an accurate pressure gauge. Recalibrate the gauge on your sprayer periodically by comparing its readings to another calibrated gauge. Also use this second gauge to measure pressure at the nozzles during calibration. The following chapter describes methods of calibrating spray equipment.

You have a choice of gauges to measure different ranges of pressures. For example, some measure from 1 to 20 psi, while others measure from 1 to 200 psi, or 1 to 500 psi, or 1 to 1,000 psi. Be sure the gauge you use is compatible with your sprayer pressure range. If your sprayer produces a maximum of 50 psi, a gauge with a range of 1 to 500 psi will be difficult to read and will have reduced accuracy. Use a gauge with a range of 1 to 100 psi for greater accuracy. The 1 to 500 psi gauge works best on sprayers that operate at maximum pressures of 300 or 400 psi (Figure 9-25). Gauges should operate at about 50% of their maximum pressure. This protects them against damage in the case of unexpected pressure surges.

When possible, use liquid-filled gauges on spray equipment. These last longer and can absorb the shock of rapid pressure changes and vibrations from the equipment. You can recognize these gauges by the liquid (glycerin) visible inside the face of the dial.

Control Valves

Use control valves to turn on and shut off liquid being pumped to the nozzles (Figure 9-26). These may be trigger-type valves on hand spray guns or lever valves controlling spray to nozzles on a boom. You can operate other control valves by cables, such as on air blast orchard sprayers, or by electric solenoids. You can even set up your sprayers so that electric solenoids control each nozzle individually.

On air blast sprayers, manufacturers usually fit nozzles to two manifolds, each with a separate control valve. This allows you to spray from either side of the sprayer or from both sides at the same time.

Field and row crop spray booms often have 2 or 3 controllable sections and special valves for these sections. In one case, a control valve for a 3-section boom has 7 spray selections available to the operator. For a boom divided into left, center, and right sections, the valve supplies spray to the

- right section only
- left section only
- center section only
- right and left sections
- right and center sections
- left and center sections
- all three sections

Electronic Sprayer Controllers. Electronic sprayer controllers allow very accurate metering of pesticide sprays. They use microcomputers to monitor and regulate spray output and/or pressure at each nozzle. Some units warn you of malfunctions of nozzles or pumps. These controllers allow you to apply consistent and precise amounts of pesticide even if the travel speed of your equipment varies. Some controllers use sensing devices to regulate the spray according to target plant size or type.

Hoses, Couplings, and Fittings

Hoses, couplings, and fittings must be strong and durable. They need to withstand the pressures produced by a spraying system and the corrosive action of spray material. Neoprene is

FIGURE 9-26.

Control valves are used to turn on or shut off spray to nozzles. Multiple valves are often used to regulate spray to different nozzles, giving the operator options to adjust the application according to the characteristics of the location.

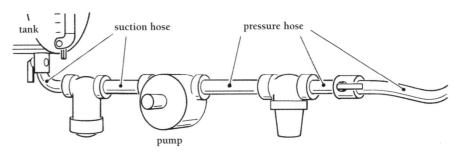

tank   suction hose   pressure hose

pump

FIGURE 9-27.

Suction hoses are used to connect the pump to the tank of the sprayer. Pressure hoses are placed between the pump and the nozzles. Suction hoses must be larger in diameter than pressure hoses and should be sturdy enough to prevent them from collapsing.

the most common material used for sprayer hoses. Use reinforced hoses to reduce chances of bursting under the pressure of the system. Leaking or ruptured hoses expose you to pesticides and release unregulated amounts of pesticide into the environment.

Two types—*pressure hoses* and *suction hoses*—connect tanks, pumps, and booms or nozzles (Figure 9-27). Use pressure hoses that can handle twice the operating pressure of your sprayer. For indoor uses, select a hose material that does not leave skid marks on floors or other surfaces.

Suction hoses that carry liquid from the tank to the pump must be larger in diameter than pressure hoses. Using hoses that are the same size or smaller than the pressure hose impedes liquid flow. This reduces the discharge rate at the nozzles and could damage the pump. Select suction hoses that are stiff enough to resist collapsing under the suction pressure of your sprayer's pump.

Fittings. Select noncorrosive couplings and fittings that can withstand the solvents used in pesticide formulations. Brass, stainless steel, and high-density plastic are common materials for these fittings. Use quick-disconnect couplings and fittings in case you need to make repairs to the system. Be sure

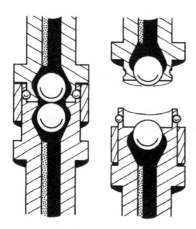

FIGURE 9-28.

A dry break coupling allows hoses containing pesticides to be disconnected from equipment without spilling any material. Spring-loaded ball bearings seal the hose openings when dry break couplings are separated.

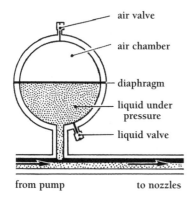

air valve
air chamber
diaphragm
liquid under pressure
liquid valve

from pump   to nozzles

FIGURE 9-29.

A surge chamber can be installed in the pressure system of a sprayer to minimize pressure fluctuations caused by the pumping action of piston and diaphragm pumps.

couplings or fittings do not reduce the internal diameter of the hoses they connect. This could cause a pressure drop at the nozzles and additional pressure on the pump.

If you need to attach or disconnect certain hoses during operation, use *dry break* couplings (Figure 9-28). These prevent pesticide leaks when you disconnect the hoses. Dry break couplings have a spring-loaded check valve that automatically plugs the disconnected hoses and fittings.

Surge Chambers

You may need to install a surge chamber on the pressure line of your sprayer. This device minimizes pressure fluctuations caused by piston and diaphragm pumps (Figure 9-29). One style of surge chamber consists of a hollow metal tank connected to the sprayer's pressure line. Air trapped in this tank compresses or expands according to changes in pressure of the pumped liquid. Compressing this air helps to minimize pressure variations.

Another type of surge chamber consists of a round tank separated by a diaphragm into two hemispheres. It has air on one side of the diaphragm and pumped liquid on the other. As pressure in the system increases, the pumped liquid distorts the diaphragm, compressing the trapped air. As a result, it moderates pressure peaks in the system. When the pumping cycle reverses, the compressed air forces liquid back into the system. This slows the rate of pressure drop. With some surge chambers, you can pump in compressed air to improve the dampening action at high pressures. You must drain liquid from some models daily to maintain air volume in the unit. If air volume in the surge chamber decreases too much, the surge chamber becomes less effective. In this case it will not adequately dampen high-pressure pulsations.

Spray Shields

When necessary, install spray shields on your boom sprayer to confine pesticide droplets and prevent drift. The shields consist of metal boxes or metal, plastic, or fabric shrouds. These surround the nozzles and confine the spray to a small area of ground or to specific plants. Attach these to the spray boom so they move with the tractor as a unit.

Closed-System Mixing Equipment

Most uses of *Danger* liquid pesticides in production agriculture require closed-system mixing equipment. Closed-system mixing equipment allows you to handle toxic liquid pesticides more safely. You do not handle opened pesticide containers, eliminating chances for accidental contact.

Some closed mixing systems use a transfer pump to move the pesticide from its original container to the sprayer tank. Other types attach to the pressure side of the sprayer. In these, the sprayer's pumping action sucks the pesticide from its container. Most devices have some type of metering device so you can measure the quantity of pesticide being transferred.

Many closed-system mixing units automatically rinse containers after they are empty. If the unit does not automatically rinse the container, use a separate rinsing device. Pump the rinsate into the spray tank.

Operators commonly install closed-system units on *nurse tanks*. A nurse tank is a special piece of equipment having a large tank with a pump and agitator. Operators use these for mixing and holding diluted pesticides. They fill one or more sprayers in the field from this unit.

Nonpowered or Hand-Operated Equipment

Nonpowered or hand-operated liquid spray equipment is comparatively inexpensive. It is also easy to use. These

FIGURE 9-30.

Aerosol dispensers used in commercial applications are attached to a hose and spray wand enabling the operator to inject liquids into cracks and crevices.

FIGURE 9-31.

Hose-end sprayers are sometimes used to apply pesticides to lawns and shrubs. They apply high volumes of dilute pesticide.

sprayers are usually simple to repair and maintain because they have only a few moving parts. You use these devices for applying pesticides to small areas or specific targets. They are handy for locations that are difficult to reach with larger equipment. Nonpowered or hand-operated equipment is lightweight, so an individual can carry most models. Some are low-pressure sprayers with small tanks. Tanks usually do not have agitators so require occasional shaking when you use wettable powder, flowable, or emulsifiable concentrate formulations. Table 9-4 is a guide to selecting the nonpowered and hand-operated devices suitable for different application needs.

Aerosol Cans. Pressure spray applicators and aerosol foggers are examples of aerosol cans. They expel a fine spray of premixed pesticide through a nozzle at the top of the can. The propellant is an inert, compressed gas. Some aerosol cans allow intermittent uses as needed, but aerosol foggers are one-time, total release units. Aerosol cans with a capacity of 1 quart or less are not reuseable. Pesticides packaged this way are popular because of their convenience.

Pest control operators use larger-volume aerosol cans for structural and greenhouse applications. Some types are refillable. Applicators can carry these on a waist belt and attach the can to a hose and spray wand (Figure 9-30). Sometimes they connect two or more cans to a single wand, allowing them to select different pesticides during the same operation. Sprays packaged in aerosol cans offer convenience and portability to professional applicators and eliminate the need for chemical mixing.

Hose-End Sprayers (Figure 9-31). Common uses for hose-end sprayers are for applying pesticides to lawns, flowers, and shrubs, usually in small areas. The sprayer combines concentrated pesticide mixtures with water from a garden hose and expels it through a high-volume nozzle. A 1- or 2-quart plastic or glass container holds the concentrated pesticide. One filling of the container produces about 20 gallons of dilute spray. Nozzles adjust for droplet size and to aim the spray in different directions. These sprayers generally have a valve to start and stop the flow of pesticide in the stream of water. Some

TABLE 9-4.

Selection Guide for Nonpowered and Hand-Operated Application Equipment for Liquid Pesticides.

	TYPE	USES	SUITABLE FORMULATIONS	COMMENTS
	AEROSOL CAN	Insect control on house or patio plants, pets, small areas, cracks and crevices, and confined spaces.	Liquids must dissolve in solvent; some dusts are available.	Very convenient. High cost per unit of active ingredient.
	HOSE-END SPRAYER	Home garden and small landscaped areas. Used for insect, weed, and pathogen control.	All formulations. Wettable powders and emulsifiable concentrates require frequent shaking.	Convenient and low-cost way of applying pesticides to small outdoor areas. Cannot spray straight up.
	TRIGGER PUMP SPRAYER	Indoor plants, pets, and small home yard areas. Used for insect and pathogen control.	Liquid-soluble formulations are best.	Low cost and easy to use.
	COMPRESSED AIR SPRAYERS	Many commercial and homeowner applications. Can develop fairly high pressures. Used for insect, weed, and pathogen control. Often used indoors for household pest control.	All formulations. Wettable powders and emulsifiable concentrates require frequent shaking.	Good overall sprayer for many types of applications. Needs thorough cleaning and regular servicing to keep sprayer in good working condition and prevent corrosion of parts.
	BACKPACK SPRAYERS	Same uses as compressed air sprayers.	All formulations. Wettable powders and emulsifiable concentrates require frequent shaking.	Durable and easy to use. Requires periodic maintenance.
	WICK APPLICATORS	Used for applying contact herbicides to emerged weeds. Agricultural and landscape uses.	Only water-soluble herbicides.	Simple and easy to use. Clean frequently.

FIGURE 9-32.

A trigger pump sprayer can be used to apply small quantities of diluted pesticide to surfaces such as houseplants or pets. It can also be used to apply some types of pesticides to confined areas.

FIGURE 9-33.

Compressed air sprayers usually hold from ½ to 5 gallons of spray mixture. Air inside the tank is compressed with a self-contained pump or a carbon dioxide cartridge. Pesticide under pressure is forced through a hose attached to an adjustable nozzle at the end of a hand-held wand.

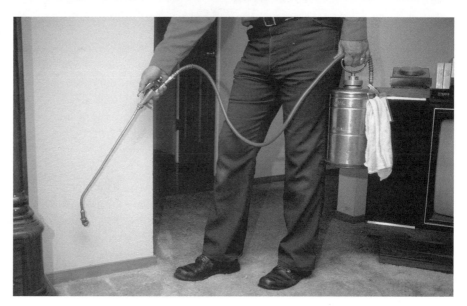

have another valve to regulate and shut off the water flow from the garden hose.

Trigger Pump Sprayers (Figure 9-32). The trigger pump sprayer is a simple liquid applicator. Squeezing a trigger forces pesticide mixtures through a nozzle, producing a fine spray. Some styles have an adjustable nozzle for controlling droplet size. You put a diluted pesticide in the plastic jar, which ranges in capacity from 1 pint to 1 gallon. Use this type of applicator to apply pesticides to small areas, such as houseplants or pets, and in confined areas.

Compressed Air Sprayers (Figure 9-33). Compressed air sprayers hold a diluted pesticide mixture in a small, airtight tank. You use a hand pump to compress air inside the tank. The compressed air forces the liquid through a hose and nozzle when you open a valve. Some models use compressed carbon dioxide cartridges as the propellant, eliminating the need for hand pumping. Metal or plastic tanks have a capacity of less than 5 gallons. Conventional tank sizes include ½, 1, 2, and 3 gallon capacities. Some compressed air sprayers have harnesses for backpack use. Larger compressed air sprayers have separate air tanks that you fill from an air compressor or portable hand pump. Hoses or pipes connect these tanks to an airtight chamber containing the diluted pesticide mixture.

Use these sprayers for treating small areas and for applying liquid pesticides indoors. Most have adjustable nozzles

FIGURE 9-34.

This type of hand-operated backpack sprayer usually requires continuous pumping action to maintain pressure for spraying. These units hold from 3 to 5 gallons of spray mixture; most have adjustable nozzles.

to control droplet size and spray pattern. For indoor uses, there are adapters to enable you to inject liquid spray into small cracks and crevices.

Backpack Sprayers (Figure 9-34). Backpack sprayers have a hand-operated hydraulic pump that forces liquid pesticides through one or more nozzles. You operate the pump by moving a hand lever up and down. Some pumps create pressures more than 100 pounds per square inch (psi). The tanks, usually made of plastic, have a capacity of around 5 gallons. These sprayers are useful in small areas where there is no access for larger equipment. Some backpack sprayers are also known as *knapsack* sprayers.

Wick Applicators (Figure 9-35). Use wick applicators, or *rope wick applicators*, to apply contact or systemic herbicides. Their basic design consists of a cloth, carpeting pad, rope, or wick that is saturated with herbicide. You wipe this wick onto the leaves of target weeds. A simple hand-held model holds liquid herbicide in its hollow handle. Liquid feeds to the pad through a series of small holes. Other types of wick applicators incorporate a boom and herbicide reservoir attached to a tractor. More elaborate versions mechanically wind ropes through the herbicide reser-

voirs. This ensures a constant and more uniform herbicide distribution.

For controlling weeds that are taller than the crop, adjust the wick applicator height to contact just the weeds. Wick applicators waste little or no pesticide. Also, no environmental contamination takes place as a result of the application process.

Powered Application Equipment

Many pesticide applications require powered equipment capable of applying high volumes of pesticide mixtures to large areas. Some units have self-contained motors, while tractors or similar external sources power others. Manufacturers equip these machines with hydraulic or mechanical agitators and pressure regulators. They also come with a variety of spray booms, hand-held spray guns, or other nozzle arrangements. Powered equipment is more complex than hand-operated equipment and often requires considerable maintenance and servicing to keep it operating properly. Table 9-5 is a guide to help you select powered liquid application equipment.

Powered Backpack Sprayers. The smallest powered sprayer consists of a backpack unit with a compact gasoline engine. The engine drives a pump that forces diluted or concentrated liquid

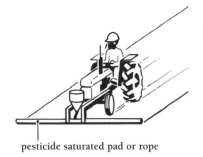

pesticide saturated pad or rope

FIGURE 9-35.

Wick applicators are used for application of contact herbicides. They can be used in areas where weeds are taller than the crop plant. Wick applicators reduce problems of drift and waste of herbicides.

TABLE 9-5.

Selection Guide for Powered Liquid Pesticide Application Equipment.

	TYPE	USES	SUITABLE FORMULATIONS	COMMENTS
	POWERED BACKPACK SPRAYER	Aquatic, landscape, right-of-way, forest, and agricultural applications.	All. Some may require agitation.	May be heavy for long periods of use. Requires frequent maintenance.
	CONTROLLED DROPLET APPLICATORS	Used for application of contact herbicides and some insecticides. Some are hand-held while others are mounted on spray boom. May also be used with air blast sprayers. Produces uniform droplet sizes.	Usually water-soluble formulations.	Plastic parts may break if handled carelessly.
	LOW-PRESSURE SPRAYER	Very common type of sprayer used in commercial applications for weed, insect, and pathogen control. Used with spray booms or hand-held equipment.	All. Equipment may include agitator.	Frequent cleaning and servicing is required. Powered by own motor or external power source.
	HIGH-PRESSURE HYDRAULIC SPRAYER	Landscape, right-of-way, and agricultural applications. Use on dense foliage and large trees or shrubs.	All. Equipment may include agitator.	Important to clean and service equipment frequently. Requires own motor or external power source. Abrasive pesticides may cause rapid wear of pumps and nozzles.
	AIR BLAST SPRAYER	For application of insecticides, fungicides, and growth regulators to trees, vines, and shrubs. Sometimes used on row crops and with livestock. Also used in aquatic areas.	All. Equipment may include agitator.	Frequent service and maintenance is required. High-horsepower motor is often needed to power pump and fan. Volutes may be used to direct spray.
	ULTRA-LOW-VOLUME APPLICATORS	Primarily used in agricultural and aquatic situations. Used with insecticides, fungicides, and growth regulators.	Usually only pesticides that dissolve in water or organic solvents.	Requires extreme care in calibration. Applies highly concentrated pesticides. Often used with a blower.
	ELECTRO-STATIC SPRAYER	Agricultural uses for applying insecticides, fungicides, and growth regulators to trees, vines, and row crops.	All. Requires agitation of some formulations.	Usually equipped with blower. Maintenance and frequent cleaning is required. Electronically charged spray droplets are attracted to target surfaces.
	AEROSOL GENERATORS AND FOGGERS	Mainly used to apply insecticides in confined areas. Used in aquatic areas for airborne insects.	Requires water- or solvent-soluble formulations.	Emitted spray is highly subject to drift. Keep equipment clean.
	CHEMICAL INJECTION PUMPS	Injects concentrated pesticides into spray boom or irrigation water. May be used with all classes of pesticides.	Requires liquid formulations.	Accurate metering is necessary to assure proper calibration. With irrigation systems, must have back-flow protection to prevent contaminating water supply.

FIGURE 9-36.

Controlled droplet applicators are designed to apply small volumes of uniform-sized droplets. These are available as hand-held units or can be mounted in groups on spray booms or on air blast sprayers.

pesticide through one or more nozzles. Air blowers, also driven by the engine, help propel spray droplets. Backpack sprayers work best for low-volume applications. This is because of their small tank sizes and inability to produce high pressures.

Controlled Droplet Applicators (Figure 9-36). Controlled droplet applicators (CDAs) apply low volumes of specific types of pesticides (usually herbicides). Rather than passing through a nozzle, the liquid pesticide mixture drops onto a spinning disc or cup. This disc has serrated edges to distribute the spray by centrifugal force. Under optimal conditions, this equipment produces droplets of a more uniform size than is possible with spray nozzles. Droplet size depends on the rotation speed of the disc and the nature of the pesticide being used—more viscous liquids produce larger droplets. Rotation speeds are adjustable between 1,000 and 6,000 rpm. As speed increases, the droplets become smaller. The size range of droplets produced by CDAs is 100 to 400 microns.

In most units, the pesticide mixture flows from a reservoir tank to the spinning disc or cup by gravitational force. This eliminates the need for a pump. An orifice in the pesticide hose controls the flow rate. In most models you can change this orifice size. Variable speed, low-voltage DC electric motors or hydraulic motors power CDAs. In some units you control the speed by changing drive belts on pulleys. Other units have electronic speed controllers. Hydraulic units accomplish speed control by adjusting the flow rate of the hydraulic fluid.

Some CDAs are inexpensive, self-contained, hand-held units. Others connect to a backpack tank by a flexible hose. You can mount one or more CDAs to a tractor boom or an all-terrain cycle (ATC). Sometimes controlled droplet applicators replace nozzles on air blast sprayers.

Uses for controlled droplet applicators include applying contact, preemergent, and postemergent herbicides. You can also use them for some insecticide and fungicide applications. Because the rotational speed of CDAs controls droplet size, you can make very low-volume applications without excessive drift. Since CDAs apply volumes between 1 quart and 3 gallons per acre, you need to calibrate them accurately. Keep low-volume applications consis-

FIGURE 9-37.

A common sprayer used for agricultural, right-of-way, forest, and landscape applications of pesticides is the low-pressure applicator like the one being used here to apply insecticides to lettuce. These apply sprays through a series of nozzles attached to a boom.

tent with pesticide label directions or current University of California recommendations.

Low-Pressure Sprayers (Figure 9-37). Low-pressure pesticide sprayers are useful tools in many different agricultural crop, turf, aquatic, and right-of-way settings. This equipment operates in the pressure range of 10 to 20 psi. You can also inject pesticides into the soil with low-pressure applicators by connecting them to soil shanks or chisels attached to a tractor tool bar. As shanks rip the soil, the unit pumps pesticide (or liquid fertilizer) below the surface. This is a common way of applying soil fumigants.

Users mount low-pressure applicators onto trailers (tag-along models) or attach them to tractors or trucks. Some models are self-propelled. Electric motors or engines provide the power for pumps in some units and others are PTO driven or hydraulically powered. Occasionally, the wheels of the trailer power the pumps (ground-wheel-driven) as you tow the unit. This method provides a relatively constant output rate even if the travel speed of the unit varies, because the pump speed is proportional to the travel speed.

Most low-pressure sprayers have tanks with a capacity of 100 gallons or more. Often you can attach two or more tanks to a tractor to increase total capacity. Low pressure usually is not suitable when you need thorough coverage of dense foliage, however. It also does not work if the spray must travel any distance, unless you use a blower.

High-Pressure Hydraulic Sprayers (Figure 9-38). High-pressure sprayers work well when spraying large areas such as orchards and field crops. You can use them also for spraying turf and landscape and right-of-way trees and shrubs. In addition, they are useful in aquatic areas and for treating livestock. This equipment forces high volumes of dilute pesticide either through hand spray guns or nozzles mounted on booms. Special boom designs improve spray coverage to all sides of crop plants. For instance, oscillating booms provide good coverage on densely foliated trees, such as citrus, and on large vines. With an oscillating boom sprayer, several high-pressure spray

FIGURE 9-38.

Oscillating boom sprayers, like the one being used here in citrus, are high-pressure units that direct large volumes of spray through dense foliage. They are used where thorough coverage is essential.

FIGURE 9-39.

An air blast sprayer has a powerful fan to move pesticide droplets through dense foliage or high into the upper parts of target trees.

nozzles rotate from side to side and up and down as the sprayer moves along. This oscillating action, coupled with high pressure and high volume, provides thorough spray coverage to all parts of target plants.

Pressures between 100 and 400 psi or more are common with high pressure sprayers. Most have large-capacity tanks, up to 2,000 gallons. High-pressure hydraulic sprayers mount on trailers, trucks, or tractors and may have a self-contained engine for powering the pump. Some are powered by a tractor PTO. With PTO-driven models, you must be careful to maintain a constant tractor engine speed to assure a uniform application rate. Many models have pressure regulators and bypass mechanisms so they work as low-pressure sprayers as well.

Air Blast Sprayers (Figure 9-39). Air blast sprayers use fans or blowers to force spray mixtures into dense foliage, to tops of trees, and across fields or aquatic areas. Proper use of air blast sprayers eliminates shingling (see Figure 6-45 on page 195) and improves pesticide coverage. Because air moves spray droplets to target surfaces, air blast sprayers do not require extremely

high pressure. They usually operate in a range between 80 and 150 psi. Most air blast sprayers have tanks ranging in capacity from 100 to 1,000 gallons. Low-volume or concentrate sprayers produce between 30 and 100 gallons of finished spray per acre. High-volume sprayers (dilute sprayers) have an output of 400 to 1,000 gallons per acre. Usually you can convert a high-volume sprayer to low volume. To do this, change the nozzle size, lower the pump output pressure, and adjust ground speed. Air blast sprayer nozzles discharge into the air stream produced by the sprayer's fan. This allows the air to break up the spray droplets and move them into dense foliage and to tree tops. Orchard and vineyard sprayers often use different sized nozzles at different locations on the manifold. Thus the sprayer applies different amounts of spray to different parts of the trees or vines (Figure 9-40). Controlled droplet applicators sometimes replace nozzles on orchard, vineyard, row crop, and livestock air blast sprayers.

Special attachments for air blast sprayers, called *volutes*, direct the spray into tall trees, around vines, across fields, and into dense foliage of vegetable crops. Different designs of

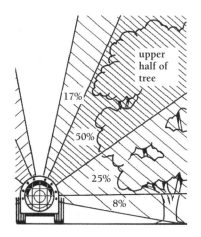

FIGURE 9-40.

An orchard air blast sprayer may be adjusted to apply greater amounts of pesticides to some parts of the tree. This is done by using several different nozzle sizes or by using more nozzles in some locations. In most situations, two-thirds of the spray output is directed to the upper half of the tree. This drawing shows an ideal pattern for most mature orchards.

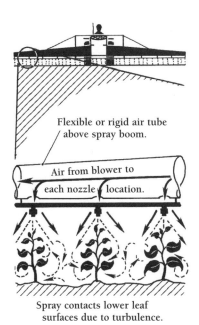

Flexible or rigid air tube above spray boom.

Air from blower to each nozzle location.

Spray contacts lower leaf surfaces due to turbulence.

FIGURE 9-41.

Air blast sprayers may also be used in row crops. As illustrated, air from a blower is carried to nozzles through a flexible or rigid tube. Pesticide droplets are distributed around the plant by the air turbulence, giving coverage to upper and lower plant surfaces.

FIGURE 9-42.

An ultra-low-volume sprayer produces low volumes of very small droplets; these are usually propelled by a fan or blower. Pesticide mixtures are much more concentrated than in higher volume sprayers.

volutes are available depending on the needs of the application.

The pumps and fans of air blast sprayers are either self-powered by a gasoline or diesel engine or externally powered by a tractor PTO. Units with large fans require 50 to 100 horsepower to drive them. You can mount some smaller sprayers to trucks or tractors, while larger ones are wheeled and designed for pulling behind tractors. Other variations include one that has the fan, pump, and spray nozzles attached to a tractor's 3-point hitch and is connected by hoses to a wheeled tank pulled behind as a separate unit. Self-propelled spraying machines, including an enclosed operator cab, are also available.

Manufacturers also produce *air assist* sprayers for use in row crops. Large-diameter tubing carries high-velocity air from a blower to each nozzle on the spray boom (Figure 9-41). This air forces the spray onto the target plants. Air turbulence circulates the spray droplets through dense foliage, cover-

ing the undersides of leaves as well as top surfaces. These sprayers apply low volumes, in the range of 3 to 15 gallons per acre.

Ultra-Low-Volume Sprayers (Figure 9-42). Ultra-low-volume (ULV) sprayers apply from 1 quart to a few gallons of spray per acre. Low-volume nozzles—or sometimes controlled droplet applicators—break up the spray into small droplets. Air from a fan or blower propels the droplets to the treatment surfaces. ULV sprayers apply highly concentrated pesticides. Mixing the pesticides with vegetable oil carriers reduces droplet evaporation. Vegetable oil also improves the spreading ability of droplets once they have contacted the target surface. ULV sprayers, powered by lightweight gasoline engines, usually have small tanks. These sprayers are smaller and much lighter than higher-volume machines. Because of the smaller droplet size and smaller blowers, ULV sprayers generally are limited to applications during low

FIGURE 9-43.

An electrostatic sprayer emits electrically charged spray droplets. These spray droplets are attracted to oppositely charged surfaces, increasing the pesticide deposition and target coverage.

winds to minimize drift and obtain satisfactory penetration and coverage.

Accurate calibration of ULV sprayers is critical because of the high concentration of pesticide being applied. There may be greater hazards to the operator with ULV sprayers because of the concentrated pesticides used.

Electrostatic Sprayers (Figure 9-43). Electrostatic sprayers apply 10 to 50 gallons per acre of pesticide in the form of small, electrically charged droplets. Droplets average about 50 microns in diameter and receive a negative electrostatic charge as they leave the sprayer volute. Because plant material has a positive electrostatic charge, these surfaces attract the spray droplets. The negatively charged spray droplets repel each other, so they do not clump together to form larger-sized droplets. Electrostatic sprayers are usually powered by a tractor PTO. A transformer connected to the tractor's electrical system creates an electrical charge of about 15,000 to 20,000 volts. Volutes of different configurations direct the spray droplets toward surfaces being treated.

These sprayers appear to be more effective if spray droplets only travel a short distance from the sprayer to the target. As the distance increases, the effect of the electrostatic charge diminishes.

Aerosol Generators and Foggers (Figure 9-44). Aerosol generators and foggers produce small airborne particles of pesticide. These units work for insect control in confined spaces such as residences, greenhouses, and warehouses.

The insecticide-laden fog produced by aerosol generators remains suspended in the air for long periods. It penetrates small cracks and inaccessible areas, killing insects on contact. Sometimes outdoor fogging controls mosquitoes and other biting or irritating insects in locations such as recreational areas. Effective insect control in outdoor areas depends mainly on proper weather. The conditions must keep the fog confined and airborne within an area long enough to contact target insects.

Thermal fog applicators use heat to generate pesticide aerosols. Other types use bifluid nozzles with high-velocity air to produce extremely fine droplets.

FIGURE 9-44.

Aerosol generators and foggers produce a fine insecticide mist that remains suspended in the air for a long period of time and penetrates cracks and inaccessible areas, killing insects on contact.

FIGURE 9-45.

Small injection pumps are used to meter pesticides into irrigation water, a technique known as chemigation.

Chemical Injection Pumps. Chemical injection pumps inject undiluted liquid pesticides directly into the nozzles, where they mix with water being simultaneously pumped from a water tank. Some injection pumps draw liquid pesticides directly from original containers, eliminating the need for mixing chemicals or cleaning tanks. When used with sprayers, chemical injection pumps allow you to apply one or more chemicals during the same operation. With this equipment you can vary the concentration of pesticide mixture during application. Some units have electronic devices that regulate the concentration of pesticide applied.

Many future possibilities exist using chemical injection systems. For example, experimental orchard sprayers use sensors and a computer system to apply pesticide amounts proportional to tree volume. They shut off the spray between trees and where trees are missing.

Chemigation. Injection pumps allow you to apply pesticides through irrigation systems, a practice known as *chemigation* (Figure 9-45). To prevent groundwater contamination through the well, regulations require automatic shutoff devices on injection pumps. These stop pesticides from being inject-

ed into the system when the irrigation water flow stops. Also, you must have safety valves to prevent possible contamination of the water supply by back flow of irrigation water.

DUST AND GRANULE APPLICATION EQUIPMENT

You do not mix granules or certain dust formulations with water, but apply them dry and undiluted. This requires special equipment, and there are unique problems with this type of application. Because dust formulations are highly susceptible to drift over great distances if applied during windy conditions, outdoor uses of dusts are limited. Their greatest use is for pest control in buildings and other confined areas. There are also formulations to control external parasites on livestock, poultry, and pets.

Granules are the dry formulations used most for pest control in landscape, agricultural, and aquatic situations. These are usually incorporated into the soil or applied to bodies of water. Table 9-6 is a guide for selecting dust and granule application equipment.

Dust Applicators

The function of a dust applicator is to combine the dust with air and spread it evenly over an area. You can choose

TABLE 9-6.

Selection Guide for Dust and Granule Application Equipment.

	TYPE	USES	SUITABLE FORMULATIONS	COMMENTS
	DUST APPLICATORS bulb applicator	for forcing dusts into small cracks and crevices	dusts	Simple, easy to use.
	compressed air duster	used to apply dusts in confined spaces such as wall voids	dusts	Avoid breathing dust.
	mechanical duster	for landscape and small agricultural areas	dusts	Avoid drift. Do not breathe dust. May have bellows to disperse dust.
	power duster	vine crops and some special applications; also used in buildings	dusts	Equipped with blower to disperse dusts. Considerable hazard of drift.
	GRANULE APPLICATORS hand-operated granule applicator	landscape, aquatic, and some agricultural areas	granules or pellets	Suitable for small areas. Easy to use.
	mechanically driven granule applicator	turf and other landscape areas; also commonly used in agricultural areas	granules or pellets	Requires accurate calibration.
	powered granule applicator	agricultural areas, usually row crops; some large landscape applications	granules or pellets	Frequent servicing and cleaning is required. Some units may have blowers to disperse granules. Others may distribute granules along a boom.

FIGURE 9-46.

Bulb applicators can be used to apply dusts to small, confined areas such as electrical outlets and cracks and crevices.

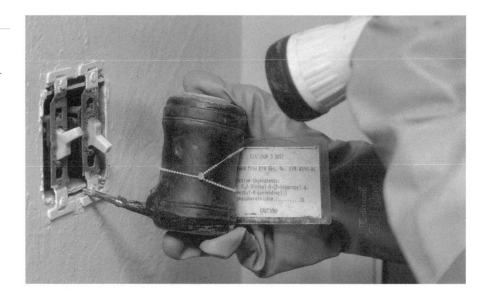

FIGURE 9-47.

A compressed air duster may be used to apply pesticide dusts in enclosed areas, wall voids, and crawl spaces and attics.

from several types of dust application equipment.

Bulb Applicators (Figure 9-46). Hand-held bulb applicators apply dusts to small confined areas, cracks, and crevices. Squeezing the bulb, which is made of rubber or a similar flexible material, expels dust-bearing air through a small tube. Some bulb dusters have attachments to extend the reach of the tube and direct the dust.

Compressed Air Dusters (Figure 9-47). Compressed air dusters move dusts through a nozzle or hose. High-velocity air picks up some pesticide from an airtight chamber and distributes it as a fine powder. Manufacturers package dust formulations of some pesticides in aerosol cans. You apply these in the same way as liquid aerosols. However, a common problem associated with dusts is their tendency to cake inside the aerosol applicator. Moisture or high humidity enhances caking. Manufacturers overcome this problem by incorporating anti-caking materials into the formulation.

Mechanical Dusters. Mechanical dusters have either a crank-operated fan and agitator or a lever-operated bellows. These devices force dust-laden air

out of a hopper. The pesticide dust passes through an orifice in the applicator or through a hose aimed by the operator. Most mechanical dusters have back or chest straps. Smaller units are hand-carried.

Power Dusters. Power dusters use fans powered by electric or gasoline motors (Figure 9-48). The small, hand-held units work well in structural settings. These units are either battery powered or plug into a standard electrical outlet. Lightweight gasoline engines power larger backpack units. From a hand-held flexible hose, operators direct pesticide dusts at targets up to 15 feet away.

Large power dusters for agricultural crops have only limited use due to environmental problems resulting from drift. These units attach to tractors. Growers use them to apply dusts in date palm gardens and to row or vine crops. There may be several nozzles on a boom. Each nozzle connects by large-diameter flexible tubing to a central blower that mixes the dust with air. Extension tubes or fan-shaped air volutes direct dusts onto target plants.

Granule Applicators

Granule applicators may be hand-operated, mechanically driven, or engine powered depending on the needs

FIGURE 9-48.

Power dusters are used to broadcast dust into confined areas. They have a blower to carry dust to treatment surfaces.

FIGURE 9-49.

A mechanically driven granule applicator may be used to apply pesticide granules to agricultural crops. Smaller versions are used for application of granular pesticides to turf.

of the application site. Aquatic weed managers mount granule applicators in boats for some aquatic applications.

Because granules are of varying sizes and shapes, equipment must accommodate size differences. *Pellet* formulations are granules of identical size and shape. When applied through specially designed applicators, pellets allow for accurate calibration. This provides more uniform application rates than is possible with other granules.

Often, granules require incorporation into the soil. Usually, operators attach tillage equipment behind the granule applicators to incorporate at the time of application.

Hand-Operated Granule Applicators. Hand-operated granule applicators usually strap to the operator's chest. Granules pass through an adjustable opening at the bottom of a cloth, metal, or plastic hopper and drop onto a spinning plate operated by a hand crank. The operator walks at a steady pace while turning the crank to achieve an even distribution of granules.

Mechanically Driven Granule Applicators (Figure 9-49). Several types of mechanically driven granule applicators are available. Some consist of ground-wheel-driven metering devices attached to a hopper. Operators attach

FIGURE 9-50.

Granules can also be applied with a back-pack granule applicator. A small gasoline engine powers a blower that disperses the granules.

several of these units to a tractor tool bar and space them according to the crop row spacing. Larger units have one large hopper connecting to several drop pipes aligned to the row spacing.

Another design of granule applicator consists of a large hopper with a chain conveyor or auger at the bottom. The chain or auger moves granules onto a spinning disc that disperses them evenly over a wide area. These applicators are ground-wheel-driven. Adjusting the openings that granules pass through regulates the rate of application. Ground speed controls swath width. Some units also have adjustable deflectors located alongside the spinning disc to regulate the swath width. Some units provide options for dispersing granules to the right, left, or both sides as needed.

Powered Granule Applicators (Figure 9-50). Small gasoline engines power backpack applicators. These applicators are similar to those used to apply liquids or dusts. A blower connected to a flexible hose aids in dispersing the granules. The operator aims the tube at the target area while walking slowly.

Another type of powered granule applicator consists of a long boom attached to a tractor or truck. Granules are augered down the boom and metered out at preset spacings. This provides for accurate calibration and even distribution of granular pesticides.

LIVESTOCK AND POULTRY APPLICATION EQUIPMENT

Pest managers use several methods to apply pesticides to livestock and poultry. Those described here are used for the external application of liquids or dusts. Several methods are used to apply pesticides to the animal's skin. In addition, veterinarians administer systemic pesticides to protect animals from internal and external parasites. Animals receive systemic pesticides through feed, by subcutaneous injections, and by mouth as pastes, capsules, or tablets.

Livestock Face and Back Rubbers and Dust Bags

Manufacturers package dry or liquid pesticide formulations into dispensing bags or other dispensing containers. Livestock managers hang or mount these in areas frequented by the animals (Figure 9-51). As the animals contact these packages, usually to scratch

FIGURE 9-51.

Certain types of pesticides are applied to livestock by means of dust bags or face and back rubbers. Small amounts of dust or liquid are deposited onto the animal each time it rubs against the device.

FIGURE 9-52.

Bait stations are helpful in preventing nontarget organisms from being exposed to the pesticide.

themselves, small amounts of pesticide are released onto their bodies. This effectively controls many different species of external parasites.

Poultry Dust Boxes

Poultry managers put dust formulations of specific pesticides in poultry dust boxes to control insects and mites infesting laying hens. Hens instinctively wallow in the boxes and pick up the dust on their feathers and skin.

Dipping Vats and Spray/Dip Machines

Livestock managers use dipping vats and spray/dip machines to control external parasites on cattle, sheep, and other large animals. They dip or spray animals so that they become totally covered with liquid pesticide. Animals enter and leave these devices through ramps.

BAIT APPLICATION EQUIPMENT

Pesticide bait formulations require special application methods. A major problem associated with baits is exposing nontarget organisms to toxic pesticides. Bait stations or bait applicators can help prevent such exposure.

Bait Stations

Bait stations hold supplies of poisoned food and attract target pests. Use types that prevent children, pets, and nontarget animals from contacting the baits (Figure 9-52). Bait stations help control flies around poultry and livestock quarters. Other types control squirrels in agricultural and right-of-way locations. Special designs also control rodents in warehouses and residential areas. Manufactures make special bait stations for managing cockroaches, ants, snails, and other invertebrates. Occasionally, bait stations are used for controlling pest birds.

Place bait stations out of the reach of nontarget organisms, pets, and children. Hang fly bait stations above poultry or livestock in poultry houses, loafing sheds, or barns. For pest bird control, managers secure V-shaped troughs high up in trees. They bait these with poisonous seeds or grains. For rodents, locate bait stations in crawl spaces, attics, and other out-of-the-way places.

Bait Applicators for Gophers and Moles

There are commercially available applicators for applying poisoned baits to control gophers and moles. Use

FIGURE 9-53.

This device is used to apply poisoned bait for control of gophers; it forms an artificial burrow that intersects with the natural burrows made by gophers. Poisoned grain is deposited in the artificial burrow.

hand-operated models to inject small quantities of poisoned bait directly into an underground burrow made by the gopher or mole. For larger areas, tractor-mounted mechanical bait applicators form baited artificial burrows that intersect natural gopher burrows (Figure 9-53). Gophers explore the artificial burrows and feed on the bait.

APPLICATION EQUIPMENT MAINTENANCE

Effective pesticide application depends on properly maintained and adjusted application equipment. Regular inspections and periodic maintenance programs help you avoid accidents or spills caused by ruptured hoses, faulty fittings, damaged tanks, or other problems.

Inspect application equipment for wear, corrosion, or damage before each use. Replace or repair faulty components. Thoroughly clean equipment after every application. Wear protective clothing, rubber gloves, and eye protection when cleaning or repairing the equipment. When not in use, store equipment in a way that prevents deterioration or damage.

Liquid Application Equipment

Preventing Problems

Take the following preventive steps to reduce problems of sprayer malfunction or breakdown and to maintain uniform and accurate application.

Use clean water. Water that contains sand or silt causes rapid pump wear and may clog screens and nozzles. Whenever possible, use water pumped directly from a well and make sure all filling hoses and pipes are clean. If you pump water from ponds or irrigation canals, filter it before putting into the sprayer tank. Also, measure the pH of the water to be sure it is adequate for the intended pesticide use. Chapter 3 describes how to check and adjust pH.

Keep screens in place. Filter screens remove foreign particles from the spray liquid. It is a nuisance to remove collected debris from the screens, but debris accumulation indicates that the screens are doing the job for which they were designed. Removing screens because they keep plugging only increases wear on the pumps and nozzles. Make sure screens are the proper size for the type of pesticide being applied. If excessive plugging does occur, try to eliminate the cause, for example, by changing water sources.

Use chemicals that are compatible with the sprayer and pump. Spray chemicals are corrosive to some metals and deteriorate rubber and plastic components. Recognize limitations in existing spray equipment. Avoid problems by modifying the equipment to accommodate the corrosive pesticides. Otherwise, use the equipment only for chemicals that are not corrosive. Sometimes it is possible to replace parts of a sprayer with corrosion-resistant materials.

Properly clean nozzles. Spray nozzles are made to precise specifications. Never use any metal object to clean or remove debris. These may damage the orifice, adversely changing the spray pattern and spray volume. Clean nozzles by flushing with clean water or a detergent solution. Remove stuck particles with a soft brush or a round wooden toothpick. Nozzle suppliers sell special brushes for this purpose. Always wear rubber gloves when handling or cleaning spray nozzles. Never blow through them with your mouth, because nozzles usually contain pesticide residues. Use an air compressor if needed, but protect your eyes and skin (Figure 9-54).

Flush sprayers before use. Use clean water to flush new sprayers and sprayers coming out of storage. This removes foreign particles, dirt, and other debris. The manufacturing process may leave metallic chips, dirt, or other residue in the tank or pump.

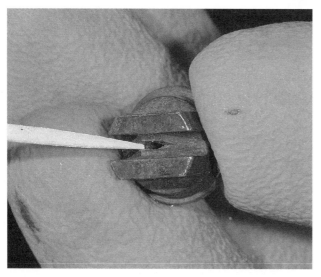 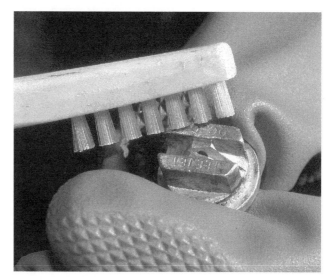

FIGURE 9-54.

To clean a clogged nozzle, use compressed air or water for flushing the orifice. Never put your mouth to a nozzle. Use a wooden toothpick or soft brush (such as an old toothbrush) to remove stuck objects. Do not use any type of metal device to remove debris, because you may damage the orifice.

Storage always subjects spraying equipment to the possibility of being contaminated with dirt, leaves, rodent debris, and rust.

Clean sprayer after use. Cleaning spray equipment at the end of each job is important. This removes residues that might contaminate future sprays or damage crops or treated surfaces. Avoid leaving pesticide mixtures in a sprayer overnight or for longer periods of time. Prolonged contact increases chances of corrosion or deterioration of sprayer components. Some pesticides settle out and may be difficult to get back into suspension after being left in an idle sprayer. After mixing them with water, certain pesticides lose their effectiveness quickly. Finally, pesticides left in an unattended sprayer may present a hazard to people, wildlife, or the environment.

If possible, apply leftover spray material to an appropriate (registered) target site. Otherwise, unused pesticide mixtures are hazardous wastes. Clean the sprayer and flush out the tank at the application site whenever possible. If this is not possible, contain the wash water and use it for mixing other pesticides of the same type. Should you not be able to use it in this manner, have it transported to a Class 1 disposal site as a hazardous waste. Never drain rinse water onto the ground or into sewer or septic lines.

Inspection and Maintenance

Perform regular inspections and periodic maintenance on spraying equipment. This keeps it in good operating condition and ready for use. Take care of simple maintenance, such as greasing bearings and drive lines, while inspecting the equipment. Always check for the following problems:

- weakened hoses
- leaking fittings
- damage to the tank or tank protective coating
- broken regulators and gauges
- worn nozzles
- worn bearings
- damaged tires (if equipped)
- other mechanical defects or wear

Equipment with self-contained engines requires additional maintenance. Check oil and water levels regularly. Change air filters, oil filters, and motor oil according to the manufacturers' recommendations. Clean and service batteries.

By spending a few minutes each day inspecting and servicing spray equipment, you increase the length of its useful life. This also helps to avoid costly breakdowns and possibly dangerous leaks. Develop a checklist for servicing and inspecting each piece of equipment to help remember what needs to be done. The checklist can also serve as a service record.

Sprayer Troubleshooting

A sprayer may not exhibit any external signs of problems but still not function properly. Problems such as lack of pressure, too much pressure, or inadequate output at the nozzles requires troubleshooting to locate and correct the cause. Table 9-7 is a guide to troubleshooting problems associated with poor sprayer performance.

TABLE 9-7.

Troubleshooting Problems Associated with Poor Sprayer Performance.

PROBLEM	POSSIBLE CAUSE
uneven spray pattern	clogged nozzles worn nozzles mismatched nozzle sizes nozzle screens not uniform boom not level hoses to nozzles or boom sections not uniform in size pressure not adjusted to operating range of nozzles foam in spray tank
clogged nozzles	rust, sand, or other contaminants in spray tank improper or missing filter screens incompatible spray mixture poorly mixed spray components agitator not working properly failure to use marine grease on mechanical agitator fittings
pressure too low	worn pump nozzles too large nozzles excessively worn air in pressure system pesticide mixture foaming broken or maladjusted pressure regulator needed pressure is beyond the capacity of the pump pump speed too slow drive belts slipping restricted or defective suction hose clogged suction strainer
pressure too high	pump speed too fast pressure regulator not working bypass system blocked, restricted, or undersized nozzles too small filter screens clogged
pump not primed	air trapped in the system suction line not completely full of liquid worn pump drive belts slipping shear pin broken on drive line foam in tank suction line blocked leak in suction hose
pesticide mixture settles out in tank	agitator insufficient or not working properly incompatible mixture tank and hoses not properly cleaned before use pH too high or too low
pulsating pressure	worn piston pump seals highly foaming tank mix
excessive drift	nozzles too small pressure too high application made during windy weather spray boom too high nozzles improperly aligned temperature too high while applying volatile materials treated surfaces not receptive failure to use a drift control agent

Sprayer Storage

Improperly storing spraying equipment can shorten its useful life. Before storing a sprayer, decontaminate and clean it thoroughly. Wear rubber gloves and appropriate protective clothing to avoid contact with pesticide residues. Remove, clean, and reinstall all filters. Partially fill the tank with clean water and add a commercial neutralizing cleaner (or ½ pound of detergent to 30 gallons of water). Circulate this solution through the system for at least 30 minutes and flush it out through the nozzles. Refill the sprayer about half full. Add more commercial cleaner according to directions or add a quart of household ammonia to each 25 gallons of water. Circulate this solution for about 5 minutes and flush a small amount through the nozzles. Shut off the sprayer and let the solution remain in the tank for 12 to 24 hours.

While the cleaning solution is soaking in the tank, thoroughly wash all external parts of the sprayer. Use detergent or ammonia solution, or use a commercial cleaner. Scrub residue off all surfaces using a bristle brush. Rinse external parts with clean water.

To prevent rusting, touch up scratched areas on all painted surfaces of the trailer, boom, tank, and accessories. Lubricate bearings to prevent them from rusting during storage.

Remove and clean nozzles and nozzle strainers. Store these in a clean plastic bag to keep them free of dirt.

After the tank has finished soaking, flush the solution out and rinse with clean water. Seal nozzle outlets with corks or plastic bags to prevent insects or dirt from getting into the lines. Remove and clean all remaining filter screens and store these in a clean plastic bag. Remove "O" rings from filters and strainers and store them in a plastic bag to prevent them from becoming brittle. Cover the tank loosely to prevent dirt, insects, and rodents from entering during storage. Do not close the tank cover tightly as this may permanently distort its rubber seal. Store the sprayer inside a building, preferably covered with a tarp for additional protection. Block up equipment that has rubber tires to remove weight from the tires and bearings. You can remove small pumps and store them in a can of new, lightweight motor oil to prevent rusting. However, if pumps have rubber or neoprene parts, do not expose them to oil.

Remove hoses used on hand-held nozzles. Coil these and hang them around a pail, basket, or other large round object. This prevents sharp bends that might cause cracks in the rubber. Never hang hoses over a nail, rack, or board. Store hoses in an area away from direct sunlight.

Release the tension from the pressure regulator and remove the "O" ring seal. Lubricate the internal cylinder of the regulator and reassemble without the "O" ring. Place the "O" ring in a plastic bag and tie it to the regulator.

Maintaining Dust and Granule Applicators

Thoroughly clean dust and granule applicators after each use. Be sure to remove all pesticide residue. Once clean, lubricate chains, auger bearings, and other moving parts according to the manufacturer's instructions. Inspect the equipment for wear and corrosion. Repair rusted or corroded areas to prevent these from getting worse.

REVIEW QUESTIONS

1. **A spray tank must be equipped with an agitator if you are using:**
   - ☐ a. Wettable powders
   - ☐ b. Soluble powders
   - ☐ c. Soluble liquids
   - ☐ d. Pesticides that dissolve in water

2. **The disadvantage of** *some* **hydraulic spray tank agitators is that they:**
   - ☐ a. Are too powerful
   - ☐ b. Cause clogging of nozzles
   - ☐ c. Cannot be used in high-pressure systems
   - ☐ d. Are not able to break up settled spray material in the tank

3. **A sight gauge is required on pesticide tanks that are:**
   - ☐ a. 20 gallons or larger
   - ☐ b. 40 gallons or larger
   - ☐ c. 50 gallons or larger
   - ☐ d. 100 gallons or larger

4. **What is a disadvantage of epoxy-coated metal spray tanks?**
   - ☐ a. They are more expensive than stainless steel tanks
   - ☐ b. They are heavier than stainless steel tanks
   - ☐ c. They do not resist alkaline materials or organic solvents
   - ☐ d. Chips or scratches can lead to serious corrosion problems

5. **What is a disadvantage of polyethylene or polypropylene spray tanks?**
   - ☐ a. They are extremely heavy
   - ☐ b. The material absorbs pesticides when scratched
   - ☐ c. They are difficult to repair when punctured
   - ☐ d. They have low resistance to acidic pesticides

6. **Which type of pump would be most suitable for a sprayer requiring an output of 25 gallons per minute at a pressure of 800 psi?**
   - ☐ a. Piston pump
   - ☐ b. Gear pump
   - ☐ c. Centrifugal pump
   - ☐ d. Roller pump

7. **Which type of pump would be most suitable for a spray situation requiring 200 gallons per minute at 100 psi?**
   - ☐ a. Piston pump
   - ☐ b. Gear pump
   - ☐ c. Centrifugal pump
   - ☐ d. Diaphragm pump

8. **The purpose of filter screens and strainers is to:**
   - ☐ a. Break up undissolved spray material
   - ☐ b. Introduce air into the spray for more effective coverage
   - ☐ c. Protect pumps and prevent clogged nozzles
   - ☐ d. Increase the sprayer's output pressure

9. **Increasing nozzle orifice size will produce:**
   - ☐ a. Smaller, uniform droplets
   - ☐ b. A greater mixture of droplet sizes
   - ☐ c. Spray droplets with a greater tendency for drift
   - ☐ d. Larger droplets

10. **To increase the uniformity of spray droplets:**
    - ☐ a. Select nozzles designed for the working pressure of your sprayer
    - ☐ b. Use fewer nozzles
    - ☐ c. Use the highest possible pressure setting
    - ☐ d. Operate your sprayer at the slowest travel speed

11. **A nozzle with a manufacturer's code of 65155 is designed to produce a volume of how many gallons per minute at 40 psi?**
    - ☐ a. 0.15
    - ☐ b. 0.65
    - ☐ c. 1.55
    - ☐ d. 6.5

12. **If your sprayer normally operates at 50 psi, it should be equipped with a pressure gauge that measures in the range of:**
    - ☐ a. 1 to 50 psi
    - ☐ b. 1 to 100 psi
    - ☐ c. 1 to 200 psi
    - ☐ d. 1 to 500 psi

13. **An advantage of controlled droplet applicators (CDAs) over spray nozzles is:**
    - ☐ a. CDAs are less expensive than nozzles
    - ☐ b. CDAs operate at higher pressures than nozzles
    - ☐ c. CDAs produce droplets of more uniform size than nozzles
    - ☐ d. CDAs are more suitable for high-volume applications than nozzles

14. **If the pressure of your sprayer drops off, this could be an indication that the:**
    - ☐ a. Pump speed is too fast
    - ☐ b. Nozzles are too small
    - ☐ c. Pump is worn
    - ☐ d. Nozzles are mismatched

15. **Which of the following** *would not* **account for an uneven spray pattern on a boom sprayer?**
    - ☐ a. Pressure in the system is adjusted to the operating range of the nozzles
    - ☐ b. Boom not level
    - ☐ c. Nozzle screens are not uniform
    - ☐ d. Foam in spray tank

10

Calibrating Pesticide Application Equipment

All pesticide application equipment must be carefully calibrated to assure that the proper amount of pesticide is applied.

THE TERM CALIBRATION refers to all the adjustments you make to be sure you apply the correct amount of pesticide to the treatment area. Failure to calibrate equipment properly is a cause of ineffective pesticide applications. In addition, inaccurate calibration always carries the potential for excessive or illegal residues remaining on treated surfaces.

This chapter discusses the steps you need to take to calibrate any type of pesticide application equipment. It does not discuss common calibration shortcuts and quick calculations. These are applicable only in specific situations or for certain types of application equipment. However, these handy techniques may be available in equipment manuals or trade journals and publications. Learn the principles of proper calibration first. Then, if appropriate, adopt a quick calibration method that applies to your equipment and special needs.

To calibrate your equipment you must first determine the amount of pesticide to apply—the application rate. *Check the pesticide label for this information.* You may need to adjust ground speed and equipment output or modify application patterns to achieve this desired rate. Once you have calibrated your equipment, check and test it periodically to be sure the calibration stays accurate. Many operators fail to understand how rapidly equipment becomes maladjusted or worn. As a result, application equipment is usually not calibrated often enough.

Table 10-1 is a list of helpful conversion factors to use when calibrating pesticide application equipment.

WHY CALIBRATION IS ESSENTIAL

The main reason for calibrating application equipment is to figure out how much pesticide to put into the tank or hopper. This assures that the correct amount of chemical is applied. It is necessary for

- effective pest control
- protecting human health, the environment, and treated surfaces
- preventing waste of resources
- controlling the volume of water applied to a given area (for liquid applications)
- complying with the law

Effective Pest Control. Manufacturers of pesticides spend millions of dollars researching ways to use their products. Their research includes determining the correct amount of pesticide to apply to effectively control target pests. Using less than the labeled amount of pesticide may result in inadequate control. This could be a waste of time and money. Inadequate amounts of pesticide also lead to problems such as pest resistance and resurgence. Using too much pesticide has adverse effects on natural enemies, target surfaces, and the environment. Higher than label rates also waste materials, but more important, they are *illegal*.

Human Health Concerns. If you apply pesticides at higher than label rates, you could endanger the health of people in the area. In addition, illegal residues may result if a pesticide is overapplied. If residues are above

TABLE 10-1.

Useful Conversion Factors for Calibration.

STANDARD MEASURE	METRIC CONVERSIONS
LENGTH 1 ft = 12 in 1 yd = 3 ft 1 mi = 5,280 ft	1 in = 25.4 mm = 2.54 cm 1 ft = 304.8 mm = 30.48 cm 1 yd = 914.4 mm = 91.44 cm = 0.914 m 1 mi = 1,609 m = 1.61 km 1mm = 0.03937 in 1 cm = 0.394 in = 0.0328 ft 1 m = 39.37 in = 3.281 ft 1 km = 3,281 ft = 0.6214 mi
AREA 1 sq in = 0.007 sq ft 1 sq ft = 144 sq in = 0.000023 sq ac 1 sq yd = 1,296 sq in = 9 sq ft 1 ac = 43,560 sq ft = 4,840 sq yd	1 sq in = 6.45 sq cm 1 sq ft = 929 sq cm 1 sq yd = 8,361 sq cm = 0.8361 sq m 1 ac = 4,050 sq m = 0.405 h 1 sq cm = 0.155 sq in 1 sq m = 1,550 sq in = 10.76 sq ft 1 h = 107,600 sq ft = 2.47 ac
VOLUME 1 tsp = 0.17 fl oz 1 tbs = 3 tsp 1 fl oz = 2 tbs = 6 tsp 1 cup = 8 fl oz = 16 tbs 1 pt = 2 cups = 16 fl oz 1 qt = 2 pt = 32 fl oz 1 gal = 4 qt = 8 pt = 128 fl oz = 231 cu in	1 fl oz = 29.5 ml = 0.0295 l 1 pt = 437 ml = 0.437 l 1 qt = 945 ml = 0.945 l 1 gal = 3785 ml = 3.785 l 1 ml = 0.033 fl oz 1 l = 33.8 fl oz = 2.112 pt = 1.057 qt = 0.264 gal
WEIGHT 1 oz = 0.0625 lb 1 lb = 16 oz 1 ton = 2,000 lb 1 gal of water = 8.34 lb	1 oz = 28.35 g 1 lb = 454 g = 0.4536 kg 1 ton = 907 kg 1 gal of water = 3.786 kg 1 g = 0.035 oz 1 kg = 35.27 oz = 2.205 lb

allowable tolerances on produce, regulators may confiscate an entire crop to protect consumers. Poorly calibrated equipment may also expose application equipment operators to concentrations of pesticide for which they are not adequately protected.

Environmental Concerns. Improper pesticide concentrations may cause environmental problems. Calibrating equipment to maintain application rates within label requirements helps protect beneficial insects and wildlife. It also reduces the potential for contaminating surface and groundwater and the air.

Protecting Treated Surfaces. Certain pesticides are phytotoxic and damage treated surfaces when used at higher than label-prescribed rates. Manufac-

turers evaluate these potential problems while testing their chemicals to determine safe concentrations. Using too much pesticide also increases chances of building up excessive residues in the soil. These buildups sometimes seriously limit the types of crops that people can grow in an area.

Preventing Waste of Resources. Using the improper amount of pesticide wastes time and adds unnecessary costs to the application. Not only are pesticides expensive, but the fuel, labor, and equipment wear and tear required to make extra applications are costly, too.

Legal Aspects. Applicators who use pesticides improperly are subject to criminal and civil charges, resulting in fines, imprisonment, and lawsuits.

Applicators are liable for injuries or damage caused by improper pesticide application.

EQUIPMENT CALIBRATION METHODS

Sidebar 19 lists the few simple tools you need to calibrate pesticide applica-tion equipment. Put these items in a small toolbox and use them only for calibration purposes (Figure 10-1). Keep your tools clean and in good working condition; *make equipment calibration a professional operation.*

Liquid application equipment and dust or granular application equipment require differing calibration techniques.

SIDEBAR 19
Tools Needed for Calibration

1. **Stopwatch.** A stopwatch is essential for timing travel speed and flow rates. Never rely on a wristwatch unless it has a stop-watch function.

2. **Measuring tape.** A 100 foot moisture- and stretch-resistant measuring tape is used for marking off the distance to be traveled and for measuring spray swath width.

3. **Calibrated liquid container.** A container having a capacity of 1 or 2 quarts, calibrated for liquid ounces, is needed for measuring spray nozzle output.

4. **Scale.** A small scale, capable of measuring pounds and ounces, is used for weighing granules collected from a granule applicator. The most accurate weight measurements can be obtained from scales having maximum capacities between 5 and 10 pounds.

5. **Pocket calculator.** A pocket calculator is needed for making calculations in the field.

6. **Pressure gauge.** An accurate, calibrated pressure gauge, with fittings compatible with spray nozzle fittings, is helpful for checking boom pressure and for calibrating the sprayer pressure gauge.

7. **Flow meter.** A flow meter, attached to a flexible hose or filling pipe, can be used for measuring the amount of water put into a tank. This device can also be used for measuring tank capacity and for determining the amount of liquid used during a calibration run. Both mechanical and electronic flow meters are available. If these are not available, a calibrated 5 gallon pail can be used instead.

8. **Flagging tape.** Colored plastic flagging tape is useful for marking off measured distances when determining applicator speed.

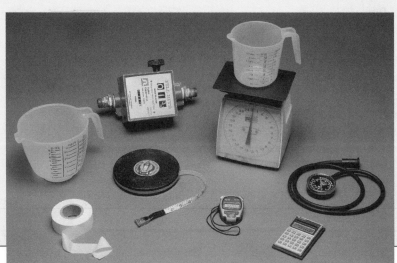

FIGURE 10-1.

A few simple tools are required for calibrating a pesticide sprayer. These include a stopwatch, measuring tape, several calibrated containers, a scale, pocket calculator, pressure gauge, flow meter, and flagging tape.

NOTE: Pesticide application equipment and the discharge from application equipment being calibrated may contain pesticide residue. Always wear rubber gloves and other protective equipment to prevent pesticide contamination of your eyes, hair, skin, clothing, and shoes. **Read** Chapter 6 for information on selecting the proper protective equipment.

Calibrating Liquid Sprayers

To monitor pump and nozzle wear, you must frequently calibrate liquid spraying equipment. Abrasive pesticides, such as wettable powders, increase the rate of wear. Pump wear decreases the amount and pressure of fluid output. Nozzle wear increases the volume of output. This usually lowers the output pressure and may produce a poor spray pattern.

The final goal is to determine how much area each tank of spray covers when the equipment moves at a known speed and operates at a known pressure. You need to measure these four factors:

- tank capacity
- travel speed
- flow rate
- spray swath width

Before making any calibration measurements, be sure to service the sprayer. Follow the servicing directions outlined in Sidebar 20.

Tank Capacity. Physically measure the capacity of the spray tank, or tanks, if the equipment has more than one. Never rely on manufacturers' tank size ratings. They may be approximate volumes, or they may not take into account fittings installed inside the tank. Also, the capacity of spray lines, pump, and filters influences tank volume. To accurately calibrate your equipment, you need to know exactly how much liquid the spray tank holds.

Situate the sprayer on a perfectly level surface. Be sure the tank is completely empty, then close all valves to prevent water leaks. Add measured amounts of clean water until you completely fill the tank. Use a flow meter attached to a hose (Figure 10-2), or a bucket or other container of known volume. A 5-gallon bucket works well for smaller sprayers. Be sure to calibrate and mark the bucket before using it to fill the tank. If you are not using a flow meter, use smaller-volume calibrated containers to top off the tank. Record the total volume of water you put into the tank. Paint or engrave this figure onto the outside of the tank for permanent reference.

While filling the tank, calibrate the tank's sight gauge. Make marks on the tank or gauge as you put in measured volumes of water. If the unit does not have a sight gauge, mark volume increments on a dipstick. Then, always keep

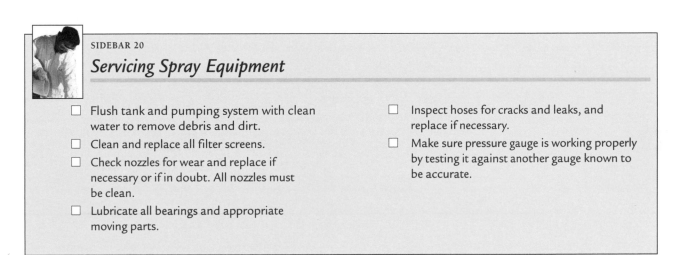

SIDEBAR 20
Servicing Spray Equipment

- ☐ Flush tank and pumping system with clean water to remove debris and dirt.
- ☐ Clean and replace all filter screens.
- ☐ Check nozzles for wear and replace if necessary or if in doubt. All nozzles must be clean.
- ☐ Lubricate all bearings and appropriate moving parts.

- ☐ Inspect hoses for cracks and leaks, and replace if necessary.
- ☐ Make sure pressure gauge is working properly by testing it against another gauge known to be accurate.

FIGURE 10-2.

Flow meters, similar to the one shown, can be used to measure the volume of spray tanks.

this dipstick with the tank. Use 1-gallon marks for tanks with a capacity of 10 gallons or less. Use increments of 5 or 10 gallons for tanks having a total capacity of 50 gallons or less. On larger tanks, use increments of 10 to 20 gallons. Once you calibrate the sight gauge or dipstick you can measure how much liquid is in the tank when it is not entirely full. Always return tanks to a level surface when reading the sight gauge or dipstick.

Travel Speed. Always measure travel speed under actual working conditions. For instance, if you are calibrating an orchard sprayer, take the water-filled tank to the orchard. Calibrate row crop and field sprayers in the fields you plan to treat. Tractors travel faster on paved or smooth surfaces than on soft dirt or clods. Never rely on tractor speedometers for mile-per-hour measurements. Tractor wheel slippage and variation in tire size due to wear produce as much as a 30% difference in actual versus indicated speed. When calibrating a backpack or hand-held sprayer, walk on terrain similar to the area that you plan to spray.

Using a 100-foot tape, measure off any convenient distance. It can be more or less than 100 feet, but calibration accuracy increases if you use longer distances (between 200 and 300 feet). Sometimes multiples of 88 feet are chosen because 88 feet is the distance covered in 1 minute while traveling 1 mile per hour. In orchards or vineyards, a given number of tree or vine spaces of known length provide a convenient reference. Indicate the beginning and end of the measured distance with colored flagging tape.

Have someone drive (or walk, if calibrating a backpack sprayer) the sprayer through the measured distance. Maintain the speed desired for an actual application. Choose a speed within a range appropriate for the application equipment. When using a tractor, note the throttle setting, gear, and rpm of the engine. The use of a positive throttle

stop is helpful so you can always return the engine to the same speed. Be sure to bring the equipment up to the actual application speed before crossing the first marker. Use a stopwatch to determine the time, in minutes and seconds, required to traverse the measured distance (Figure 10-3). For best results, repeat this process 2 or 3 times and take an average. Follow the procedure in Sidebar 21 to calculate the actual speed of the equipment.

Flow Rate. Measure the actual output of the sprayer when nozzles are new, then periodically thereafter to accommodate for nozzle wear. Manufacturers provide charts showing output of given nozzle sizes at specified sprayer pressures. However, you should check output under actual conditions of operation. Manufacturer's charts are most accurate when using new nozzles. Used nozzles may have different output rates because of wear. However, even new nozzles may have slight variations in actual output. Sprayer pressure gauges may not be accurate, which further adds error to the output estimate determined from charts.

You measure liquid sprayer output in gallons per minute. Select from one of the two methods described below, depending on the type of sprayer you are calibrating. The first method works for low-pressure sprayers and small hand-held units. It involves collecting a volume of water emitted out of individual nozzles over a measured time. The second method, for airblast and high-pressure sprayers, measures *output* of the sprayer over a known period.

Collection Method for Low-Pressure and Small Hand-Held Sprayers. Calibrate low-pressure sprayers by measuring the amount of spray emitted from nozzles. These include low-pressure boom sprayers, backpack sprayers, and controlled droplet applicators. If the sprayer has more than one nozzle, collect liquid from each separately. This allows you to compare each nozzle's output and

SIDEBAR 21

Calculating Speed of Application Equipment

1. Convert minutes and seconds into minutes by dividing the seconds (and any fraction of a second) by 60.

■ EXAMPLE

Your trip took 1 min and 47.5 sec.
47.5 sec ÷ 60 sec/min = 0. 79 min

Add these amounts together:
1 min + 0.79 min = 1.79 min

2. Get the average run time by adding the *converted* minutes from each run and dividing by the number of runs.

■ EXAMPLE

Three runs were made
Run #1 = 1 min, 47.5 sec = 1.79 min
Run #2 = 1 min, 39.8 sec = 1.66 min
Run #3 = 1 min, 52.0 sec = <u>1.87</u> min
　　　　　　　　　　Total = 5.32 min

5.32 min ÷ 3 runs = 1.77 min/run average time

3. Divide the measured distance by the average time. This will tell you how many feet were traveled per minute.

■ EXAMPLE

The measured distance is 227 feet.
227 ft ÷ 1.77 min = 128.25 ft/min

4. If you wish to determine the speed in miles per hour, divide the feet-per-minute figure by 88 (the number of feet traveled in 1 minute at 1 mile per hour).

■ EXAMPLE

128.25 ft/min ÷ 88 ft/min/mi/hr = 1.46 mi/hr

FIGURE 10-3.

Measure off a known distance when calculating the speed of travel of the application equipment.
Use a stopwatch to time the travel of the sprayer through the measured distance.

FIGURE 10-4.

To determine the output from each nozzle, collect liquid over a measured period of time. Make sure the sprayer is operating at the pressure that would be used under actual field conditions. Wear rubber gloves and eye protection, because the liquid may contain traces of pesticide.

points out any malfunction or wear. You need a stopwatch and calibrated container for making measurements. Wear rubber gloves to avoid skin contact with the liquid. Stand upwind from the nozzles to prevent fine mist or spray from contacting your face and clothing. Wear eye protection to prevent getting spray droplets in your eyes.

For low-pressure power sprayers used in agricultural, right-of-way, and landscape applications, fill the tank at least half full with water. Start the sprayer and bring the system up to normal operating pressure. Operate hydraulic agitators if they will operate during the application. This is important because hydraulic agitators divert some liquid from the nozzles and often lower the pressure in the system. Most power sprayers have a limited operating pressure range depending on the type of pump and type of power unit. Never attempt to operate equipment beyond its normal working range, because this may damage the pump. If you are calibrating a PTO-driven sprayer, be sure that the tractor engine rpm is the same as that used in the speed calibration. If this is not the same, the pump output pressure will be different. Adjust the pressure to the requirements of the spray situation and nozzle manufacturer's recommendations. Check the pressure by attaching a calibrated pressure gauge at either end of the boom, replacing one of the nozzles. Open the valves to all nozzles and note the pressure,

make adjustments as necessary, then remove the gauge.

While all nozzles are operating at the proper pressure, collect about 15 to 30 fluid ounces of liquid from each nozzle (Figure 10-4). Use a stopwatch to determine the time in seconds required to collect each volume.

When calibrating backpack sprayers, pump the unit as you would during an actual application. Collect spray in a calibrated container for a measured time. Compressed air sprayers lose pressure during operation, so you must frequently pump them up. To calibrate, fill the tank about half full with water. This provides a sufficient volume of air to keep the pressure more uniform.

For some types of controlled droplet applicators, you can disconnect the hose and orifice from above the spinning disc or cup. After doing this, collect liquid into a calibrated container over a measured time. The liquid must flow through the orifice.

Record the volume of liquid collected from each nozzle or orifice and the time in seconds to collect each amount. Use a format similar to the form in Sidebar 22. Determine the output in fluid ounces per second for each nozzle by dividing the volume by the seconds required to collect it. Convert ounces per second into gallons per minute by multiplying the result by the constant 0.4688. This constant represents 60 seconds per minute divided by 128 fluid ounces per gallon.

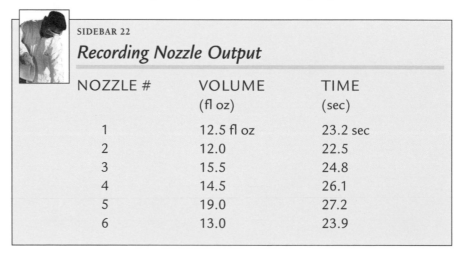

SIDEBAR 22

Recording Nozzle Output

NOZZLE #	VOLUME (fl oz)	TIME (sec)
1	12.5 fl oz	23.2 sec
2	12.0	22.5
3	15.5	24.8
4	14.5	26.1
5	19.0	27.2
6	13.0	23.9

SIDEBAR 23

Calculating Gallons per Minute for Low-Pressure Sprayers

1. Determine the gallons per minute output of each nozzle by dividing the fluid ounces collected by the time (in seconds) and multiplying the result by 0.4688.

▪ EXAMPLE

Nozzle	fl oz ÷ sec			×	0.4688	=	gpm
1	12.5 ÷ 23.2	=	0.539	×	0.4688	=	0.253
2	12.0 ÷ 22.5	=	0.533	×	0.4688	=	0.250
3	15.5 ÷ 24.8	=	0.625	×	0.4688	=	0.293
4	14.5 ÷ 26.1	=	0.556	×	0.4688	=	0.261
5	19.0 ÷ 27.2	=	0.699	×	0.4688	=	0.328
6	13.0 ÷ 23.9	=	0.544	×	0.4688	=	0.255

Total Output = 1.640 gpm

2. Compute the percentage of variation from the rated nozzle output. Divide the actual gallons per minute output by the rated output. Subtract 1 from this number and multiply by 100.

▪ EXAMPLE

Nozzle	Actual gpm ÷ Rated gpm			Subtract 1.00			Multiply by 100	=	Percent variation
1	0.253 ÷ 0.250	=	1.012	−1.00	=	0.012	× 100	=	1.2
2	0.250 ÷ 0.250	=	1.000	−1.00	=	0.000	× 100	=	0.0
3	0.293 ÷ 0.250	=	1.172	−1.00	=	0.172	× 100	=	17.2
4	0.261 ÷ 0.250	=	1.044	−1.00	=	0.044	× 100	=	4.4
5	0.328 ÷ 0.250	=	1.312	−1.00	=	0.312	× 100	=	31.2
6	0.255 ÷ 0.250	=	1.020	−1.00	=	0.020	× 100	=	2.0

Output among nozzles will usually vary. In the example in part 1 in Sidebar 23, the output ranges from 0.250 gallons per minute to 0.328 gallons per minute. Assume that the rated capacity (as given by the manufacturer) for these nozzles at the recommended operating pressure is 0.250 gallons per minute. The variation among nozzles should not be greater than 5%. The output of any nozzle should not exceed the manufacturer's rated output by more than 10%. Figure the percentage of variation as shown in the example in part 2 in Sidebar 23. Divide the actual output by the rated output. Subtract 1.00 from this figure, then multiply by 100 to obtain the percentage of variation. Nozzles 3 and 5 in this example exceed

these amounts and therefore must be replaced. However, whenever you replace any nozzles, recheck the flow rate of all the nozzles. Changing one nozzle may affect the pressure in the whole system. After changing nozzles, readjust the pressure regulator to maintain the desired pressure. Part 1 of Sidebar 24 shows how to recalculate the output in gallons per minute after replacing worn nozzles.

Spray check devices are calibration aids that provide a visual representation of the spray pattern. Place this portable device under a boom and collect the output from several nozzles. After collection, rotate the device from a horizontal to a vertical position. The liquid drains into a series of evenly spaced glass vials. Floats inside these vials rise to the top of the liquid. You then can see variations in liquid levels, pinpointing nozzle problems and poor nozzle height adjustment.

Measured Release Method for Air Blast or High-Pressure Sprayers. Due to the air blast and high pressures of larger sprayers, you cannot collect the spray from the nozzles. Therefore, find the output of the sprayer over time by measuring how much water the sprayer used.

Start by moving the sprayer to a level surface and fill the tank to its maximum with clean water. Fill the tank to a level that you can duplicate when refilling. A convenient technique is to fill the tank with clean water to the point where it just begins to overflow. Use low-volume, low-pressure water, such as from a garden hose, for topping off the tank. Check for leaks around tank seals and in hoses. All nozzles must be clean and operating properly or the results will be inaccurate.

Stand upwind and operate the sprayer at its normal operating speed and pressure. Open the valves to all nozzles, starting a stopwatch at the same time. Continue to run the sprayer for several minutes, then close the valves to all nozzles. Record the elapsed time that the nozzles operated (Figure 10-5).

SIDEBAR 24

Recalculating Output after Replacing Worn Nozzles

1. Replace worn nozzles (numbers 3 and 5 in this example) and remeasure the output of all nozzles on the boom. Recalculate the gallons per minute for each nozzle. Add these rates together to determine the total output of the sprayer.

■ EXAMPLE

Nozzle	fl oz ÷ sec			×	0.4688	=	gpm
1	12.5 ÷ 23.2	=	0.539	×	0.4688	=	0.253
2	12.0 ÷ 22.5	=	0.533	×	0.4688	=	0.250
3	13.3 ÷ 24.5	=	0.542	×	0.4688	=	0.254
4	14.5 ÷ 26.1	=	0.556	×	0.4688	=	0.261
5	15.2 ÷ 28.3	=	0.537	×	0.4688	=	0.252
6	13.0 ÷ 23.9	=	0.544	×	0.4688	=	0.255

Total Output = 1.525 gpm

2. Check to see that all nozzles are within 5% of the rated capacity of these nozzles.

■ EXAMPLE

Nozzle	Actual gpm ÷ Rated gpm			Subtract 1.00			Multiply by 100	=	Percent variation
1	0.253 ÷ 0.250	=	1.012	−1.00	=	0.012	× 100	=	1.2
2	0.250 ÷ 0.250	=	1.000	−1.00	=	0.000	× 100	=	0.0
3	0.254 ÷ 0.250	=	1.016	−1.00	=	0.016	× 100	=	1.6
4	0.261 ÷ 0.250	=	1.044	−1.00	=	0.044	× 100	=	4.4
5	0.252 ÷ 0.250	=	1.008	−1.00	=	0.008	× 100	=	0.8
6	0.255 ÷ 0.250	=	1.020	−1.00	=	0.020	× 100	=	2.0

Using the site gauge or dipstick, check to see how much liquid the sprayer used. Otherwise, use a flow meter attached to a low-pressure filling hose and refill the sprayer to the original level. Record the gallons of water used; this volume is the amount of liquid sprayed during the timed run. Repeat this process two more times to get an average of sprayer output. Determine the sprayer output in gallons per minute by using the calculations shown in Sidebar 25.

Swath Width. The final measurement needed to complete calibration is the width of the spray swath being applied by the sprayer. Figure 10-6 illustrates

SIDEBAR 25

Calculating Gallons per Minute for High-Pressure Sprayers

1. Record the elapsed time during each trial run and the amount of liquid sprayed:

EXAMPLE

Run #	Time	Volume
1	1 min 45 sec	37.5 gal
2	1 min 30 sec	33.5 gal
3	1 min 50 sec	38.0 gal

2. Convert the time from minutes and seconds to minutes by dividing the seconds by 60 and adding this decimal to the minutes.

EXAMPLE

Run #	min	sec	sec ÷ 60	=	min
1	1	45	0.75	=	1.75
2	1	30	0.50	=	1.50
3	1	50	0.83	=	1.83

3. Divide the collected gallons for each run by the minutes, resulting in gallons per minute.

EXAMPLE

Run #	gal ÷ min	=	gpm
1	37.5 ÷ 1.75	=	21.4
2	33.5 ÷ 1.50	=	22.3
3	38.0 ÷ 1.83	=	20.8

4. Add all the gallon-per-minute figures and divide this total by the number of runs (3 in this example) to get the average gallon-per-minute output.

EXAMPLE

Run #	gpm
1	21.4
2	22.3
3	20.8
Total =	64.5

64.5 ÷ 3 = 21.5 gpm average output

FIGURE 10-5.

It is not possible to collect the sprayed liquid from some types of sprayers. To determine the amount of liquid expelled by these sprayers: (1) fill the tank to a known level; (2) run the sprayer under normal conditions for a timed period; and (3) refill the tank to its original level, measuring the amount of water used.

spray swath widths for various application situations. For multiple-nozzle boom-type sprayers, the swath is the width of the boom plus the distance between one pair of nozzles. You can also calculate swath width by multiplying the number of nozzles by the nozzle spacing. (Number of nozzles × nozzle spacing = swath width.) When making a pesticide application with a boom sprayer, overlap the spray by the same amount as the nozzles on the boom

overlap (Figure 10-7). Adjust the boom height so that there is approximately a 30% overlap of spray from adjacent nozzles on the boom (Figure 10-8). Position nozzles at the exact height they would be during an actual application. Check the spray boom to make sure it is level. An unleveled boom causes uneven spray distribution (Figure 10-9). Align fan nozzles as illustrated in Figure 10-10 to give an even spray distribution.

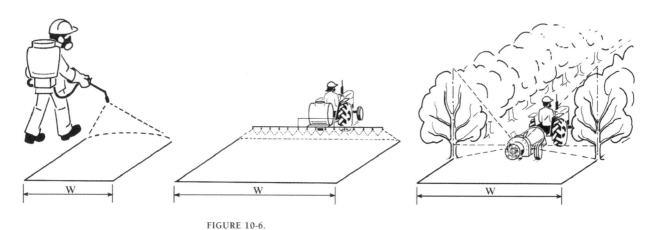

FIGURE 10-6.

A spray swath is the horizontal width being covered with spray material during a single pass. Swath width is measured differently, depending on the type of pesticide application.

FIGURE 10-7.

Spray from adjacent swaths should overlap by the same amount as spray from nozzles on the spray boom overlaps (usually about 30% of the spray pattern of one nozzle). To do this, allow one nozzle-width spacing between swaths as illustrated here.

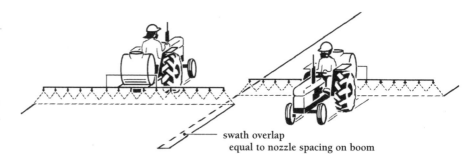

swath overlap equal to nozzle spacing on boom

FIGURE 10-8.

Under normal conditions, flat fan nozzles on a spray boom must be spaced so there is a 30% overlap of the spray emitted by adjacent nozzles. This provides for a uniform distribution of spray.

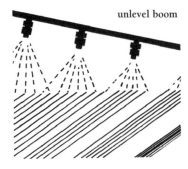

FIGURE 10-9.

An unlevel spray boom will cause an uneven pesticide application.

FIGURE 10-10.

The spray pattern will be uneven if nozzles are not aligned properly on the spray boom. Rotate nozzles about ten degrees from the axis of the boom to prevent droplets from adjacent nozzles from touching, but still allow for proper overlap of the spray pattern.

When applying spray as separate bands or strips, the swath width is equal to the combined width of each band. It does not include the unsprayed spaces between bands (Figure 10-11).

When spraying crop plants on both sides of the sprayer in an orchard or vineyard, the spray swath is equal to the width of the tree or vine row (Figure 10-12). If you spray only one side of the

row, the swath is one-half the width of the tree or vine spacing (Figure 10-13). Use a tape measure to determine tree or vine row width. Take several measurements within the orchard or vineyard to check if row spacing is uniform and consistent. Average the results if you find any variation (Figure 10-14).

It is convenient to know the number of trees or vines per acre. This allows

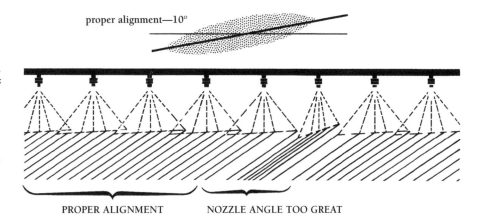

proper alignment—10°

PROPER ALIGNMENT   NOZZLE ANGLE TOO GREAT

FIGURE 10-11.

Swath width from banded applications is determined by adding the widths of the individual bands.

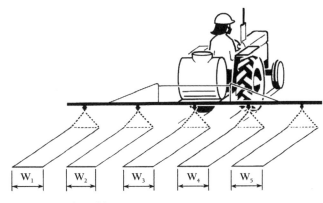

W_1 W_2 W_3 W_4 W_5

Swath Width = $W_1 + W_2 + W_3 + W_4 + W_5$

FIGURE 10-12.

In orchards or vineyards, if plants on both sides of the sprayer are being sprayed simultaneously with an air blast sprayer or high-pressure boom sprayer, the swath width is the distance between plant rows.

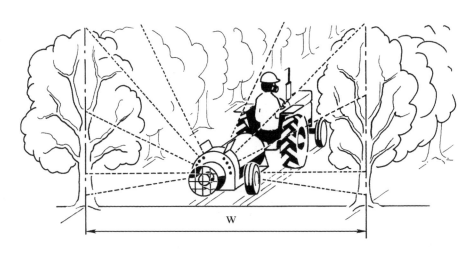

W

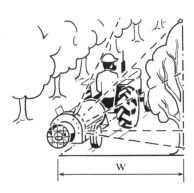

FIGURE 10-13.

When spray is emitted from only one side of an orchard or vineyard airblast sprayer, the swath width of each pass is one-half the plant row spacing.

FIGURE 10-14.

Swath width for pesticide sprays in orchards and vineyards should be measured from the center of one tree or vine row to the center of the adjacent row. Take several measurements in different locations to check for variation in plant spacing. If variation exists, average the measurements.

FIGURE 10-15.

Swath width for herbicide strip sprays in orchards and vineyards should be measured only to the center of the tree or vine row and should not include overlap.

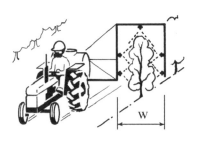

FIGURE 10-16.

Sometimes spray can be applied to both sides of a plant or vine row through a specially designed, horseshoe-shaped boom arrangement. Several plant rows can often be sprayed at the same time with these applicators. Spray swath width is the distance between opposing nozzles. If multiple rows are sprayed, the swath width is the sum of the distances.

you to adjust an air blast sprayer to apply a given volume of water per acre. After spraying out a tank of known volume, count the number of trees or vines completely sprayed. Then, calculate the area that you sprayed. You can increase or decrease travel speed slightly to apply less or more liquid per acre. You can also change nozzle sizes.

Measure swath width for herbicide strip sprays in orchards and vineyards to the center of the tree or vine row. Do not include overlap (Figure 10-15). Unless you apply the herbicide to the entire orchard or vineyard floor, the actual sprayed area is less than the total planted area.

Some applications use an inverted "U"-shaped boom to apply pesticides to the tops and both sides of vines or plants in a row (Figure 10-16). Sometimes these booms cover a row on each

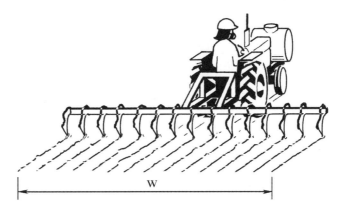

FIGURE 10-17.

Subsoil chisels spaced along a tractor's tool bar are used to inject pesticides into the soil. When pesticides are injected into the soil, the swath width is usually considered to be the width of the tool bar.

side of the tractor. Swath width for this type of equipment is equal to the distance between opposing nozzles.

You can inject pesticides into the soil by using special subsoil chisels spaced along a tractor-mounted tool bar. Assume that you are applying pesticides to the entire subsurface area in most soil injection applications. This swath width is equal to the number of chisels multiplied by the space between the chisels on the tool bar (Figure 10-17). When you inject pesticides as bands, the swath width is the sum of all the band widths, similar to surface band applications.

Measure the swath width of a backpack sprayer from the spray pattern produced on the ground in a test run. Keep the nozzle at the height held during an actual application. Maintain this height always to prevent variation in swath width. Nozzles of these types of sprayers usually provide a uniform spray pattern. Overlap swaths only enough to assure a uniform application pattern. Use the same method to measure swath width of controlled droplet applicators.

Determining the Amount of Pesticide to Use. Use tank volume, travel speed, flow rate, and swath width to calculate the total area covered with each tank of material. Knowing this

value allows you to determine how much pesticide to put into the tank. Choose from two calculation methods. One applies to pesticides applied by the acre. The other is for applications made by the square foot, such as landscape treatments or sprays in confined areas. See Sidebars 26 and 27.

Figure 10-18 is an example of how to combine calibration formulas onto a single sheet for in-field use. This example shows a calibration worksheet designed for orchard sprayers. You can make similar sheets for other types of pesticide sprayers.

To prevent waste of pesticide material, accurately measure the area you plan to treat. Then, mix only the amount of chemical needed.

Changing Sprayer Output

Once you calibrate a sprayer, you have determined its output rate for a specific speed. There may be times when you need to change this output rate. These include

- accommodating variations in foliage
- different plant spacing
- special requirements of the treatment area
- the need to travel at a faster or slower speed
- compensating for nozzle or pump wear

SIDEBAR 26

How Much Pesticide to Put into the Spray Tank (pesticides applied on a per-acre basis)

1. First, determine the area that can be treated in 1 minute. Divide the spray swath width by 43,560 (the number of square feet in 1 acre) and multiply the result by the travel speed in feet per minute. The result will be the acres treated per minute. In the example in Sidebar 21, page 289, travel speed was calculated to be 128.25 feet per minute. Assuming the swath width is 12 feet, the calculation would be:

■ EXAMPLE

(12 ft ÷ 43,560 sq ft/ac) × 128.25 ft/min = 0.0353 ac/min

In this example, when a swath 12 feet wide is being sprayed, 0.0353 acres are covered in 1 minute.

2. Next, determine the gallons of liquid being applied per acre. Divide the gallons per minute figure by the acres per minute:

■ EXAMPLE

1.525 gal/min ÷ 0.0353 ac/min = 43.2 gal/ac

3. Then, determine the number of acres that can be treated with a full tank. Divide the actual measured volume of the spray tank (or tanks) by the gallon per acre figure. Assume the tank holds 252.5 gallons when filled:

■ EXAMPLE

252.5 gal/tank ÷ 43.2 gal/ac = 5.84 ac/tank

4. Finally, determine how much pesticide to put in the tank. Multiply the number of acres per tank by the recommended rate per acre of pesticide; check the pesticide label for this information. (If the label calls for "active ingredient" see the "Active Ingredient Calculations" section on page 307.)

■ EXAMPLE

Pesticide Label Says		Acres per Tank		Amount of Pesticide to Put in Tank
1.5 lb/ac	×	5.84	=	8.76 lb
3 qt/ac	×	5.84	=	17.52 qt
2 gal/ac	×	5.84	=	11.68 gal
1 pt/ac	×	5.84	=	5.84 pt

SIDEBAR 27

How Much Pesticide to Put into the Spray Tank (pesticides applied by the square foot)

1. Determine how many square feet can be treated in 1 minute. Multiply the speed as determined by the procedures in Sidebar 21, page 289, by the swath width. In this example, assume a single-nozzle hand-operated sprayer is being used to apply a swath width of 2.5 feet at a speed of 128.25 feet per minute.

■ EXAMPLE

128.25 ft/min × 2.5 ft = 320.63 sq ft/min

2. Next, determine the volume of spray, in gallons, that will be applied to 1 square foot. Divide the gallon per minute output (from Sidebar 23) of the sprayer by the square feet per minute. For this example, assume that the backpack unit sprays 0.05 gallons per minute.

■ EXAMPLE

0.05 gal/min ÷ 320.63 sq ft/min = 0.000156 gal/sq ft

3. Then, find out how many square feet can be sprayed with one tank. Divide the number of gallons per square foot into the measured tank capacity. For this example assume that the tank holds 3 gallons.

■ EXAMPLE

3 gal/tank ÷ 0.000156 gal/sq ft = 19,230 sq ft/tank

4. Finally, determine how much pesticide to put in the tank. First, read the pesticide label; it will tell you the amount of pesticide to apply. Normally, the label will tell you how much to apply per square foot (or per 100 or 1,000 square feet) or per acre. (If the label calls for "active ingredient" see the "Active Ingredient Calculations" section on page 307.)

■ EXAMPLE A

If the label gives the dosage rate per 1, 100, or 1,000 square feet, multiply that rate by the square-feet-per-tank as determined in step 3:

Pesticide Label Says	×	Square Feet per Tank	=	Amount of Pesticide to Put in Tank
3 fl oz per 1,000 sq ft	×	19,230	=	57.69 fl oz
¾* fl oz per 1,000 sq ft	×	19,230	=	14.42 fl oz
1 oz per 100 sq ft	×	19,230	=	192.3 oz

*The fraction ¾ is converted to its decimal equivalent 0.75 to complete this calculation.

■ EXAMPLE B

If the pesticide label gives the dosage rate in units of pesticide per acre, convert square feet per tank (from step 3) to acres per tank by dividing it by 43,560 (the number of square feet in 1 acre):

19,230 sq ft/tank ÷ 43,560 sq ft/ac = 0.441 ac/tank

Then, multiply the labeled rate per acre by the number of acres per tank:

Pesticide Label Says	×	Acres per Tank	=	Amount of Pesticide to Put in Tank
1.5 lb/ac	×	0.441	=	0.661 lb (10.6 oz)
3 qt/ac	×	0.441	=	1.32 qt (42.2 fl oz)
2 gal/ac	×	0.441	=	0.882 gal (7.1 pt)
1 pt/ac	×	0.441	=	0.441 pt (7.1 fl oz)

ORCHARD SPRAYER CALIBRATION

Grower: <u>D. BROWN</u>   Date: <u>1-29-1999</u> Sprayer Type: <u>AIR BLAST</u>

CHECK: ☑ 1. Filter screens and strainers clean?
           ☑ 2. Tank clean and free of scale and sediment?
           ☑ 3. Pressure gauge operating?
           ☑ 4. Nozzles working properly?

Sprayer operating pressure: <u>100</u> psi

I-A. GALLONS/HOUR (Method I—using nozzle chart from manufacturer's catalog)

Nozzle Size	Number (N)		Rated Output (gallons/minute)		Minutes per Hour		Gallons per Hour
D2-25	8	×	0.25	×	60	=	120
D4-25	8	×	0.45	×	60	=	216
		×		×	60	=	
				TOTAL GALLONS PER HOUR		=	336

I-B. GALLONS/HOUR (Method 2—measurement)
1. Fill sprayer to verifiable level.
2. Run sprayer for a measured period of time (T), spraying
   under the same conditions as in the orchard.   T = <u>3.53</u>
3. Refill sprayer, measuring the amount of water used (GAL) in gallons.   GAL = <u>20.4</u>
4. Calculate: gallons/hour = (GAL × 60)/T   TOTAL GALLONS/HOUR = <u>346.7</u>

II. MILES/HOUR
1. Establish distance (D) in feet.   D = <u>253</u>
2. Measure elapsed time for sprayer to travel the distance.
   Make 3 runs and average results.
   a. First run time   = <u>1.05</u> minutes.
   b. Second run time = <u>1.15</u> minutes.
   c. Third run time   = <u>1.13</u> minutes.
3. Average of three runs (T) = <u>1.11</u> minutes.
4. Calculate miles per hour:
   MPH = (D/T)/88   MPH = <u>2.59</u>

III. ACRES/HOUR
1. Measure width of tree row (W) in feet.   W = <u>22</u>
2. Calculate miles per acre:
   miles/acre = (43,560/W)/5,280   MILES/ACRE = <u>0.375</u>
3. Calculate acres per hour:
   acres/hour = MPH/(miles/acre)   ACRES/HOUR = <u>6.91</u>

IV. GALLONS/ACRE
   (gallons/hour)/(acres/hour) = gallons/acre   GALLONS/ACRE = <u>50.17</u>

FIGURE 10-18.

A worksheet such as this Orchard Sprayer Calibration Worksheet can be helpful in recording and computing the figures necessary for calibration. Similar worksheets can be developed for other types of sprayers. (In this example, notice the difference between the rated output of the nozzles and the actual output. Nozzles are worn.)

V. ACRES/TANK

Tank size = <u>500</u> gallons/tank

(gallons/tank)/(gallons/acre) = acres/tank   ACRES/TANK = <u>9.97</u>

VI. AMOUNT OF PESTICIDE/TANK

Recommended amount of pesticide/acre = <u>2.5 lb.</u>

(pesticide/acre) × (acres/tank) = pesticide/tank   PESTICIDE/TANK = <u>24.9 lb.</u>

VII. CALIBRATION CHECK

1. Tree spacing (S) = <u>22</u> × <u>22</u> feet   S = <u>484</u>

2. Trees per acre (T) = 43,560/S   T = <u>90</u>

3. Count the actual number of trees sprayed (N)

   with one tank: N = <u>918</u>

4. Actual acres sprayed = N/T   ACTUAL ACRES = <u>10.2</u>

5. Calculated acres per tank

   (from "V" above)   CALCULATED ACRES/TANK = <u>9.97</u>

6. Percent accuracy = calculated acres/actual acres x 100   ACCURACY = <u>97.7%</u>

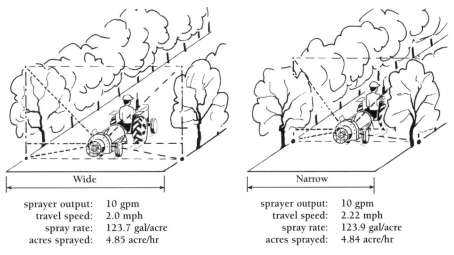

FIGURE 10-19.

Changes in row spacing in an orchard or vineyard affect the amount of spray being applied per acre. Increasing or decreasing ground speed can accommodate for the difference in spacing so the correct amount of pesticide per acre will be applied. Variations in the size of trees or vines may also influence the rate of application.

	Wide		Narrow
sprayer output:	10 gpm	sprayer output:	10 gpm
travel speed:	2.0 mph	travel speed:	2.22 mph
spray rate:	123.7 gal/acre	spray rate:	123.9 gal/acre
acres sprayed:	4.85 acre/hr	acres sprayed:	4.84 acre/hr

Sprayer must travel faster to keep spray application rate the same.

You can make several adjustments, either alone or in combination, to effectively increase or decrease sprayer output within a limited range.

Changing Speed. The simplest way to adjust the volume of spray being applied is to change the travel speed of the sprayer. A slower speed results in more liquid being applied, while a faster speed reduces the application rate. You may need such adjustments when swath width changes slightly. This would be the case in orchards or vineyards where plant spacing differs from block to block (Figure 10-19). Changing the travel speed eliminates the need for altering the concentration of chemical in the spray tank. However, there are limits to the amount of speed change you can make. Operating application equipment too fast is a common error and will result in poor coverage. Operating it too slow results in runoff, waste, and an increase in application time and cost. To determine how much to increase or decrease your speed, put in the new swath width and rework the calculations shown in Sidebar 26 or Sidebar 27.

Changing Output Pressure. As nozzles begin to wear, the spray volume will increase. When a pump begins to wear it becomes less efficient and the nozzle output drops off. Adjusting the pressure regulator to increase or decrease output pressure will change the spray volume slightly. Increasing pressure increases the output, while decreasing pressure lowers it. However, to double the output volume you must increase the pressure by a factor of four. This is usually beyond the capabilities of a spraying system. The working pressure range of the sprayer pump limits this adjustment. Whenever pressure in the system changes, remeasure the nozzle output (see Sidebar 22, page 290). Then, rework the calibration calculations. Increasing pressure breaks the spray up into finer droplets. Lowering pressure too much reduces the effectiveness of nozzles by altering the spray pattern.

Changing Nozzle Size. The most effective way to change the output volume of a sprayer is to install nozzles of a different size. Larger nozzles increase volume, while smaller ones reduce volume. Changing nozzles usually alters the pressure of the system and requires an adjustment of the pressure regulator. Adjust the output volume of disc-core nozzles by changing either the disc or the core. Sometimes you need to replace both. Be aware that changes in either the core or disc will also change the droplet size and spray pattern. Use tables included in nozzle manufacturers' catalogs as a guide for estimating output of different combinations. Whenever you change any nozzles, recalibrate the sprayer and refigure its new total output.

Calibrating Dry Applicators

The techniques for calibrating dry applicators are similar in many ways to those used for liquids. However, calibrate granule applicators for each type of granular pesticide you apply. Also, recalibrate this equipment each time weather or field conditions change. Granules vary in size and shape from one pesticide to the next, influencing their flow rate from the applicator hopper. Temperature and humidity, as well as field conditions, also influence granule flow.

Before beginning to calibrate a dry applicator, be sure that it is clean and all parts are working properly. Most equipment requires periodic lubrication. Always wear rubber gloves to prevent contact with residues on the equipment. Calibrating granule applicators involves using actual pesticides, so wear the label-prescribed personal protective equipment. Some formulations are dusty and may require respiratory protection.

You must measure three variables when calibrating a dry applicator:
- travel speed
- output rate
- swath width

Travel Speed. Determine travel speed in feet per minute in the same manner as you would for liquid applicators. Follow the instructions given on page 288. Fill up the applicator hoppers so you can measure speed under actual operating conditions.

Output Rate. To determine the output rate, fill the hopper or hoppers with the granular pesticide. Most granule applicator hoppers have ports with adjustable openings for granules to pass through. Refer to the manufacturer's instructions to determine the approximate opening for the rate and speed you need. Once you set the approximate opening, use one of the following three methods to determine the actual output rate.

1. *Measure the Quantity of Granules Applied to a Known Area.* The easiest way to calibrate a granule applicator is to collect and weigh the granules applied to a known area. Use this method when working with broadcast applicators. Spread out a plastic tarp of known size on the ground. Then operate the broadcast applicator at a known speed across the tarp (Figure 10-20). Place the granules collected by the tarp into a container and weigh them. Use the calculations shown in the example in Sidebar 28 to figure the amount of granular pesticide applied per acre or other unit of area.

2. *Collect a Measured Amount of Granules Over a Known Period of Time.* Collecting and weighing measured quantities of granules is similar to calibrating a liquid boom sprayer with multiple nozzles. Use this method for granule applicators with multiple ports. While operating the applicator at a normal speed, collect granules from one port at a time. Record the time required to collect each sample. Weigh samples separately, then use the calculations shown in Sidebar 29 to find the output rate.

3. *Refill the Hopper After a Measured Period of Time.* Use this method with hand-operated equipment or when applying small quantities. It also works best when you have several applicators on a boom. Fill the hopper or hoppers to a known level and operate the equipment for a measured time. When finished, weigh the quantity of granules required to refill the hoppers to their original levels. Use the calculations shown in the example in Sidebar 30 to compute the output rate. Settling of granules in the hoppers may cause this method to be less accurate than the two methods listed above.

Swath Width. To measure the swath width, operate the equipment under actual field conditions. Whenever possible, place cans, trays, or other containers at even intervals across the application swath. Use these to collect granules. Weigh the granules collected in each container separately to determine the distribution pattern. You can operate some spreaders over a strip of black cloth or plastic. This gives you a rapid visual assessment of granule distribution and swath width. Applicators that apply bands or inject granules into the soil do not have devices to disperse granules from side to side. You

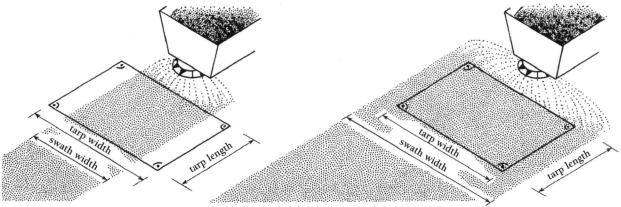

Area measurement: swath width × tarp length

Area measurement: tarp width × tarp length

FIGURE 10-20.

To determine the area of granules being applied, measure the swath width across a plastic tarp and multiply this by the length of the tarp. If the swath is wider than the tarp, the area is computed by multiplying the length by the width of the tarp.

SIDEBAR 28

Calculating Granule Output Rate by Measuring the Quantity Applied to a Known Area

1. Spread a 10 foot by 10 foot (or larger) plastic tarp on the ground and measure its length and width. Multiply the length by the width to determine the area of the tarp.

■ EXAMPLE

Tarp size = 10 ft by 12 ft
Tarp area = 10 × 12 = 120 sq ft

2. Fill the hopper or hoppers of the granule applicator, adjust the output ports to the recommended opening, and travel across the tarp at a known speed while granules are being broadcast.

3. Measure the swath width of the granules that were applied (see Figure 10-20) and compute the area of the swath. If the swath is wider than the tarp, the area figure to be used is equal to the area of the tarp. If the swath is narrower than the tarp, multiply the swath width by the length of the tarp.

4. Transfer all the granules on the tarp into a container and weigh them.

5. Multiply the weight of the granules collected (in pounds) by the area (acre, 1,000 square feet, or 100 square feet) given on the label. (An acre is 43,560 square feet.) Divide the result by the area of the swath.

■ EXAMPLE

Assume the swath width of granules being applied equals 15 feet. Therefore use the tarp area of 120 square feet in the calculations. (If the swath width was less than the tarp width, for example 8 feet, the area would then be 8 feet × 12 feet = 96 square feet.) Multiply the weight (in pounds) by the labeled area and divide the result by the tarp or swath area:

Weight = 8 oz × 16 oz/lb = 0.5 lb

$$\frac{0.5 \text{ lb} \times 43,560 \text{ sq ft/ac}}{120 \text{ sq ft}} = 181.5 \text{ lb/ac}$$

In this illustration, the granule applicator is broadcasting 181.5 pounds of material per acre. If the label calls for a greater amount, open the port more or slow the speed of travel of the applicator. If the label calls for a lesser amount, close the port some or speed up the rate of travel. Once an adjustment has been made, repeat this calibration procedure.

SIDEBAR 29

Calculating Granule Output Rate by Collecting a Measured Amount over a Known Period of Time

1. Adjust the hopper opening according to manufacturer's instructions suggested for your required application rate. If no information is available, begin with an intermediate setting.

2. Operate the equipment at the speed of an actual application. Collect granules in a clean container, such as a pan or bag, before they drop to the ground. Use a stopwatch to determine the time required to collect each volume. If granules are dispersed through more than one opening, collect and time the output from each. Because some units drop granules onto a spinning disc for dispersal, it may be necessary to disable the disc by disconnecting the drive chain or belt to prevent granule loss during collection. For smaller units, collect the discharge into a bag placed over the outlet. Be sure granules are moved away from the port quickly enough to prevent clogging.

3. Weigh the output from each port separately to detect any variability; if necessary, adjust ports to equalize flow rates. Collections should be weighed in ounces.

4. Determine the output in pounds per hour. Divide each weight by the collection time and multiply by 0.0625, (the number obtained by dividing 1 minute by 16 ounces per pound; this number will convert ounces per minute into pounds per minute).

■ EXAMPLE

The following is an example of an output collected from a granule applicator with six ports, although the same calculations would apply if only one port were used. Hopper openings were adjusted following manufacturer's recommendations for an application of 200 pounds per acre:

Port #	Ounces	Time (min)
1	29.5	0.25
2	33.0	0.28
3	31.5	0.26
4	29.0	0.25
5	33.0	0.27
6	30.0	0.26

Port #	oz ÷ min = oz/min × 0.0625 = lb/min
1	29.5/0.25 = 118.0 × 0.0625 = 7.375
2	33.0/0.28 = 117.9 × 0.0625 = 7.369
3	31.5/0.26 = 121.2 × 0.0625 = 7.575
4	29.0/0.25 = 116.0 × 0.0625 = 7.250
5	33.0/0.27 = 122.2 × 0.0625 = 7.638
6	30.0/0.26 = 115.4 × 0.0625 = 7.213

44.420

5. Determine total pounds per minute output by adding the individual outputs of each port. In this example the total output is 44.42 pounds per minute.

6. Use the technique shown in Sidebar 31, page 306, to calculate the rate per acre or other unit of area.

determine swath width by adding the widths of individual bands.

Application Rate. Use the example in Sidebar 31 to calculate the actual rate of granules being applied per acre or other unit of area. If your calculations do not correspond to the labeled rate, adjust the equipment and repeat the calibration procedure. Motorized and hand-operated applicators apply granules at a fixed output, independent of ground speed. When ground speed increases, you apply fewer granules per unit of area. When ground speed decreases, you apply more material. With this type of equipment you can adjust application rate by adjusting the size of the

SIDEBAR 30

Calculating the Rate of Output by Refilling the Hopper after a Measured Period of Time

1. Fill the hopper or hoppers to a known level with granules.

2. Operate the equipment for a measured period of time at a known speed.

3. Weigh the amount of granules required to refill the hopper or hoppers to their original level. If multiple hoppers are being used, be sure each is applying approximately the same amount of granules. If a significant variation exists, adjust the ports and repeat steps 1 through 3.

Hopper Number	Operating Time (min)	Weight of Granules (lb)
1	2.5	6.2
2	2.5	6.1
3	2.5	6.1
4	2.5	6.3
5	2.5	6.1
6	2.5	<u>5.9</u>
		36.7

4. Convert the output to pounds per minute by dividing the total weight from all hoppers by the time they were operated.

■ EXAMPLE

In this example, six applicators are used together on a boom. They have been adjusted so that they all apply approximately the same amount of granules:

■ EXAMPLE

36.7 lbs ÷ 2.5 min = 14.68 lbs/min

5. Use the technique shown in Sidebar 31 (below) to calculate the rate per acre or other unit of area.

SIDEBAR 31

Calculating Rate per Acre or Other Unit of Area

1. Determine the acres per minute being treated by dividing the swath width by 43,560 (the number of square feet in an acre) and multiplying the result by the speed of travel. In this example the swath width is 30 feet and the application speed is 352 feet per minute (4 miles per hour).

■ EXAMPLE

(30 ft [swath] ÷ 43,560 sq ft/ac) × 352 ft/min = 0.242 ac/min

2. Determine the pounds of formulated pesticide being applied per acre by dividing the output rate of the granule applicator (as computed from the calculations performed in Sidebars 28, 29, or 30) by the acres per minute calculated in step 1. This example uses 44.42 pounds per minute as the output rate.

■ EXAMPLE

44.42 lb/min ÷ 0.242 ac/min = 183.6 lb/ac

port opening and by changing the speed of travel.

The output of ground-wheel-driven granule applicators varies according to the ground speed. If ground speed increases, the applicator runs faster and the output rate is greater. When the ground speed slows down, output decreases because the applicator runs slower. The result of this automatic change in output is that the equipment applies nearly the same amount of material per acre or other unit of area no matter what speed it travels. The equipment has minimum and maximum operating speeds determined by the manufacturer, however. You change the application rate by increasing or decreasing the size of the port openings. In some units, you also change drive gears or sprockets to change the speed of the metering mechanism.

CALCULATION FOR ACTIVE INGREDIENT, PERCENTAGE SOLUTION, AND PARTS PER MILLION SOLUTIONS

Not all pesticide recommendations call for dry or liquid formulated amounts of pesticide per unit of area.

Research work sometimes requires a pesticide application rate in pounds of active ingredient (a.i.) per unit of area. Some labels require that pesticides be mixed as a percentage solution or be diluted to parts per million (ppm). Before adding pesticide to the spray tank, read and understand the dilution instructions on the label.

Active Ingredient (a.i.) Calculations

Pesticides are seldom available in their pure state. Manufacturers formulate them into a pest control product by combining them with adjuvants and inert ingredients such as carriers and solvents. Therefore, only a portion of any formulated product, whether dry or liquid, is pure pesticide. This portion is the *active ingredient* (a.i.). Some University of California and other pesticide use guidelines call for a.i. if there are several formulations available. Because different manufacturers often sell different formulations, using a.i. calculations allows you to apply the same amount of actual pesticide to a unit of area no matter what formulation you use.

Manufacturers list the percentage of active ingredient on product labels. Labels of liquid pesticides give the percentage by weight of active ingredient. They also tell how many pounds of active ingredient are in 1 gallon of formulation (Figure 10-21). Labels of dry formulations list the percentage by weight of active ingredient. Use the calculations in Sidebar 32 to make active ingredient calculations with liquid formulations. Use Sidebar 33 for dry formulations and Sidebar 34 for granular formulations.

Active Ingredient: Chlorothalonil (tetrachloroisophthalonitrile) 40.4%
Inert Ingredients: 59.6%
Total: 100.0%

Keep Out of Reach of Children
WARNING—AVISO
Si usted no entiende la etiqueta, busque a alguien para que se la explique a usted en detalle.
(If you do not understand the label, find someone to explain it to you in detail.)

See side panel for additional precautionary statements.

FIGURE 10-21.

To determine the percentage of active ingredient in a pesticide formulation, check the pesticide label. Liquid formulations list active ingredient as the number of pounds per gallon of formulation. Dry formulations list active ingredient as the total percentage of the weight.

SIDEBAR 32
Liquid Formulations

Assume that a sprayer has been calibrated and found to spray 7.5 acres per tank. You have a recommendation to apply 1.5 pounds a.i. of chlorothalonil per acre to control rust on snap beans, and have been supplied with a liquid formulation containing 4.17 pounds a.i. of chlorothalonil per gallon.

1. Determine the number of acres that can be treated with 1 gallon of formulation by dividing the pounds of a.i. per gallon by the recommended pounds of a.i. per acre.

■ EXAMPLE

4.17 lb a.i. per gal ÷ 1.5 lb a.i. per ac = 2.78 ac/gal

2. Divide the known acre capacity of your tank by the acres per gallon:

■ EXAMPLE

7.5 ac/tank ÷ 2.78 ac/gal = 2.7 gal/tank

This is the number of gallons of formulated chlorothalonil that should be put into the tank for spraying 7.5 acres of crop.

SIDEBAR 33
Powder Formulations

The calibrated sprayer you are using covers 7.5 acres per tank, and you have a recommendation to apply 1.5 pounds a.i. of chlorothalonil per acre for control of rust on snap beans. You are provided with a wettable powder formulation that, according to the label, contains 75% chlorothalonil.

1. Convert the percentage of a.i. to a decimal by dividing by 100 (or simply move the decimal point two places to the left).

■ EXAMPLE

75% = 0.75 lb a.i./lb formulation

2. Divide the recommended amount of a.i. by the amount of a.i. in the formulation.

■ EXAMPLE

1.5 lb a.i. per ac ÷ 0.75 lb a.i. per lb formulation = 2 lb formulation/ac

3. Multiply the pounds of formulation per acre by the number of acres per tank to find out how much material to put into the tank.

■ EXAMPLE

2 lb form/acre × 7.5 ac/tank = 15 lb/tank

SIDEBAR 34

Granular Formulations

You are given a recommendation for application of 0.50 lb a.i. of ethoprop per 1,000 square feet of turf for control of nematodes. You are provided with a granular formulation containing 10% active ingredient (0.1 pound of a.i. per pound of formulation).

1. Convert the percent a.i. to a decimal and divide this into the recommended application rate:

■ EXAMPLE

0.5 lb a.i. per 1000 sq ft ÷ 0.1 lb a.i. per lb formulation = 5 lb formulation

2. Calibrate the granule applicator so that it applies 5 pounds of formulated ethoprop per 1,000 square feet.

TABLE 10-2.

Parts per Million (ppm).

ppm	DECIMAL SOLUTION	PERCENTAGE
1 ppm	0.000001	0.0001%
10 ppm	0.00001	0.001%
100 ppm	0.0001	0.01%
1,000 ppm	0.001	0.1%
10,000 ppm	0.01	1.0%
100,000 ppm	0.1	10.0%
1,000,000 ppm	1.0	100.0%

Percentage Solutions

Sometimes label recommendations require that the pesticide be mixed as a percentage solution. You mix the active ingredient to get a known concentration regardless of the sprayer output rate. You mix percentage solutions on a weight-to-weight basis (w/w), meaning pounds of a.i. per pound of water. Sidebar 35 provides an example of calculating a percentage solution with liquid formulations. Sidebar 36 shows those for dry formulations.

Parts per Million (ppm) Solutions

You must mix certain pesticides in parts per million (ppm) concentrations.

These are the same as percentage solutions. For example, a 100 ppm solution is equal to a 0.01% solution (Table 10-2). The ppm designation represents the parts of active ingredient of pesticide per million parts of water. Parts per million dilutions are a common way of measuring very diluted concentrations of pesticides. When calculating parts per million, use the formulas in Sidebar 37 if you are mixing dry formulations with water. For liquid formulations, use the formulas in Sidebar 38.

SIDEBAR 35

Percentage Solution—Liquid Formulations

To prepare a percentage solution using liquid formulations, you need to know the volume of the spray tank, the weight of active ingredient per gallon of formulation, and the weight of a gallon of water. The weight of water is a constant, being approximately 8.34 pounds. Assume you have measured the volume of the spray tank and find that it holds 264.5 gallons of water. You are given a recommendation to apply a 1% solution of glyphosate for control of aquatic weeds using a high-pressure sprayer with a hand-held spray nozzle. The formulation of glyphosate that you are to use contains 5.4 pounds of active ingredient per gallon.

1. Find the total weight of the liquid in the filled tank by multiplying 264.5 gallons by 8.34 pounds per gallon:

■ EXAMPLE

264.5 gal × 8.34 lb/gal = 2,205.93 lb

2. Multiply this weight by 0.01 (1%) to determine the weight of a.i. required to mix a 1% solution:

■ EXAMPLE

2,205.93 × 0.01 = 22.06 lb

3. Divide the required weight of a.i. by the weight of a.i. in the formulation. The result is the number of gallons of liquid formulation that should be added to 264.5 gallons of water to achieve a 1% solution:

■ EXAMPLE

22.06 lb a.i. ÷ 5.4 lb a.i./gal = 4.1 gal formulation

In this example, one tank of liquid should contain 4.1 gallons of glyphosate formulation. The total volume of water combined with the glyphosate formulation should equal 264.5 gallons, the capacity of the tank. You would therefore use 260.4 gallons of water and 4.1 gallons of formulated glyphosate.

Note: These calculations give a close approximation of the amount of liquid formulation to add to the tank to achieve a known percentage solution. The mathematics for a more exact figure are more complex and unnecessary for this type of work.

SIDEBAR 36

Percentage Solution—Dry Formulations

Dry formulations require similar calculations for percentage solutions. First, from the label, determine the percent of a.i. in the dry formulation. Assume for this example that it is 75% a.i.; 1 pound of dry formulation would contain 0.75 pound of pesticide active ingredient. You need to mix a 1% spray solution of this formulation in the 264.5 gallon tank.

1. Find the total weight of the liquid in the filled tank by multiplying 264.5 gallons by 8.34 pounds per gallon:

■ EXAMPLE

264.5 gal × 8.34 lb/gal = 2,205.93 lb

2. Multiply this weight by 0.01 (1%) to determine the weight of a.i. required to mix a 1% solution:

■ EXAMPLE

2,205.93 × 0.01 = 22.06 lb

3. Divide the weight of a.i. by the decimal equivalent of the percent of a.i. in the formulation. The result is the number of pounds of formulation that should be added to 264.5 gallons of water to achieve a 1% solution:

■ EXAMPLE

22.06 lb = 29.41 lb formulation

Add 29.41 pounds of wettable powder to 264.5 gallons of water to achieve a 1% solution.

SIDEBAR 37

Calculating a Parts per Million Dilution for Dry Formulations

Assume you are given a recommendation requiring a 100 ppm concentration of oxytetracycline to be mixed in a 500 gallon tank. Oxytetracycline is used for control of fire blight on pear trees. The formulation you have is a wettable powder containing 17% a.i.

1. Find the total weight of the liquid in the filled tank by multiplying 500 gallons by 8.34 pounds per gallon:

■ EXAMPLE

500 gal × 8.34 lb/gal = 4,170 lb/tank

2. Determine how many pounds of a.i. are required for 1 pound of spray solution:

■ EXAMPLE

100 ppm = 100 parts a.i. ÷ 1,000,000 parts solution = 0.0001

It will require 0.0001 pounds of a.i. for each pound of solution to achieve a 100 ppm mixture.

3. Determine how many pounds of a.i. are required for a tank of solution, using the weight of the liquid in the tank:

■ EXAMPLE

4,170 lb/tank × 0.0001 lb a.i. = 0.417 lb a.i.

4. Divide the weight of a.i. by the decimal equivalent of the percent of a.i. in the formulation. The result is the number of pounds of formulation that should be added to 500 gallons of water to achieve a 100 ppm solution:

■ EXAMPLE

0.417 lb a.i. ÷ 0.17 lb a.i./lb form = 2.45 lb formulation

SIDEBAR 38

Calculating a Parts per Million Dilution for Liquid Formulations

Assume that a pesticide contains 5.4 pounds of a.i. in 1 gallon of formulation. You are required to prepare a 100 ppm concentration in a 500 gallon tank.

1. Find the total weight of the liquid in the filled tank by multiplying 500 gallons by 8.34 pounds per gallon:

■ EXAMPLE

500 gal/tank × 8.34 lb/gal = 4,170 lb/tank

2. Determine how many pounds of a.i. are required for 1 pound of spray solution:

■ EXAMPLE

100 parts a.i ÷ 1,000,000 parts sol = 0.0001

It will require 0.0001 pounds of a.i. for each pound of solution to achieve a 100 ppm mixture.

3. Determine how many pounds of a.i. are required for a tank of solution, using the weight of the liquid in the tank:

■ EXAMPLE

4,170 lb/tank × 0.0001 lb a.i. = 0.417 lb a.i./tank

4. Divide the required weight of a.i. by the pounds of a.i. per gallon to determine how many gallons of formulation are required. Since this will probably be a small number, multiply by 128 ounces per gallon to convert to ounces.

■ EXAMPLE

0.417 lb a.i./tank ÷ 5.4 lb a.i./gal = 0.0772 gal/tank

0.0722 gal/tank × 128 fl oz/gal = 9.88 fl oz/tank

Adding 9.88 fluid ounces of this formulated pesticide to 500 gallons of water will result in a 100 ppm solution.

REVIEW QUESTIONS

1. **Which of the following is the *main* reason for accurately measuring pesticides being put into your spray tank?**
   - ☐ a. To save money
   - ☐ b. To avoid illegal overapplication
   - ☐ c. To achieve uniform droplet sizes
   - ☐ d. To prevent overfilling the spray tank

2. **Frequent calibration of your application equipment will assure that you:**
   - ☐ a. Are using the correct amount of pesticide for effective pest control
   - ☐ b. Always use the maximum amount of pesticide allowed by law
   - ☐ c. Will never have pest problems
   - ☐ d. Can make effective pesticide applications during severe weather conditions

3. **Which of the following could be a result of *proper* equipment calibration?**
   - ☐ a. Better spray coverage during high winds
   - ☐ b. Unnecessary loss of time and money
   - ☐ c. Inadequate pest control
   - ☐ d. Effective pest control

4. **Why must you accurately measure the capacity of your spray tank?**
   - ☐ a. Tank manufacturer capacity ratings may be inaccurate
   - ☐ b. To be able legally to use more pesticide product per acre than prescribed by the pesticide label
   - ☐ c. Accurate measurement of the tank is unnecessary for proper calibration
   - ☐ d. To comply with federal laws

5. When making a pesticide application, increasing travel speed of the spraying equipment will:
   - ☐ a. Increase the amount of pesticide applied per acre
   - ☐ b. Decrease the amount of pesticide applied per acre
   - ☐ c. Have no effect on the amount of pesticide applied per acre
   - ☐ d. Improve coverage of the pesticide being sprayed

6. If sprayer output is not changed, what will you need to do to the travel speed of the application equipment to maintain the same rate per acre when the swath width narrows from 20 to 15 feet?
   - ☐ a. Decrease speed
   - ☐ b. Increase speed
   - ☐ c. Maintain the same speed
   - ☐ d. Triple the speed

7. Which of the following *is not* a good reason for calibrating pesticide application equipment?
   - ☐ a. Effective pest control
   - ☐ b. So equipment can be operated faster
   - ☐ c. Protecting human health, the environment, and treated surfaces
   - ☐ d. Complying with the law

8. For calibration, which four factors need to be measured?
   - ☐ a. Travel speed, sprayer pressure, number of nozzles, and nozzle height
   - ☐ b. Swath width, size of area to be treated, travel speed, and sprayer pressure
   - ☐ c. Tank capacity, travel speed, swath width, and sprayer output (flow rate)
   - ☐ d. Nozzle height, size of area to be treated, travel speed, and swath width

9. To double the output volume of a sprayer by increasing pressure, you must adjust the pressure regulator to increase the pressure by a factor of:
   - ☐ a. Two
   - ☐ b. Three
   - ☐ c. Four
   - ☐ d. Five

10. Your calibrated sprayer with a 300-gallon tank will cover 4.2 acres. You plan to apply an herbicide at a label rate of 1.5 pounds per acre. How much of this herbicide will you put into the spray tank?
    - ☐ a. 4.2 pounds
    - ☐ b. 4.5 pounds
    - ☐ c. 6.3 pounds
    - ☐ d. 12.6 pounds

11. It takes your equipment 3 minutes to travel 264 feet. How fast, in miles per hour, is the equipment traveling?
    - ☐ a. 1
    - ☐ b. 2
    - ☐ c. 3
    - ☐ d. 4

12. By measuring the output of each nozzle on the spray boom, you discover that the sprayer output is 256 ounces in 30 seconds. What is the output of the sprayer in gallons per minute?
    - ☐ a. 2
    - ☐ b. 3
    - ☐ c. 4
    - ☐ d. 5

13. How many acres can you treat if your sprayer holds 419 gallons and you've calibrated it to spray 80 gallons per acre?
    - ☐ a. 3.2
    - ☐ b. 4.8
    - ☐ c. 5.2
    - ☐ d. 6.3

14. A boom sprayer with flat fan nozzles is applying 6 strips, each one being 24 inches wide. What is the swath width you would use for calibration?
    - ☐ a. 2 feet
    - ☐ b. 4 feet
    - ☐ c. 6 feet
    - ☐ d. 12 feet

15. It took 24 gallons to refill an airblast sprayer after running it for 3 minutes. What is the sprayer's output in gallons per minute?
    - ☐ a. 5
    - ☐ b. 8
    - ☐ c. 10
    - ☐ d. 16

WER SHEET FOR REVIEW QUESTIONS

Chapter 1
1. d
2. d
3. c
4. b
5. c
6. c
7. d
8. a
9. a
10. c
11. b
12. c
13. d
14. c
15. c

Chapter 2
1. a
2. c
3. a
4. c
5. c
6. d
7. a
8. d
9. b
10. a
11. c
12. b
13. a

Chapter 3
1. b
2. a
3. c
4. d
5. d
6. d
7. c
8. b
9. b
10. c
11. b
12. b
13. c
14. d
15. d

Chapter 4
1. d
2. c
3. c
4. c
5. a
6. d
7. b
8. b
9. a
10. a
11. d
12. c
13. c
14. a
15. d

Chapter 5
1. a
2. c
3. b
4. b
5. c
6. c
7. d
8. a
9. a
10. a
11. d
12. c
13. c
14. c
15. a
16. c
17. b

Chapter 6
1. d
2. c
3. a
4. b
5. d
6. c
7. c
8. c
9. b
10. a
11. b

12. d
13. d
14. b
15. a
16. c
17. c
18. c

Chapter 7
1. b
2. d
3. a
4. d
5. c
6. b
7. c
8. c
9. b
10. a

Chapter 8
1. b
2. b
3. d
4. a
5. d
6. c
7. a
8. c
9. a
10. b
11. a

Chapter 9
1. a
2. d
3. c
4. d
5. c
6. a
7. c
8. c
9. d
10. a
11. c
12. b
13. c
14. c
15. a

Chapter 10
1. b
2. a
3. d
4. a
5. b
6. b
7. b
8. c
9. c
10. c
11. a
12. c
13. c
14. d
15. b

Glossary

24(c) registration. see *special local need registration (SLN)*.

abiotic. nonliving factors, such as wind, water, temperature, or soil type or texture.

abraded. a surface that has been roughened or scratched.

absorb. to soak up or take in a liquid or powder.

acaricide. a pesticide used to control mites.

accidental misapplication. an unintentional, incorrect application of a pesticide.

accumulate. to increase in quantity within an area, such as in the soil or tissues of a plant or animal.

acetylcholine. a short-acting neurotransmitter, widely distributed in the body, that transmits nerve signals between nerves and muscles, nerves and sensory organs, or nerves and other nerves.

acidic. pertaining to a solution or substance that has a pH lower than 7.0.

acidifier. an adjuvant used to lower the pH (or acidify) the water being mixed with a pesticide. Pesticides often break down more slowly if the spray water is slightly acid. Acidifiers are also referred to as acidulators.

acidulator. see *acidifier*.

action threshold. in pest management, the level of pest damage or pest infestation that warrants some type of control action.

activator. an adjuvant that increases the activity of a pesticide by reducing surface tension or speeding up penetration through insect or plant cuticle.

active ingredient (a.i.). the material in the pesticide formulation that actually destroys the target pest or performs the desired function.

acute effect. an illness that becomes apparent soon after an exposure to a pesticide occurs.

acute onset. pertaining to symptoms of pesticide-related injury that appear soon after the exposure incident.

additive effect. an increase in toxicity brought about by combining one pesticide with another. The increased toxicity is no greater than if an equal volume of either pesticide is used alone, however.

adjuvant. a material added to a pesticide mixture to improve or alter the deposition, toxic effects, mixing ability, persistence, or other qualities of the active ingredient.

adrenergic. having an impact on the natural adrenal or other hormone systems of an organism.

adsorb. to take up and hold on surface.

aerosol. very fine liquid droplets or dust particles often emitted from a pressurized can or aerosol generating device.

aestivation. dormancy during summer or periods of high temperature or a dry season.

agitator. a mechanical or hydraulic device that stirs the liquid in a spray tank to prevent the mixture from separating or settling.

agricultural commissioner. the official in each county in California who has the responsibility for enforcing the state and federal pesticide regulations and issuing permits for restricted-use pesticides. County agricultural commissioners and their staff frequently inspect pesticide applications and application sites. All agricultural uses of pesticides must be reported monthly to county agricultural commissioners.

agricultural use. a classification of certain pesticides that limits their use to production agriculture settings.

air assist sprayer. a sprayer that uses air to move spray droplets to the target surface. See also *air blast sprayer*.

air blast sprayer. a sprayer that uses a high-powered fan to carry spray droplets to target surfaces. Airblast sprayers are usually used on tall plants such as trees or vines

air gap. a space between the filling hose and the liquid in the pesticide tank that prevents backflow of pesticide liquids into the water source. The air gap should be a minimum of 2 times the diameter of the filling hose or pipe.

algae. aquatic, nonvascular plants (singular: alga.)

alkaline. pertaining to a solution or substance that has a pH greater than 7.0.

alkylating. involves changes to biologically important molecules that alter their function; an alkylating agent causes replacement of hydrogen atoms on molecules by an alkyl group.

allowable tolerance. the maximum amount of pesticide residues that may remain on treated produce or other food items once the these items become available to consumers.

all-terrain cycle. a three- or four-wheeled motorcycle-like vehicle used for applying low volumes of pesticides in agricultural areas and open lands.

amphibian. a cold-blooded organism such as a frog, toad, or salamander.

anemometer. an instrument used for measuring wind speed.

animal kingdom. one of two groups of living organisms, the other being the plant kingdom.

anionic. pertaining to materials that contain negatively charged ions; a characteristic of some types of surfactants that helps prevent pesticides from being washed off treated surfaces.

annual. a type of plant that passes through its entire life cycle in one year or less.

antagonistic effect. reduced toxicity or effectiveness as a result of combining one pesticide with another.

antibiotic. a substance produced by a living organism, such as a fungus, that is toxic to other types of living organisms. Sometimes used as a pesticide.

anticoagulant. a type of rodenticide that causes death by preventing normal blood clotting.

apiary. a place where bees are kept, such as a bee hive.

application frequency restriction. a limitation on the number of times a particular pesticide may be applied to the same crop or site in a growing season or other period of time.

application pattern. the course the applicator follows through the area being treated with a pesticide.

application rate. pertaining to the amount of pesticide that is applied to a known area, such as an acre.

application swath. see *swath* and *swath width*.

aquatic. pertaining to water, such as aquatic weeds or aquatic pest control.

aquifer. an underground formation of sand, gravel, or porous rock that contains water. The place where groundwater is found.

arsenical pesticide. a type of pesticide that contains some form of arsenic.

arthropod. an animal having jointed appendages and an external skeleton, such as an insect, a spider, a mite, a crab, or a centipede.

artificial respiration. see *rescue breathing*.

attractant. a substance that attracts a specific species of animal to it. When manufactured to attract pests to traps or poisoned bait, attractants are considered to be pesticides.

attractive nuisance. a legal principle referring to an area (such as public or private land) or object that is or could be hazardous to people but that exerts some compelling attraction (especially to children).

auger. a spiral-shaped shaft used for moving pesticide dusts or granules from a hopper to a moving belt or disk for application.

augmentation. the process of building up a population of natural enemies in an area by bringing in additional eggs, larvae, or adults of that species.

avicide. a pesticide used to control pest birds.

axonic. affecting the axons or long fibers of nerve cells; impairing normal nerve function by interfering with the conduction of a nerve impulse along a nerve.

back siphoning. the process that permits pesticide-contaminated water to be sucked from a spray tank back into a well or other water source. Back siphoning is prevented by providing an air gap or check valve in the pipe or hose used to fill a spray tank.

backflow. see *back siphoning*.

backpack sprayer. also known as a knapsack sprayer, a small portable sprayer carried on the back of the person making the pesticide application. Some backpack sprayers are hand-operated and others are powered by small gasoline engines.

bacterium. a unicellular microscopic plantlike organism that lives in soil, water, organic matter, or the bodies of plants and animals. Some bacteria cause plant or animal diseases. (plural: bacteria.)

bait. a food or foodlike substance that is used to attract and often poison pest animals.

bait station. a box or similar device designed to hold poisoned bait for controlling rodents, insects, or other pests. Bait stations usually have baffles or small openings to prevent access to the bait except by the target pest.

band treatment. the application of liquid or dry pesticides in bands or strips, usually to the soil, rather than over the entire area.

belly grinder. a hand-operated device used to apply pesticide granules. The device straps to the front of the operator, who then turns a crank while walking forward through the treatment area.

beneficial. pertaining to being helpful in some way to people, such as a beneficial plant or insect.

biennial. a plant that completes part of its life cycle in one year and the remainder of its life cycle the following year.

bifluid nozzle. a special nozzle used for producing extremely fine droplets. Fluid is broken up into small droplets by passing through a high-velocity airstream.

bind (chemically). a chemical reaction in which molecules of one substance attach to molecules of another substance, forming a bond that can only be broken through another chemical reaction.

binding agent. a special type of adjuvant, similar to glue, that is designed to prevent a sprayed pesticide from washing or rubbing off the treated surface.

bioaccumulation. the gradual buildup of certain pesticides within the tissues of living organisms after feeding on lower organisms containing smaller amounts of these pesticides. Animals higher up on the food chain accumulate greater amounts of these pesticides in their tissues.

biochemical. pertaining to a chemical reaction that takes place within the cells or tissues of living organisms.

biological activity. activity involving the biological processes of living organisms, as opposed to physical or mechanical activity.

biological control. the action of parasites, predators, pathogens, or competitors in maintaining another organism's numerical density at a lower average than would occur in their absence. Biological control may occur naturally in the field or be the result of manipulation or introduction of biological control agents by people.

biological factors (in pesticide resistance). factors such as life cycles, life stages, physical attributes, and others that protect certain organisms from the toxic effects of pesticides.

biology. knowledge about the life habits of a plant or animal.

biotic. pertaining to living organisms, such as the influences living organisms have on all pest populations.

black light trap. a device that uses ultraviolet light to attract insects.

blocking (photosynthesis). preventing plants from carrying out photosynthesis (converting sunlight into energy for plant growth and other functions) by interfering with one or more of the chemical processes that must take place to accomplish this.

boom. a structure attached to a truck, tractor, or other vehicle, or held by hand, to which spray nozzles are attached.

boom applicator. a pesticide application device having multiple nozzles spaced along a boom, making it possible to spray a wide swath. Boom applicators are usually used for herbicide application and for other pesticides in field and row crops.

botanical. derived from plants or plant parts.

brand name. the registered or trade name given to a pesticide by its manufacturer or formulator. A specific pesticide may be sold under several brand names.

breakdown. the process by which chemicals, such as pesticides, decompose into other chemicals.

broad spectrum pesticide. a pesticide that is capable of controlling many different species or types of pests.

broadcast application. a method of applying granular pesticides by dispersing them over a wide area using a spinning disc or other mechanical device.

broadleaves. one of the major plant groups, known as dicots, with netveined leaves usually broader than grasses. Seedlings have two seed leaves (cotyledons); broadleaves include many herbaceous plants, shrubs, and trees.

brood. pertaining to a group of young or newly hatched individuals, such as termites.

buffer. an adjuvant that lowers the pH of a spray solution and, depending on its concentration, can maintain the pH within a narrow range even if acidic or alkaline materials are added to the solution.

buffer area. a part of a pest-infested area that is not treated with a pesticide to protect adjoining areas from pesticide hazards.

buffer strip. an area of a field left unsprayed for the purpose of protecting nearby structures or sensitive areas from drift. The minimum buffer strip is usually one swath width.

buffer zone. see *buffer strip*.

caking. the process by which pesticide dusts pack and clump together, preventing proper application.

calibration. the process used to measure the output of pesticide application equipment so that the proper amount of pesticide can be applied to a given area.

California Department of Pesticide Regulation (DPR). the state agency responsible for regulating the use of pesticides in California.

carbamate. a class of pesticides commonly used for control of insects, mites, fungi, and weeds. N-methyl carbamate insecticides, miticides, and nematicides are cholinesterase inhibitors.

carcinogenic. having the ability to produce cancer.

cardiopulmonary resuscitation (CPR). a procedure designed to restore normal breathing after breathing and heartbeat have stopped.

carrier. the liquid or powdered inert substance that is combined with the active ingredient in a pesticide formulation. May also apply to the water or oil that a pesticide is mixed with prior to application.

caste. a subgroup having specialized duties within a population of insects. Some termite species, for example, have worker, soldier, and reproductive castes.

cationic. pertaining to materials that contain positively charged ions. Some surfactants include cationic materials to improve mixing and absorption by the target pest.

catkin. an inflorescence that hangs down by its own weight; its flowers are usually of one sex.

caustic. quality of a chemical describing its ability to burn or injure the skin, eyes, or mouth and intestinal lining.

Caution. the signal word used on labels of the least toxic pesticides; these pesticides have an oral LD_{50} greater than 500 and a dermal LD_{50} greater than 2,000.

CDA. see *controlled droplet applicator.*

certified pesticide applicator. a person who has demonstrated through an examination process the ability to safely handle and apply highly hazardous restricted-use pesticides.

certified private applicator. a property owner, manager, or responsible person employed by the property owner or manager who has demonstrated through an examination process the ability to safely handle and apply restricted-use pesticides on the property under their control.

chemical name. the official name given to a chemical compound to distinguish it from other chemical compounds.

chemigation. the application of pesticides to target areas through an irrigation system.

CHEMTREC. a chemical-industry-supported organization that provides assistance and advice on pesticide emergencies. The telephone number of CHEMTREC is 1-800-424-9300.

chlorinated hydrocarbons. also known as organochlorines, a class of pesticides that contain a chlorine atom incorporated into an organic molecule. They were frequently used for insect and mite control, but most early forms of these compounds have now been banned due to environmental persistence or other problems. DDT, chlordane, toxaphene, dieldrin, and dicofol are examples of some of the earlier-developed chlorinated hydrocarbons.

chlorotic. a yellowing or bleaching of normally green leaves due to a nutrient deficiency, disease, pest damage, or other disorder.

cholinesterase. an essential enzyme found in many living organisms, including human beings, that deactivates the chemical *acetylcholine* that is responsible for transmitting nerve impulses between nerves and between nerves and muscles. Without proper cholinesterase activity, which allows the nerve signals to stop at the appropriate time, nerves and muscles do not function properly.

chronic. pertaining to long duration or frequent recurrence.

chronic illness. an illness that will last for long periods of time. Cancer, respiratory disorders, and neurological disorders are examples of chronic illnesses that have been associated with exposures to some types of pesticides.

class 1 disposal site. a disposal site for toxic and hazardous materials such as pesticides and pesticide-contaminated wastes.

class 2 disposal site. a disposal site for nontoxic and nonhazardous materials such as household and commercial waste. Sanitary landfills are class 2 disposal sites.

classical biological control. a pest control method that uses natural enemies and is directed toward pests that are not native to a geographical area. Classical biological control involves locating the native home of an introduced pest and finding suitable natural enemies that can be imported, reared, and released into the area where the pest has been established.

classified oils. spray oils with distillation properties defined by the California grade system, developed in 1925 by Ralph H. Smith of UC Riverside.

closed mixing system. a device used for measuring and transferring liquid pesticides from their original container to the spray tank. Closed mixing systems reduce chances of exposure to concentrated pesticides. Closed mixing systems are usually required when mixing liquid materials with the signal word *Danger.*

coalescent effect. the unique mode of action observed when two or more pesticides having different modes of action are combined.

common name. the recognized, nonscientific name given to plants or animals. The Weed Science Society of America and the Entomological Society of America publish lists of recognized common names. Many pesticides also have common names, separate from their brand names and chemical names.

compatibility agent. an adjuvant that improves the ability of two or more pesticides to combine.

compatible. the condition in which two or more pesticides mix without unsatisfactory chemical or physical changes.

competition. the struggle between different organisms for the same resources, such as water, light, nutrients, or space.

confined area. areas such as buildings or greenhouses, attics, crawl spaces, or holds of ships that may have restricted air circulation and therefore promote buildup of toxic fumes or vapors from a pesticide application.

contact poison. a pesticide that provides control when target pests come in physical contact with it.

control agent. organisms or chemicals that reduce populations of pests, such as natural enemies and pesticides. Also, certain types of adjuvants that reduce the tendency for a pesticide spray to drift.

controlled droplet applicator (CDA). an application device that produces more-uniformly-sized liquid droplets by passing liquid over a notched, spinning disk.

convulsions. contortions of the body caused by violent, involuntary muscular contractions. Convulsions can be a symptom of pesticide poisoning.

corrosive materials. certain chemicals that react with metals or other materials. Some pesticides are corrosive, and special handling requirements are needed when using these.

cotyledon. the first leaf or pair of leaves of a sprouted seed. Grasses (monocots) have a single cotyledon while broadleaved plants (dicots) have a pair of cotyledons.

coverage. the degree to which a pesticide is distributed over a target surface.

coverall. a one- or two-piece garment of closely woven fabric that covers the entire body except the head, hands, and feet, and must be provided by the employer as personal protective equipment. Coverall differs from, and should not be confused with, work clothing that can be required to be provided by the employee.

CPR. see *cardiopulmonary resuscitation*.

crop stage. the stage of development of agricultural crops, such as seedling, flowering, fruit set, etc. Different pests attack crops at different stages of development.

cross resistance. a condition where an organism that has developed resistance to one type or group of pesticides is also resistant to other similar or dissimilar pesticides even though the organism has never been exposed to those pesticides.

cumulative effect. poisoning symptoms that only appear after several repeated doses over a period of time, indicating that the toxic effect is building up in the system of the poisoned individual.

cuticle. the outer protective covering of plants and arthropods that aids in preventing moisture loss.

Danger. the signal word used on labels of highly hazardous pesticides—those pesticides with an oral LD_{50} less than 50 or a dermal LD_{50} less than 200 or those having specific, serious health or environmental hazards.

deactivation. the process by which the toxic action of a pesticide is reduced or eliminated by impurities in the spray tank, by water being used for mixing, or by biotic or abiotic factors in the environment.

decontaminate. the most important step in reducing potential injury when someone has been exposed to a pesticide. Decontamination involves thoroughly washing the exposed skin with soap and water or flushing the exposed eye with a gentle stream of running water.

deficient oxygen condition. a condition where the oxygen concentration in air falls below 19%, thus making an area highly hazardous. High levels of pesticide vapors in a confined area can displace oxygen, creating a deficient oxygen condition. Supplied-air respirators (SCBAs) are required to be worn when entering areas with deficient oxygen conditions.

defoaming agent. an adjuvant that eliminates foaming of a pesticide mixture in a spray tank.

defoliant. a pesticide used to remove leaves from target plants, often as an aid in harvesting the plant.

degradation. the breakdown of a pesticide into an inactive or less active form. Environmental conditions, impurities, or microorganisms can contribute to the degradation of pesticides.

dehydration. the process of a plant or animal losing water or drying up.

delayed mixture. an incompatibility or adverse effect between two pesticides that were applied to the same target but at different times.

deposition. the placement of pesticides on target surfaces.

deposition aid. an adjuvant that improves the ability of a pesticide spray to reach the target.

dermal. pertaining to the skin. One of the major ways pesticides can enter the body to possibly cause poisoning.

dermatitis. inflammation, itching, or irritation of the skin caused by pesticide exposure.

desiccant. a material that removes water from plants or arthropods or destroys the waxy coatings that protect these organisms from water loss. Desiccants are one of the types of pest control agents used for weeds and arthropods and are also used to defoliate certain plants before harvest.

detoxify. the process that is used to render a chemical nontoxic. Some organisms can detoxify pesticides through internal biological processes.

diluent. the inert liquid or powdered material that is combined with the active ingredient during manufacture of a pesticide formulation. Also, the water, petroleum oil, or other liquid in which the formulated pesticide is mixed before application.

directions for use. the instructions found on pesticide labels indicating the proper procedures for mixing and application.

disease. a condition, caused by biotic or abiotic factors, that impairs some or all of the normal functions of a living organism.

dispersion. the act of spreading pesticide droplets, dusts, or granules widely over a target area.

disposal site. see *Class 1 disposal site* and *Class 2 disposal site.*

dissolve. to pass into solution.

dormant. to become inactive during winter or periods of cold weather.

dose. the measured quantity of a pesticide. Often the size of the dose determines the degree of effectiveness, or, in the case of poisoning of nontarget organisms, the degree of injury.

drift. the movement of pesticide dust, spray, or vapor through the air away from the application site.

dry flowable. a dry, granular pesticide formulation intended to be mixed with water for application. When combined with water, a dry flowable will be similar to a wettable powder. Dry flowable formulations are measured by volume rather than weight.

dust. finely ground pesticide particles, sometimes combined with inert materials. Dusts are applied without mixing with water or other liquid.

dynes/cm. a dyne is the unit of force in the metric system equal to the force that would give a free mass of 1 gram an acceleration of 1 centimeter per second per second.

early-entry worker. an employee who must enter a pesticide application site to perform cultural activities before the expiration of the restricted-entry interval.

ecological. an approach that considers the interrelationship between living organisms and the environment.

economic damage. damage caused by pests to plants, animals, or other items that results in loss of income or a reduction of value.

economic injury threshold. the point at which the value of the damage caused by a pest exceeds the cost of controlling the pest, therefore making it practical to use a control method.

effective life. the period of time that an applied pesticide remains toxic enough to adequately control pests for which it was intended.

efficacy. the ability of a pesticide to produce a desired effect on a target organism.

electrostatic. an electrical charge that causes a pesticide liquid or dust to be attracted to the target surface.

emergence. the appearance of a plant through the surface of the soil.

emergency exemption from registration. a federal exemption from regular pesticide registration sometimes issued when an emergency pest situation arises for which no pesticide is registered that has a tolerance on the crop in question.

emulsifiable concentrate. a pesticide formulation consisting of a petroleum-based liquid and emulsifiers that enable it to be mixed with water for application.

emulsifier. an adjuvant added to a pesticide formulation to permit petroleum-based pesticides to mix with water.

emulsion. droplets of petroleum-based liquids (oils) suspended in water.

encapsulation. a process by which tiny liquid droplets or dry particles are contained in polymer plastic capsules to slow their release into the environment and prolong their effectiveness. Sometimes encapsulation lowers hazards to people mixing or applying pesticides.

endangered species. rare or unusual living organisms whose existence is threatened by people's activities, including the use of some types of pesticides.

environment. all of the living organisms and nonliving features of a defined area.

environmental contamination. spread of pesticides away from the application site into the environment, usually with the potential for causing harm to organisms.

Environmental Protection Agency (EPA). the federal agency responsible for regulating pesticide use in the United States.

enzyme. a complex chemical compound produced and used by a living organism to induce or speed up chemical reactions without being itself permanently altered.

epidermis. the outer layer of skin of vertebrates or the cellular layer of tissue beneath the cuticle of invertebrates.

eradicant. a pesticide that is used to destroy a pest organism such as a fungus.

eradication. the pest management strategy that attempts to eliminate all members of a pest species from a defined area.

establishment number. a number assigned to registered pesticides by the U.S. Environmental Protection Agency that indicates the location of the manufacturing or formulation facilities of that product.

estivation. see *aestivation*.

evaporate. the process of a liquid turning into a gas or vapor.

exclusion. a pest management technique that uses physical or chemical barriers to prevent certain pests from getting into a defined area.

exotic. a pest from another country, one that is not native to the local area.

exposure. the unwanted contact with pesticides or pesticide residues by people, other organisms, or the environment.

extender. an adjuvant that enhances the effectiveness or effective life of a pesticide by some means such as screening ultraviolet light, slowing down volatilization, or improving sticking qualities.

fallow. cultivated land that is allowed to lie dormant during a growing season.

farm advisors. University of California specialists in most counties of California who serve as resources for residents of the state on pest management, water management, soil management, nutrition, and many other issues.

fencerow. the strip of soil under a fence. Fencerows are common places for weed growth in cultivated areas because the fence blocks access to the cultivation equipment.

fibrous. thin, long, and multibranching roots forming a dense clump.

field incompatibility. an incompatibility between pesticides mixed together in a spray tank that occurs during application. Field incompatibility may result from changes in the temperature of the water used in the mix or changes in the length of time the spray mixture has been in the tank.

fieldworker. an employee of a farming operation who performs cultural practices on crops or agricultural soil.

fieldworker training. specific training mandated by the U.S. Environmental Protection Agency and the state of California to assist fieldworkers in protecting themselves from pesticide residues when they work in areas that have received pesticide applications. Training is required if fieldworkers enter areas during a 30-day period after the expiration of a restricted-entry interval.

FIFRA. the Federal Insecticide, Fungicide, and Rodenticide Act. This is the federal law that regulates pesticide registration, labeling, use, and disposal in the United States.

filamentous. long and threadlike.

first aid. the immediate assistance provided to someone who has received an exposure to a pesticide. First aid for pesticide exposure usually involves removal of contaminated clothing and washing the affected area of the body to remove as much of the pesticide material as possible. First aid is not a substitute for competent medical treatment.

fit check. the procedure that must be carried out each time a person puts on an organic vapor filtering respirator. The fit check involves: (1) properly adjusting the straps, (2) closing off the filters with the hands and inhaling to check for air leaks around the face seal, and (3) closing off the exhalation valve and exhaling to check for air leaks through the filters.

fit test. a test that must be performed to check the proper fit of an organic vapor filtering respirator. Fit tests must be performed each time a new respirator is issued. A detecting agent, such as isoamyl acetate or irritant smoke, is used to check the seal of the respirator's facepiece to the wearer's face.

flow rate. the amount of pesticide being expelled by a pesticide sprayer or granule applicator per unit of time.

flowable. flowable formulations consist of finely ground particles of pesticide active ingredient mixed with a liquid, along with emulsifiers, to form a concentrated emulsion. These liquids are mixed with water for dilution prior to spraying.

fog. a spray of very small pesticide-laden droplets that remain suspended in the air.

foliage. the leaves of plants.

formulation. a mixture of active ingredient combined during manufacture with inert materials. Inert materials are added to improve the mixing and handling qualities of a pesticide.

frass. solid fecal material produced by insect larvae.

fruiting bodies. special structures produced by fungi that contain the spores by which the organisms reproduce.

fume. the vapor phase of some pesticide active ingredients.

fumigant. vapor or gas form of a pesticide used to penetrate porous surfaces for control of soil-dwelling pests or pests in enclosed areas or storage.

fumigation. the process of controlling certain pests by exposing them to an atmosphere of toxic gas inside an enclosed area or under tarped soil.

fungicide. a pesticide used for control of fungi.

fungus. multicellular lower plant lacking chlorophyll, such as a mold, mildew, rust, or smut. The fungus body normally consists of filamentous strands called the mycelium and reproduces through dispersal of spores. (plural: fungi.)

general-use pesticide. pesticides that have been designated for use by the general public as well as by licensed or certified applicators. General-use pesticides usually have minimal hazards and do not require a permit for purchase or use.

generic pesticide. a pesticide not protected by a patent; one that may be manufactured by many different companies.

genetic factors (in pesticide resistance). inherited factors that an organism uses to resist the effect of a pesticide; these might include certain behaviors, timing of life stages, physical attributes, or physiological mechanisms.

granule. a dry formulation of pesticide active ingredient and inert materials compressed into small, pebble-like shapes.

groundwater. fresh water trapped in aquifers beneath the surface of the soil; one of the primary sources of water for drinking, irrigation, and manufacturing.

ground-wheel-driven. a trailer-mounted dry or liquid pesticide applicator that gets the power to drive a pump, auger, or spinning disc from the movement of one of the trailer wheels as the unit is towed.

habitat. the place where plants or animals live and grow.

half-life. the period of time that must elapse for a pesticide to lose half of its original toxicity or effectiveness.

hand lens. a small magnifying glass used in monitoring for plant pests.

handler. a person who mixes, loads, transfers, applies (including chemigation), or assists with the application (including flagging) of pesticides; who maintains, services, repairs, cleans, or handles equipment used in these activities; who works with unsealed pesticide containers; who adjusts, repairs, or removes treatment site coverings; who incorporates pesticides into the soil; who enters a treated area during any application or before the REI has expired; or who performs crop advisor duties.

harvest interval. a period of time as indicated by the pesticide label that must elapse after a pesticide has been applied to an edible crop before the crop can be harvested legally.

hazard communication program. part of California's pesticide regulations that requires employers to provide information about pesticides and pesticide applications at the workplace.

hazardous materials. materials, including many pesticides, that have been classified by regulatory agencies as being harmful to the environment or to people. Hazardous materials require special handling and must be stored and transported in accordance with regulatory mandates.

hazardous waste. a hazardous material for which there is no further use. Remains from pesticide spill cleanup are often hazardous wastes. Hazardous wastes can be disposed of only through special hazardous material incineration or by transporting to a Class 1 disposal site.

heat stress. potentially life-threatening overheating of the body under working conditions that lack proper preventive measures, such as drinking plenty of water, taking frequent breaks in the shade to cool down, and removing or loosening personal protective equipment during breaks. California regulations require that pesticide handlers receive training on recognizing, avoiding, and treating heat stress.

HEPA. see *high-efficiency particulate air filter.*

herbaceous. a plant that is herblike, usually having little or no woody tissue.

herbicide. a pesticide used for the control of weeds.

hibernation. the process of passing the winter in a resting or nonactive state.

high-efficiency particulate air filter. special filtering medium designed to remove extremely small particles from the air.

honeydew. the sweet, sticky fluid secreted by some plant-feeding insects such as aphids, and scales. Coatings of honeydew on leaf and fruit surfaces promote the buildup of a fungus known as sooty mold. Ants, bees, wasps, and other insects feed on honeydew and may protect the plant-feeding insects from attack by other insects.

hormonal herbicide. a special type of herbicide that controls weeds by changing growth rates or patterns.

hormone. a chemical produced in the cells of a plant or animal that produces changes in cells in another part of the organism's structure.

host. a plant or animal species that provides sustenance for another organism.

host resistance. the ability of a host plant or animal to ward off or resist attack by pests or to be able to tolerate damage caused by pests.

host-free area. an area where certain plants that serve as hosts to specific types of pests are forbidden by law to be grown. Establishing host-free areas is a way of controlling some pests.

host-free period. a period of time, usually each year, when certain plants are prohibited from being grown as a way of controlling some pests.

hydrolysis. a chemical process that involves incorporating a water molecule into another molecule.

hygiene. as it applies to pesticide exposure, hygiene involves washing exposed body areas promptly to remove pesticide residues.

hypha. a threadlike fiber that makes up the mycellium of a fungus. (plural: hyphae)

impermeable. having the ability to resist penetration by a substance or object.

impregnate. an item, such as a flea collar, that has been manufactured with a certain pesticide in it. Impregnates usually emit small, localized quantities of pesticide over an extended period of time.

incompatibility. a condition in which two or more pesticides are unable to mix properly or one of the materials chemically alters the other to reduce its effectiveness or produce undesirable effects on the target.

incompatible mixture. the result when two or more pesticides are combined and they react to make the mixture unusable.

incorporate. to move a pesticide below the surface of the soil by discing, tilling, or irrigation. To combine one pesticide with another.

indexing. a method used to classify plant diseases.

inert. not having any chemical activity.

inert ingredients. all materials in the pesticide formulation other than the active ingredient. Some inert ingredients may be toxic or hazardous to people.

infection. the establishment of a microorganism within the tissues of a host plant or animal.

infestation. a troublesome invasion of pests within an area such as a building, greenhouse, agricultural crop, or landscaped location.

inflorescence. the reproductive shoot system of a plant that bears flowers.

ingest. to take into the body through the mouth, such as eating or swallowing.

inhalation. the method of entry of pesticides through the nose or mouth into the lungs.

inhibit. to prevent something from happening, such as a biochemical reaction within the tissues of a plant or animal.

inorganic. derived from rock or mineral sources rather than biological or biochemical sources. Usually refers to materials whose molecules do not contain carbon and hydrogen atoms.

insect growth regulator (IGR). a type of insecticide that controls certain insects by disrupting the normal process of development from immature to reproductive life stages.

insectaries. laboratories having growth chambers where insects are hatched and reared, often for commercial purposes.

insecticide. a pesticide used for the control of insects. Some insecticides are also labeled for control of ticks, mites, spiders, and other arthropods.

instar. the period between molts in larvae of insects. Most larvae pass through several instars; these are usually given numbers such as 1st instar, 2nd instar, etc.

integrated pest management (IPM). a pest management program that uses life history information and extensive monitoring to understand a pest and its potential for causing economic damage. Control is achieved through multiple approaches including prevention, cultural practices, pesticide applications, exclusion, natural enemies, and host resistance. The goal is to achieve long-term suppression of target pests with minimal impact on nontarget organisms and the environment.

intentional misapplication. the deliberate improper use of a pesticide, such as exceeding the label rate or applying the material to a site not listed on the label.

interactive effect. interaction when two or more pesticides are mixed, producing greater or lesser toxicity to the target pests or changing the mode of action.

interval. the legal period of time between when a pesticide is applied and when workers are allowed to enter the treated area or produce can be harvested. See *preharvest interval* and *restricted-entry interval*.

introduced pest. a pest that is transported from its native area to a location where it previously did not exist. Some pests are introduced accidentally while others have been introduced intentionally.

inversion. a weather phenomenon in which cool air near the ground is trapped by a layer of warmer air above. Vapors of pesticides applied during an inversion can become trapped and concentrated and move away from the treatment area with the potential to cause damage or injury at some other location.

invert emulsion. an emulsion where water droplets are suspended in an oil rather than the oil droplets being suspended in water.

invertebrate. any animal not having an internal skeleton or shell, such a insects, spiders, mites, worms, nematodes, and snails and slugs.

ion. an atom or molecule that carries a positive or negative electrical charge due to losing or gaining electrons through a chemical reaction.

ionize. the process in which a chemical converts into ions when it dissolves in water or other liquid.

irreversible injury. a health condition caused by certain exposures to some pesticides in which there is no medical treatment or recovery.

knapsack sprayer. See *backpack sprayer.*

knowledge expectations. the breadth of knowledge about an occupation or procedure, such as pesticide handling, that a person performing this job is expected to have. Regulations establish minimal expectations for pesticide applicators, and certification examinations test a person's knowledge of these expectations.

labeling. the pesticide label and all associated materials, including supplemental labels, special local needs registration information, and manufacturer's information. The pesticide label is a legal document.

larva. the active immature form of insects that undergo metamorphosis to reach adulthood. (plural: larvae.)

LC$_{50}$. the lethal concentration of a pesticide in the air or in a body of water that will kill half of a test animal population. LC$_{50}$ values are given in micrograms per milliliter of air or water (μg/ml).

LD$_{50}$. the lethal dose of a pesticide that will kill half of a test animal population. LD$_{50}$ values are given in milligrams per kilogram of test animal body weight (mg/kg).

leaching. the process by which some pesticides move down through the soil, usually by being dissolved in water, with the possibility of reaching groundwater.

lethal. capable of causing death.

lethal concentration. see *LC$_{50}$*.

lethal dose. see *LD$_{50}$*.

life stage. the development stages living organisms pass through over time. Plants and animals (especially insects) pass through several life stages during which their susceptibility or tolerance to pesticides varies.

long-term health problem. a pesticide-related illness or disease that may extend over months, years, or a lifetime.

material safety data sheet (MSDS). an information sheet provided by a pesticide manufacturer describing chemical qualities, hazards, safety precautions, and emergency procedures to be followed in case of a spill, fire, or other emergency.

medical facility. a clinic, hospital, or physician's office where immediate medical care for pesticide-related illness or injury can be obtained.

mesh. the number of wires per inch in a screen, such as a screen used to filter foreign particles out of spray solutions to keep nozzles from becoming clogged. Mesh is also used to describe the size of pesticide granules, pellets, and dusts.

metabolic inhibitor. a chemical that interferes with normal activity within the cells of living organisms.

metabolism. the total chemical process that takes place in a living organism to utilize food and manage wastes, provide for growth and reproduction, and accomplish all other life functions.

metal organic. a type of pesticide made up of organic molecules that include metal ions such as zinc, copper, iron, arsenic, and mercury.

metamorphosis. the changes that take place in certain types of living organisms, such as insects, as they develop from eggs through adults. In some families of insects the young do not resemble adults.

microbial pesticide. pertaining to pesticides that consist of bacteria, fungi, or viruses used for control of weeds, invertebrates, or (rarely) vertebrates.

microencapsulated. a pesticide formulation in which particles of the active ingredient are encased in plastic capsules; pesticide is released after application when the capsules break down.

micron. a very small unit of measure: 1/1,000,000th of a meter.

microorganism. an organism of microscopic size, such as a bacterium, virus, fungus, viroid, or mycoplasma.

mimic. to copy or appear to be like something else.

minimal exposure pesticides. specific high-hazard pesticides identified in the California law that have special requirements for handling. Only certified commercial applicators may apply or supervise the application of minimal exposure pesticides.

mitigation. the process of making a problem, such as a pest infestation, less severe.

mixing. the process of opening pesticide containers, weighing or measuring specified amounts, and transferring these materials into application equipment, all in accordance with instructions found on pesticide labels.

mode of action. the way a pesticide reacts with a pest organism to destroy it.

molluscicide. a pesticide used to control slugs and snails.

molting. a process of shedding the outer body covering or exoskeleton in invertebrates such as insects and spiders. Molting usually takes place to allow the animal to grow larger.

monitoring (pest). the process of carefully watching the activities, growth, and development of pest organisms over a period of time, often utilizing very specific procedures.

monocot. a member of a group of plants whose seedlings have a single cotyledon; some monocots are known as grasses.

Monthly Pesticide Use Report. a form that must be completed and submitted to the local agricultural commissioner's office by the tenth of the month following any month in which pesticides are applied to an agricultural crop.

MSDS. see *Material Safety Data Sheet*.

mutagenic. a chemical that is capable of causing inheritable abnormalities in living organisms.

mycelium. the vegetative body of a fungus, consisting of a mass of slender filaments called hyphae. (plural: mycelia.)

mycoplasma. a microorganism intermediate between viruses and bacteria, capable of causing diseases in plants.

narcotic. the mode of action of some insecticides resulting in a prolonged sleeplike state from which the target insects may not recover.

narrow-range oil. horticultural oils with 10 to 90 percent distillation ranges of approximately 60° to 80°F (10 mm hg), and 50 percent distillation points from 412° to 440°F. Used for dormant or summer application.

National Institute for Occupational Safety and Health (NIOSH). the federal agency that tests and certifies respiratory equipment for pesticide application.

native. refers to animals or plants that are indigenous to an area.

natural enemy. an organism that can kill a pest organism; includes predators, pathogens, parasites, and competitors.

necrosis. localized death of living tissue.

negligent application. a pesticide application in which the applicator fails to exercise proper care or follow label instructions, potentially resulting in injury to people or surrounding areas.

nematicide. a pesticide used to control nematodes.

nematode. elongated, cylindrical, nonsegmented worms. Nematodes are commonly microscopic; some are parasites of plants or animals.

neoprene. a synthetic rubber material used to make gloves, boots, and clothing for protection against pesticide exposure.

NIOSH. see *National Institute for Occupational Safety and Health.*

no observable effect level. see *NOEL.*

nocturnal. being active during the night as opposed to daytime activity.

NOEL. no observable effect level. The NOEL is the maximum dose or exposure level of a pesticide that produces no noticeable toxic effect on test animals.

nonionic. pertaining to an adjuvant that dissolves in the spray solution without producing positively or negatively charged particles.

nonpoint pollution source. pollution from pesticides or other materials that arises from their normal or accepted use over a large general area and extended period of time.

nonselective. a pesticide that has an action against many species of pests rather than just a few.

nontarget organism. animals or plants within a pesticide-treated area that are not intended to be controlled by the pesticide application.

Notice of Intent. oral or written notification to the agricultural commissioner, as specified by the commissioner, prior to the use of a pesticide. A condition of a Restricted-Use Permit.

notification. see *oral notification* and *posting.*

noxious. something that is harmful to living organisms, such as a noxious weed.

occasional pest. a pest that does not recur regularly, but causes damage from time to time as a result of changing environmental conditions or other factors.

ocular. pertaining to the eye—this is one of the routes of entry of pesticides into the body.

offsite movement. any movement of a pesticide from the location where it was applied. Offsite movement occurs through drift, volatilization, percolation, water runoff, crop harvest, blowing dust, and by being carried away on organisms or equipment.

operator identification number. the number assigned to an operator of agricultural or other property, as defined in California regulations, where pesticides will be applied. Operator identification numbers are used in the pesticide use reporting process.

oral. through the mouth—this is one of the routes of entry of pesticides into the body.

oral notification. a method used to notify workers of pesticide applications on property where they are employed.

organic. a pesticide whose molecules contain carbon and hydrogen atoms. Also may refer to plants or animals which are grown without the addition of synthetic fertilizers or pesticides.

organic agriculture. growing of agricultural commodities without the use of certain synthetic chemicals and fertilizers. For pest control, organic agriculture utilizes naturally occurring substances as well as cultural, mechanical, and biological methods.

organism. any living thing.

organophosphate. a commonly used class of pesticides. Organophosphates are organic molecules containing phosphorous. Some organophosphates are highly toxic to people. Most break down in the environment very rapidly.

ornamental. cultivated plants that are grown for purposes other than food or fiber.

output rate. the amount of pesticide mixture discharged by pesticide application equipment over a measured period of time. The usual output rate for liquid sprayers, measured in gallons per minute.

overwinter. the process of passing through the winter season. Many living organisms survive harsh weather conditions as seeds, eggs, or certain resting stages.

palmate. refers to leaves shaped like the palm of a hand with the veins radiating out from a central location.

panicle. a flower head of a plant in which the lateral branches of the raceme are branched.

parasite. a plant or animal that derives all its nutrients from another organism. Parasites often attach themselves to their host or invade the host's tissues. Parasitism may result in injury or death of the host.

pathogen. a microorganism that causes a disease.

pellet. a pesticide formulation consisting of the dry active ingredient and inert materials pressed into uniform-sized granules.

penetrate. to pass through a surface such as skin, protective clothing, plant cuticle, or insect cuticle. Also refers to the ability of an applied spray to pass through dense foliage.

percolation. the process by which water flows downward through permeable soil. During percolation, water may dissolve or leach out pesticides and other chemicals in the soil and carry them downward.

perennial. a plant that lives longer than two years—some may live indefinitely. Some perennial plants lose their leaves and become dormant during winter; others may die back and resprout from underground root or stem structures each year. The evergreens are perennial plants that do not die back or become dormant.

persistent pesticide. a pesticide that remains active in the environment for long periods of time because it is not easily broken down by microorganisms or environmental factors.

personal hygiene. see *hygiene*.

personal protective equipment (PPE). devices and garments that protect handlers from exposure to pesticides. These include coveralls, eye protection, gloves and boots, respirators, aprons, and hats.

pest resurgence. see *resurgence*.

pesticide. any substance or mixture of substances intended for preventing, destroying, repelling, or mitigating any insects, rodents, nematodes, fungi, or weeds, or any other forms of life declared to be pests, and any other substance or mixture of substances intended for use as a plant regulator, defoliant, or desiccant.

pesticide deposition. see *deposition*.

pesticide formulation. the pesticide as it comes from its original container, consisting of the active ingredient blended with inert materials.

pesticide handler. see *handler*.

pesticide residue tolerance. the maximum amount of pesticide residue allowable by law that can remain on edible commodities that enter the food distribution system.

pesticide resistance. genetic qualities of a pest population that enable individuals to resist the effects of certain types of pesticides that are toxic to other members of that species.

Pesticide Safety Information Series. a series of informational sheets developed and distributed by the California Department of Pesticide Regulation pertaining to handling pesticides, personal protective equipment, emergency first aid, medical supervision, etc.

pesticide use hazard. the potential for a pesticide to cause injury or damage during handling or application.

pesticide use record. a record of pesticide applications made to a specific location.

pH. a measure of the concentration of hydrogen ions in a solution—as the number of hydrogen ions increase, the pH reading gets lower and the solution becomes more acid.

phenology model. a mathematical model, based on studies of an organism, that enables people to predict the timing of the life cycles of the organism.

pheromone. a chemical produced by an animal to attract other animals of the same species.

photosynthesis. the process by which plants convert sunlight into energy.

physiological. pertaining to the functions and activities of living tissues.

phytotoxic. injurious to plants.

plant growth regulator (PGR). a pesticide used to regulate or alter the normal growth of plants or the development of plant parts.

plant kingdom. one of two groups of living organisms, the other being the animal kingdom.

plantback restriction. a restriction that limits the type of commodity that can be grown in an area for a designated period of time after a certain pesticide has been used.

point pollution source. pollution of the soil or groundwater caused by spilling or dumping quantities of a toxic material in one location.

postapplication cleanup. washing of application equipment, personal protective equipment, and other items used during a pesticide application to remove pesticide residues.

postemergent. an herbicide applied after emergence of a specified weed or crop.

posting. the placing of signs around an area to inform workers and the public that the area has been treated with a pesticide.

postsynaptic. refers to an effect that takes place beyond the synapse (or junction between two nerves or between nerves and muscles or other organs).

potency. the toxicity of a pesticide.

potentiation. an increase in the toxicity of a pesticide brought about by mixing it with another pesticide or chemical.

pour-on. a ready-to-use formulation or diluted mixture of pesticide for control of external parasites on livestock. The liquid is usually poured along the back of the animal.

powder. a finely ground dust containing active ingredient and inert materials. This powder is mixed with water before application as a liquid spray.

power take-off. a special shaft connected to the rear, front, or side of a tractor and certain other types of equipment that uses the engine of the tractor or other equipment to power external devices such as sprayers, mowers, hydraulic pumps, etc.

ppb. parts per billion.

PPE. see *personal protective equipment.*

ppm. parts per million.

precautionary statements. the section on pesticide labels where human and environmental hazards are listed; personal protective equipment requirements are listed here as well as first aid instructions and information for physicians.

precipitation. the process by which solid particles settle out of a solution, such as a formulated pesticide in a spray tank.

predaceous. having the habit of hunting and eating other animals.

predacide. a pesticide used for control of predaceous mammals such as coyotes.

preemergent. the action of an herbicide that controls specified weeds as they sprout from seeds before they push through the soil surface.

preharvest interval. a period of time as set by law that must elapse after a pesticide has been applied to an edible crop before the crop can be harvested legally. Pesticide labels provide information on preharvest intervals.

preplant. an herbicide that has been incorporated into the soil to control weeds prior to planting crop seeds.

pressure. the amount of force applied by the application equipment pump on the liquid pesticide mixture to force it through the nozzles.

pressure gauge. an instrument on liquid pesticide application equipment that measures the pressure of the liquid being expelled.

private applicator. individuals who apply pesticides on agricultural property under their control and for their own benefit or needs.

private applicator certification. see *certified private applicator.*

propellant. a material, such as compressed air or gas, used to propel spray liquids or dusts to target surfaces.

protectant. a pesticide that provides a chemical barrier against pest attack.

protective clothing. garments of personal protective equipment that cover the body, including arms and legs.

protein synthesis. the process by which cells in living organisms build complex chemical chains known as proteins.

protozoan. minute, single-celled organism belonging to the phylum Protozoa. Protozoans are common in the soil and water; some are parasitic on animals.

psi. pounds per square inch.

PTO-driven. see *power take-off.*

pupa. in insects having complete metamorphosis, the resting life stage between larval and adult forms. (plural: pupae.)

pyrethroid. a synthetic pesticide that mimics pyrethrin, a botanical pesticide derived from certain species of chrysanthemum flowers.

qualified trainer (for agricultural fieldworkers and agricultural pesticide handlers). a person who is a certified private or commercial applicator, an agricultural pest control adviser, a registered forester, agricultural biologist, UC farm advisor, or who has completed a DPR-approved train-the-trainer course.

quarantine. a legally imposed period of time during which the movement of certain items (such as produce) within a designated area is restricted to prevent the spread of pests.

raceme. a flower stalk with one central stem, with or without a terminal flower, and bearing lateral flowers or small bunches of flowers.

rate. the quantity or volume of liquid spray, dust, or granules that is applied to an area over a specified period of time.

recombination. an occurrence in which a pesticide breaks down and then combines with other chemicals in the environment to produce a different compound than what was originally applied.

recommendation. a written document prepared by a licensed pest control adviser that prescribes the use of a specific pesticide or other pest control method.

red cell and plasma cholinesterase determination. the blood test used to detect exposure to organophosphate and n-methyl carbamate insecticides.

registration and establishment numbers. identification numbers assigned by the U.S. Environmental Protection Agency and the California Department of Pesticide Regulation and found on pesticide labels.

regularly handle. handling pesticides during any part of the day for more than six calendar days in any 30-consecutive-day qualifying period beginning on the first day of handling. Any day spent on loading pesticides while exclusively using a closed system or mixing only pesticides sealed in water-soluble packets is not included for any employee who has a baseline blood cholinesterase level established pursuant to Section 6728(c)(1).

regulations. the guidelines or working rules that a regulatory agency uses to carry out and enforce laws.

regulatory control. management of pests by the passage of laws and regulations that restrict activities which would promote pest buildup.

REI. see *restricted-entry interval*.

repellent. a pesticide used to keep target pests away from a treated area by saturating the area with an odor that is disagreeable to the pest.

rescue breathing. also known as artificial respiration. Given mouth-to-mouth to assist or restore breathing to a person overcome by pesticides. Rescue breathing is given if the victim has a pulse.

reservoir. a population of pests within a local area. Also an organism harboring plant or animal pathogens.

residual action. the pesticidal action of material after it has been applied. Most pesticide compounds will remain active several hours to several weeks or even months after being applied.

residue. traces of pesticide that remain on treated surfaces after a period of time.

resistance. see *pesticide resistance* or *host resistance*.

respiration. the metabolic process in plants and animals in which, among other things, oxygen is exchanged for carbon dioxide or carbon dioxide is exchanged for oxygen.

respiratory equipment. a device that filters out pesticide dusts, mists, and vapors to protect the wearer from respiratory exposure during mixing and loading, application, or while entering treated areas before the restricted-entry interval expires.

restricted materials permit. see *restricted-use permit*.

restricted-entry interval (REI). a period of time that must elapse between application of a pesticide and when it is safe to allow people into the treated area without requiring they wear personal protective equipment and receive early-entry worker training.

restricted-use permit. a permit, issued by county agricultural commissioner offices, that enables growers to possess and apply restricted-use pesticides. Restricted-use permits can only be issued to certified applicators.

restricted-use pesticide. highly hazardous pesticides that can only be possessed or used by commercial applicators who have a valid Qualified Pesticide Applicator license or certificate or private applicators who have passed a written exam administered by the local agricultural commissioner thereby demonstrating that they understand the proper methods of handling, using, and disposing of these materials.

restrictive statement. a statement on a pesticide label that restricts the use of that pesticide to specific areas or by designated individuals.

resurgence. the sudden increase of a pest population after some event, such as a pesticide application.

reversible injury. a pesticide-related injury (or illness) that can be reversed through medical intervention and/or the body's healing process.

rhizome. an underground stem of certain types of plants.

rinsate. the liquid derived from rinsing pesticide containers or spray equipment.

rodenticide. a pesticide used for control of rats, mice, gophers, squirrels, and other rodents.

rope wick applicator. a device used to apply contact herbicides onto target weed foliage with a saturated rope or cloth pad.

route of exposure. the way a pesticide gets onto or into the body. The four routes of exposure are dermal (on or through the skin), ocular (on or in the eyes), respiratory (into the lungs), and ingestive (through swallowing).

rpm. revolutions per minute.

ruffling. an application technique in which spray is applied with oscillating motion or an air blast so the droplets come in contact with all of the target plant's leaf surfaces.

runoff. the liquid spray material that drips from the foliage of treated plants or from other treated surfaces. Also the rainwater or irrigation water that leaves an area—this water may contain trace amounts of pesticide.

safety cab. an enclosed cab installed on a tractor to protect the operator from pesticide exposure. The cab includes an air filtering system.

saprophyte. an organism that lives on dead or decaying organic matter.

secondary pest. an organism that becomes a serious pest only after a natural enemy, competitor, or primary pest has been eliminated through some type of pest control method.

Section 18 Exemption. see *emergency exemption from registration*.

selective pesticide. a pesticide that has a mode of action against only a single or a small number of pest species.

self-contained breathing apparatus (SCBA). see *supplied-air respirator*.

service container. any container designed to hold concentrate or diluted pesticide mixtures, including the sprayer tank, but not the original pesticide container.

shelf life. the maximum period of time that a pesticide can remain in storage before losing some of its effectiveness.

shingling. the clumping or sticking together of plant foliage caused by the force of a liquid spray. Shingling prevents spray droplets from reaching all surfaces of the foliage and may result in poor pest control.

sight gauge. a device on a pesticide sprayer or configuration of the spray tank that permits the operator to view the level of liquid in the tank.

signal word. one of three words (*Danger, Warning, Caution*) found on every pesticide label to indicate the relative hazard of the chemical.

site. the area where pesticides are applied for control of a pest.

site identification number. the number assigned to a location where pesticides are to be applied.

site of action. the location within the tissues of the target organism where a pesticide acts.

skin absorption. the passage of pesticides through the skin into the blood stream or other organs of the body.

skull and crossbones. the symbol on pesticide labels that are highly poisonous. Always accompanied by the signal word *Danger* and the word "Poison."

SLN. see *special local need registration.*

slurry. a watery mixture containing pesticide powder. Slurries leave a thick coating of pesticide residue on treated surfaces.

soil mobility. a variable characteristic of a pesticide, based on its chemical nature. Highly mobile pesticides leach rapidly through the soil and may contaminate groundwater. Immobile pesticides, or those with low soil mobility, remain tightly attached to soil particles and are resistant to leaching.

soil profile. the characteristics and differences of soil at different depths.

soluble. able to dissolve completely in a liquid.

soluble powder. a pesticide formulation in which the active ingredient and all inert ingredients completely dissolve in water to form a true solution.

solution. a liquid that contains dissolved substances, such as a soluble pesticide.

solvent. a liquid capable of dissolving certain chemicals.

sorptive dust. a fine powder used to destroy arthropods by removing the protective wax coating that prevents water loss.

source reduction. sanitation practices.

special local need registration (SLN). also known as 24(c) registration, the registration of a pesticide for treatment of a local or specific pest problem where no registered pesticide is available.

speed of travel. the speed that the operator moves the pesticide application equipment through the area being treated. It is necessary to calculate the speed of travel in order to calibrate pesticide application equipment.

spore. a reproductive structure produced by some plants and microorganisms that is resistant to environmental influences.

spot treatment. a method of applying pesticides only in small, localized areas where pests congregate, rather than treating a larger, general area.

spray check device. a special piece of equipment that measures and visualizes the output from the nozzles on a spray boom. This device provides rapid visualization of differences in output between nozzles.

spreader. an adjuvant that lowers the surface tension of treated surfaces to enable the pesticide to be absorbed.

statement of practical treatment. a section of the pesticide label that provides information on treating people who have been exposed to the pesticide. This includes emergency first aid information.

statement of use classification. a special statement found on labels of some highly hazardous pesticides indicating that their use is restricted to people who are qualified through a certification process.

sterilant. a pesticide used for control of rodents by preventing their reproduction.

sticker. an adjuvant used to prevent pesticides from being washed or abraded off treated surfaces.

stolon. an aboveground runner stem found in some species of plants.

stomach poison. a pesticide that kills target animals who ingest it.

structural pest. a pest such as a termite or wood rot fungus that destroys structural wood in buildings.

subcutaneous injection. injecting a substance, such as a drug, under the skin.

sublethal dose. a pesticide dose insufficient to cause death in the exposed organism.

summer oils. narrow-range oil applied during the growing season.

superior oils. term given to more highly refined paraffinic oils in the late 1940s. When used today, refers to most oils available (e.g., narrow-range oils), but excludes very heavy dormant emulsions that have low unsulfonated residues. All narrow-range oils are superior oils, but not all superior oils are narrow-range oils.

supplemental label. additional instructions and information not found on the pesticide label because the label is too small but legally considered to be part of the pesticide labeling.

supplied-air respirator. a tightly fitting face mask that is connected by hose to an air supply such as a tank worn on the back of the person using the respirator or to an external air supply. Supplied-air respirators permit people to enter oxygen-deficient areas or areas where there are highly toxic pesticide vapors.

suppression. the pest management strategy that attempts to reduce pest numbers below an economic injury threshold or to a tolerable level.

supreme oils. refers to a specific product (Volck Supreme Oil), but often used incorrectly to indicate any superior or narrow-range oil. The distillation midpoint is higher and the 10 to 90 percent distillation range is wider than other narrow-range oil formulations.

surface active agent. see *surfactant*.

surface coverage. the degree to which a spray or dust covers the surface of leaves or other objects being treated.

surface tension. forces on the surfaces of liquid droplets that keep them from spreading out over treated surfaces.

surface water. water contained in lakes or ponds or flowing in streams, rivers, and canals.

surfactant. surface active agent. An adjuvant used to improve the ability of the pesticide to stick to and be absorbed by the target surface.

susceptible life stage. the life stage of a pest organism that is most susceptible to a pesticide used to control it. In general, insects are most susceptible during the larval or juvenile stage; weeds are usually most susceptible during the seedling stage.

suspension. fine particles of solid material distributed evenly throughout a liquid such as water or oil.

swath. the area covered by one pass of the pesticide application equipment.

swath width. the width of the area covered by spray droplets or granules as the application equipment moves through. The swath width must be measured to calibrate application equipment.

symptom. any abnormal condition caused by a pesticide exposure that can be seen or felt or that can be detected by examination or laboratory tests.

synaptic. pertaining to the junctions between nerves or between nerves and muscles and other organs. In many organisms, nerve impulses are carried across these junctions by the chemical *acetylcholine*.

synergism. a reaction in which a chemical that has no pesticidal qualities can enhance the toxicity of a pesticide it is mixed with.

synthesized. applying to pesticides that are manufactured through chemical processes rather than occurring naturally.

systemic pesticide. a pesticide that is taken up into the tissues of the organism and transported to other locations where it will affect pests.

tag-along. a liquid or dry pesticide applicator mounted on a wheeled trailer and pulled behind a tractor or other powered vehicle.

tailwater. the water that collects at the lower end of a field during or after irrigation.

tank mix. a mixture of pesticides or fertilizers and pesticides applied at the same time.

target. either the pest that is being controlled or surfaces within an area that the pest will contact.

temperature inversion. see *inversion*.

teratogenic. a chemical that is capable of causing noninheritable birth abnormalities.

thickener. an adjuvant that increases the viscosity of the spray solution so that larger droplets are formed by the nozzles; thickeners are used to control drift.

threshold. see *economic injury threshold*.

threshold limit value (TLV). the airborne concentration of a pesticide in parts per million (ppm) that produces no adverse effects over a period of time.

TLV. threshold limit value.

tolerance. the ability to endure the impact of a pesticide or pest without exhibiting adverse effects. The maximum amount of pesticide residue that is permitted on produce or other edible animal or agricultural crop products.

toxicant. a substance that, at a sufficient dose, will cause harm to a living organism.

toxicity. the potential a pesticide has for poisoning an exposed organism.

toxicity category. the three classifications of pesticides that indicate the approximate level of hazard. The three categories are indicated by the signal words *Danger*, *Warning*, and *Caution*.

toxicity testing. a process in which known doses of a pesticide are given to groups of test animals and the results observed.

toxicology. the study of toxic substances on living organisms.

tracking powder. a fine powder that is dusted over a surface to detect or control certain pests such as cockroaches or rodents. For control, the inert powder is combined with a pesticide; the animal ingests this powder when it cleans itself and becomes poisoned.

training record. the document, signed by the trainer, employer, and trainee, used to record the dates and types of pesticide safety training received.

translocate. the movement of pesticides from one location to another within the tissues of a plant.

treated surface. the surface of plants, soil, or other items that were contacted with pesticide spray, dust, or granules for the purpose of controlling pests.

treatment area. see *site*.

treatment threshold. see *action threshold*.

triple rinse. the process of partially filling an empty pesticide container, replacing the lid, shaking the container, then emptying its contents into the spray tank. This procedure is performed three times to assure that most of the pesticide residue is removed. Triple-rinsed containers can be offered for special pesticide container recycling or taken to a Class 2 disposal site.

tuber. an underground vegetative reproductive structure of some types of plants. Tubers are characterized by small scalelike leaves.

ultra-low-volume (ULV). a pesticide application technique in which very small amounts of liquid spray are applied over a unit of area; usually ½ gallon or less of spray per acre in row crops to about 5 gallons of spray per acre in orchards and vineyards.

umbel. a flower head in which all the flower stalks originate at or near one point.

unclassified oils. spray oils that do not meet the distillation properties defined by the California grade system.

unloader. a sensitive valvelike mechanism used on high-pressure applicators that diverts the liquid back into the tank when nozzles are shut off to prevent a rapid buildup of pressure in the system that would possibly damage the pump. When the flow to the nozzles is turned back on, the unloader quickly restores pressure to them.

unregistered crop. any crop that is not listed on the pesticide label. Pesticides can only be applied to crops that are specifically listed on the label.

unregistered site. any site, such as a right-of-way or pond, that is not listed on the pesticide label. Legal uses of pesticides require that they be applied to listed or registered crops or sites.

unsulfonated residue (UR). a measure of purity of petroleum oils used as pesticides. Oils used for insecticides and acaricides must have a minimum UR rating based on the grade or type of oil. Oils with higher UR ratings are safer for use on plants.

use restrictions. special restrictions included on the pesticide label or incorporated into state or local regulations that specify how, when, or where a specific pesticide may be used.

vaporize. to transform from a spray of droplets to a foglike vapor or gas.

vector. an organism, such as an insect, that can transmit a pathogen to plants or animals.

vertebrate. the group of animals that have an internal skeleton and segmented spine, such as fish, birds, reptiles, and mammals.

viroid. a microorganism that is much smaller than a virus and is not enclosed in a protein coat. Some viroids produce disease symptoms in certain plants.

virus. a very small organism that multiplies in living cells and is capable of producing disease symptoms in some plants and animals.

viscosity. a physical property of a fluid that affects its flowability. More-viscous fluids flow less easily and produce larger spray droplets.

volatile. able to pass from liquid or solid into a gaseous stage readily at low temperatures.

volatilization. the process of a pesticide liquid or solid passing into a gaseous stage.

volute. a metal ductlike structure used to direct the air flow from a sprayer fan. Spray nozzles are often positioned near the outlet of the air flow. Volutes enable pesticide-laden air to be directed to tree tops or other hard-to-reach areas.

Warning. the signal word used on labels of pesticides considered to be moderately toxic or hazardous. Pesticides that are assigned the signal word *Warning* based on toxicity usually have an oral LD_{50} between 50 and 500 and a dermal LD_{50} between 200 to 2,000.

watershed. an area of land that drains its surface water into a defined watercourse or body of water.

water-soluble concentrate. a liquid pesticide formulation that dissolves in water to form a true solution.

wettable powder. a type of pesticide formulation consisting of an active ingredient that will not dissolve in water, combined with a mineral clay and other inert ingredients and ground into a fine powder.

wetting agent. an adjuvant used in pesticide mixtures to lower the surface tension of spray droplets, enabling them to come in close contact and spread out over target surfaces, especially those containing fine hairs or waxy layers.

work clothing. garments such as long-sleeved shirts, short-sleeved shirts, long pants, short pants, shoes, and socks. Work clothing is not considered personal protective equipment although pesticide product labeling or regulations may require specific work clothing during some activities. Work clothing differs from and should not be confused with a coverall. While coveralls must be provided by the employer, work clothing can be required to be provided by the employee. Short-sleeved shirts and short pants are only considered acceptable work clothing under conditions expressly permitted by pesticide product labeling.

Worker Protection Standard (WPS). the 1992 amendment to the Federal Insecticide, Fungicide, and Rodenticide Act (FIFRA) that makes significant changes to pesticide labeling and mandates specific training of pesticide handlers and workers in production agriculture, commercial greenhouses and nurseries, and forests.

Index